Operations Research in
Research and Development

Operations Research in Research and Development

proceedings of a conference at Case Institute of Technology

edited by
BURTON V. DEAN

Associate Professor of Operations Research
Case Institute of Technology

John Wiley & Sons, Inc., New York · London

64 /   623

To my wife, Barbara

Preface

This book presents the collection of papers on Research and Development Management Systems problems delivered at a conference at Case Institute of Technology. The general objective of these papers is to present applications of the methodology of operations research to the solution of some research and development management problems. A few papers dealing with both methodology and problems of a pioneering nature are presented in this book.

For our purpose a research and development management system is a behavioral system, consisting of men and facilities, with multiple and sometimes conflicting goals and objectives. The system operations consist of the performance of research and decision acts, where the responsibility for decision making is usually shared among groups having specified areas of responsibility, annual budgets, and completion schedules. Communications exist among groups whose essential outputs are ideas or developments, usually to serve another department within the organization. Each decision maker has a number of alternate courses of action (e.g., new project initiation, project termination, project delay or speed-up) and a number of desired outcomes (e.g., project implementation, project payoff, research group growth). The outputs of such systems are often probabilistic, involving difficult and important problems of measurement and evaluation of output efficiency. In this brief description of a research and development management system there may be noted many of the elements that are used by operations researchers in the description of classical management systems.

Research and development has been referred to as the fastest growing "industry" in the United States. Our national and economic growth depends to a great extent on the productivity and efficiency of this industry. At present time over 1,000,000 people are employed in the industry at an annual cost of about 3% of our gross national product. Some segments of this industry are very large and complex, as, for example, the National Aeronautics and Space Administration, which employs over 20,000 people and spends 2 billion dollars annually. Since 1940, the dollar expenditure growth of the industry has been exponential or at a constant rate, whereas the manpower growth has been linear, or at a constant amount. Thus in many research and development organizations there are problems of budgeting, scheduling, evaluation, selection, sequencing, timing, and control similar to those that have occurred in other company areas. In addition, at the national and international levels, there are significant problems of policy making which have been recognized only recently. In all areas of the management of this industry there are major demands for the development of scientific attitudes and methods. It is our hypothesis that operations research, as one of the applied sciences, can contribute to the solution of many of the important problems.

It is worthwhile to point out some basic requirements for the development and application of scientific methods to research and development management problems. First, a development of models of the research process and system is required, where the relevant factors are introduced. Of particular importance is the need for analytic descriptions of the behavior of small, task-oriented, creative groups. Second, a need exists for a research management theory where system optimization, simulation, and analysis may be effectively utilized. Third, a major requirement exists for an increase in the number and variety of education and research programs in research and development management.

A number of acknowledgments to individuals and groups are in order. Dr. Russell L. Ackoff, Director of the Operations Research Group, formulated the initial suggestion on conducting a conference on recent applications of operations research and has consistently attempted to broaden the scope and usefulness of operations research. Professor Vernon C. Mickelon, Head, Department of Management, encouraged the idea of a conference, as well as courses and research theses in this important area. The Office of Special Studies, National Science Foundation, has supported research at Case Institute of Technology on research budgeting and project selection problems. Case Institute of Technology has consistently provided the environment and facilities for curricula, research, and conferences in operations research and management. The Special Programs Office, under Mr. Herbert Schultz, managed the many details of this conference. Finally, Mrs. Grace White and her excellent secretarial staff prepared and proofread the manuscript.

BURTON V. DEAN

Cleveland, Ohio
April 1963

Contents

1.

A Proposal for Strengthening
U. S. Technology, *Ellis A. Johnson*

This chapter is concerned with *the continuing difficulty of U. S. technology and its management to achieve its full and great potential, to compete successfully with the USSR in the application of science to certain aspects of military technology and space,* and with *the growing danger that Western Europe, Japan, and perhaps the USSR, whose rates of increase in industrial productivity already exceed ours, might eventually surpass us in productivity because of superiority in the application of science.* This chapter is also concerned with possible actions we might take to remedy this situation.

Although the situation in the application of science to technology is not satisfactory, we agree with the President's Science Advisory Committee that so far "American science is second to none in the world, and the Federal Government, on balance, has played a highly constructive role in supporting it."[1] The role, influence, and success of the National Science Foundation, the National Institutes of Health, the Department of Agriculture, and the Office of Naval Research in this respect are especially gratifying.

The chapter summarizes evidence of U. S. backwardness and factors which have influenced U. S. technology, states the nature of the problems involved in managing U. S. technology, gives an example of the factors that affect R & D (research and development) effectiveness and that might be changed, primarily by government help as has been the case for basic research, and finally proposes actions that might be taken.

[1] *Scientific Progress, The Universities, and the Federal Government,* President's Science Advisory Committee, November 12, 1960.

1

THE EVIDENCE

There are real symptoms of trouble in the management of the application of science in the United States and, indeed, in the whole free world. We regard with dismay the pre-eminence of the Soviet Union in several of the most important military weapons systems and in space, and the fact that their *rate* of advance in the application of science and engineering to weapons systems and production systems has been 50 percent faster than ours in some of the most critical areas. Considering resources, capabilities, and experience, the reverse would have been expected.

It is instructive, as an example, to evaluate the relative progress of the United States and the Soviet Union in thermonuclear weapon systems. Much has been learned and published in the press of Soviet atomic developments from test identifications, Soviet releases, interchanges during the International Geophysical Year, and the Atoms for Peace Conferences in 1955 and 1958. The known military atomic weapons operations and tests in the U. S. and the USSR spell out the relative pace of research and development step by step. The USSR *rate* has been almost 1½ times that of the U. S. Figure 1 represents the time pattern of some of the more or less accepted achievements in terms of specific advances in atomic development. The data have been taken from public sources. In this figure, a time scale is used for the abscissa, a 45° line is arbitrarily drawn to represent U. S. progress, with notable testing events by the U. S. placed *on* this line at the date of the event. The equivalent Soviet event is then placed at the same ordinate level but at the date of the Soviet event. The relative slope of the two lines then is the measure of relative rate of progress. Although this representation is crude and inexact, it has the virtue of providing an easily grasped over-all "statistical trend" estimate of relative U. S.–USSR rate of progress. All indications are that the USSR lag noted at the time of their first atomic explosion has been overcome during the succeeding decade. A table of comparable events and the source of the information are given in the Appendix at the end of this chapter.

The first Soviet atomic test in 1949 surprised most U. S. experts because it came so early. The first U. S. hydrogen bomb test came in 1952, the Soviet's in 1953; but the USSR had the first air-drop of an H-bomb (USSR, 1955; U. S., 1956). Intercontinental jet bombers were reported operational for both countries in the same year (1955). Our Nautilus was launched in 1955—a "scoop" for the U. S. in atomic submarines.

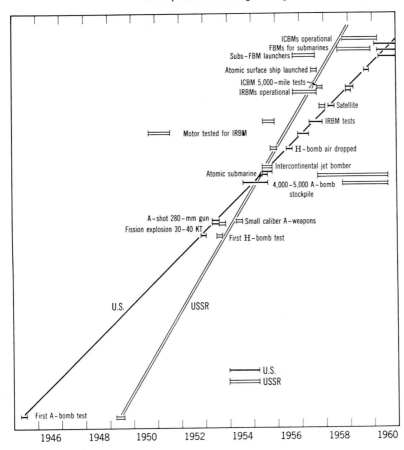

FIGURE 1.   Lead time: U. S.-USSR nuclear weapons and carriers.

In missile carriers for atomic weapons, the Russians outplanned and outproduced us. They tested a motor in 1951 for a projected intermediate-range missile, with faith that they could package a *small* H-bomb. We waited for the bomb before starting the missile. IRBM's were reported to have been operational in Russia in 1955. There are news notices of Soviet IRBM submarine launchers as early as 1955. Our submarine firings of the Polaris made headlines in the U. S. in 1959–1960. The high thrust of the rocket motors and the extensive payloads of Soviet space satellites are indicative of advanced capabilities available in Soviet weapons development.

In all public estimates on stockpiles of atomic bombs, a wide margin in numbers is attributed to the U. S. But if the Soviets have "enough" in terms of their estimate of strategic and tactical requirements, then relative quantity need not be directly proportional to military value.

The significant point, regardless of possible error in element or timing, is that the U. S. had a minimum lead of 4 years in the strategic weapons system field in 1945, and the Soviets, with extraordinary expenditure of effort and great effectiveness in development, currently (1962) have as good a political and military balance in atomic weapons and carriers as the U. S. and perhaps better. This was accomplished with a technical labor force approximately equivalent to that of the U. S. To the free nations of the West, the Soviet "steep upward curve" in selected areas of technical development was technically unexpected and, in its military significance, unnerving.

In spite of our current over-all economic and military advantages, we are disturbed by these immediate and obvious symptoms of U. S. inferiority in the *rate of application* of scientific knowledge to selected areas of weapons systems development. We have inferred, perhaps wrongly, that the situation is a direct consequence of too few U. S. scientists and engineers and inadequate funds. To counter this trend, and as a matter of common sense, many authorities have proposed increases in the number of students educated for science and technology and in the funds provided for both research and its application. Similarly, many have urged that our educational policies be re-examined in view of the fact that the Soviet technical labor force is expanding at a much greater rate than our own. The number of college-eligible secondary school graduates in the U. S. will almost double during this decade, bringing into being an educational crisis of apparently unmanageable proportions,[2,3] with anticipatory preparation not yet taken. Educational bills falter in Congress, and the advice of the President's Scientific Advisory Committee is not translated into action.

In industry we are disturbed because our rate of improvement of per capita productivity is less than that of either the Soviet Union or of our allies. Especially striking is the exceedingly stable rate of increase of U. S. GNP (gross national product)—at 2.7 percent a year for the past *century*. Is this rate invulnerable to improvement as a result of R & D progress?

Even our machine tool industry, key to our productivity in which we have always excelled, is subject to unprecedented and keen competition from abroad. The fact that the automated presses of the

2 "Investing in Scientific Progress," National Science Foundation Report, NSF 61-27, Washington, D. C., 1961.

3 See footnote 1.

Treasury Department which print our currency are of English manufacture is an example of acknowledged superiority of foreign automation in one particular area. The per capita productivity of Denmark is now estimated at 80 percent of U. S. productivity as compared to 30 percent prior to World War II! Saulnier's estimate of progress in Italy and Japan is flattering to those countries—the difficulties there lie in the problems related to the need for greater associated political progress.

Thus, although we find ourselves at present the most powerful nation in the world in productivity and military power, as well as in science, we fear that the continuation of this superiority is endangered by our conservative policies, our unwillingness to make great enough present sacrifices (in education and science) to improve the future, our lack of great elan, our lack of long-range planning, and our consequent sluggish advance. We must infer that within a few decades we may be matched and surpassed in technical achievements and innovation by other countries of the world, friends as well as enemies, unless we do take decisive actions to remedy our faults.

There is general agreement that one of the primary means for maintaining our rate of advance in national well-being and power is a higher level and more efficient use of applied research and development, the mainspring of innovation in the modern world. Education comes first, but since production of more technical personnel has a very long lead time, the question is whether, as an immediate measure, we can in addition improve the over-all management of our existing great resources in research and development. In further detail, what techniques of management can be used to improve research and development at the level of the research group, the company, the government department, and at the national level?

THE NATURE OF THE PROBLEM

It is important to recapitulate the evidence on the close relationship and dependence among innovation, organized R & D, education, and national welfare if we are to estimate the increased effort needed to maintain economic superiority in the U. S.

R & D is the modern tool used to organize the art of invention and innovation useful to man. From antiquity, relatively unorganized innovation has had revolutionary effects on man's society, as indicated in Figure 2. This example, taken from a paper by Max Petterson[4] shows the growth of the population of England as a function of the

[4] Max Petterson, "Main States of Social Evolution in Man," *Nature*, Vol. 184, No. 4684, August 8, 1959, pp. 481–482.

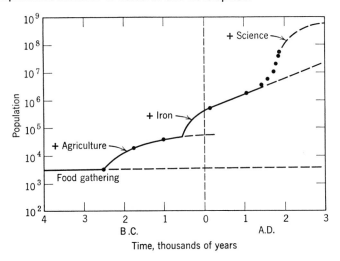

FIGURE 2.   Population growth of England and Wales.

major innovations of the last few thousand years. These innovations, first the introduction of agriculture, then of iron, and then of science, made possible the growth of the English population from a few thousand to tens of millions, and during the two centuries, economic well-being was established with the consequent release of Britain from endemic starvation.

Figure 3 shows the correlations between expenditures on organized research and development and the economy of several countries,[5] and Figure 4 a similar correlation of percent R & D expenditures for U. S. industries versus increase in plant capacity.[6]

Both Figures 3 and 4 neglect the lag between R & D expenditures and increases in productivity, capital investment, and other economic effects. Thus the crude correlation shown in Figures 3 and 4 indicates only approximately the possible relationships. We need to develop a more adequate model for R & D effort that does take into account both time lag and economic results. Still, the general relationships shown are inductively defensible and are believed to repre-

[5] Income data: U. S. Statistical Office and International Cooperation Administration. R & D data: Organization for European Economic Cooperation; Department of Scientific and Industrial Research, United Kingdom; Defense Research Board, Canada; Français de Recherche Operationelle, France, ORO-AFFE (American Forces Far East).

[6] *Management of New Products*, Booz, Allen, and Hamilton, 1960.

sent cause and effect relationships. The difficulty of developing an adequate model lies in the difficulty of obtaining reliable data (Chapter 2).

At this stage of our understanding, we can be content with claiming that these correlations, as a part of a positive feedback system, do provide adequate evidence to support the hypothesis of a cause and effect relationship, and that a policy of heavy investment in research and development produces long-range, increased growth in industry and in national prosperity.[7]

The economy of any country and the per capita income is, of course, critically dependent upon the social drive of the country in question, its internal organization, policies governing tax structure

[7] Ellis A. Johnson and Herbert E. Striner, "Research and Development, Resources Allocation and Economic Growth," speech before International Federation of Operational Research Societies, Aix-en-Provence, France, September 1960, The Johns Hopkins University Operations Research Office, Bethesda, Maryland.

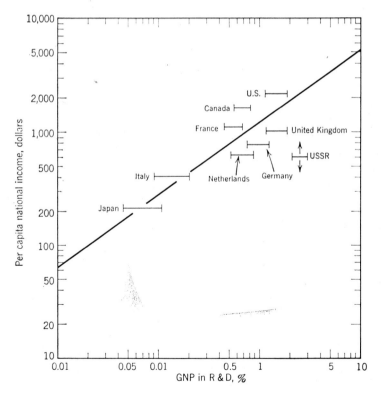

FIGURE 3.   Percentage of GNP in R & D.

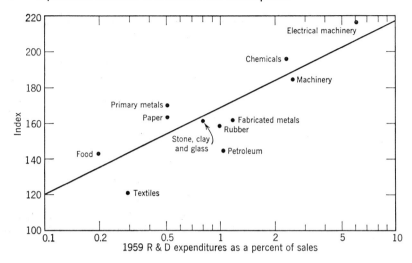

FIGURE 4. Comparison of R & D expenditures to increases in plant capacity, 1950–1959. (1950 industrial capacity index = 100.)

and capital investment, opportunities for individual profit, encouragement of competition, patent law, and availability of national resources, as well as many other factors. However, it is contended that there remains a causal relationship of dominating importance between the over-all effort spent on research and development and the per capita national income, since today, in contrast to the past, the per capita income is primarily dependent on the use of new mechanisms and new ways of using energy that can be provided only by organized R & D. Concerning this problem, Sumner Slichter has rightly stated:

By and large, the Government has shown grossly inadequate appreciation of the importance of research to the community. Government research expenditures, it is true, are larger and have been growing rapidly, but they have been forced mainly by military considerations. . . .

But outside the field of military research, the Government support of research is only a small fraction of the amount that would yield enormous returns to the community. Indeed, it is safe to say that there is no field where larger Government expenditures would produce as rich a return as greater outlays on research . . . and also on the necessary foundations for research, the education of talented people.[8]

[8] Sumner H. Slichter, "Technological Research as Related to the Growth of the Economy," *Proceedings of a Conference on Research and Development and Its Impact on the Economy,* NSF-58-36 1958, p. 117.

As will be shown later, the difficult problems of inflation and of the efficiency in R & D management make the measure in terms of monetary investment a rather poor guide to the total effort in research and development, although to date, dollar support of R & D has been accepted as an adequate measure of effort.

It is essential that we appreciate the source of the funds supporting the R & D effort as well as the organization executing R & D, since the donor of the funds usually exercises a dominating influence on the effectiveness of the research. Figure 5 shows that the source of support of basic research has evolved from a situation in which basic research, once supported primarily by university and foundation funds, has reached a point where it is supported largely by Government funds (much of this, as Slichter pointed out, military funds).[9]

Again, the assumption of a 1-to-1 ratio between number of pages in scientific journals and the amount of basic research can and has been criticized. In spite of the objections related to relative merit of articles, duplication in publication, and suppression (for reasons of industrial and/or national security or censorship) by both industry and Federal Government, Figure 5 is considered to give with rather high accuracy the actual relative relationships in the sponsorships of basic research. Figure 6 shows that over-all, increased fiscal support of

* Helen S. Milton and Ellis A. Johnson, *Sponsorship of Research—A Survey of Scientific Literature*, ORO-TP-42, Operations Research Office, the Johns Hopkins University, September 1961.

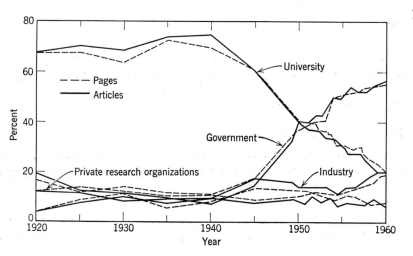

FIGURE 5. National sponsorship of basic research, 1920–1960, by percentages of articles and pages. (Survey of 50 scientific journals.)

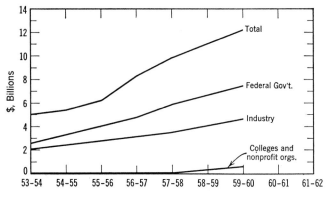

FIGURE 6.   Annual U. S. Expenditures on R & D.

R & D has come largely from Federal funds which now contribute over one-half of *all* research and development funds spent in the U. S. If the trend continues, within a few decades the Federal Government may be providing up to 80 to 90 percent.   For this reason we stress that Federal appropriations and policy for R & D deserve the most critical scrutiny by the Government, not only because of the enormous effect of R & D on our general well-being but also because the Government provides a large and increasing part of the money for direct support of R & D.   On the other hand, almost all of *execution* of applied research and development has been by industry.   Excepting basic research, only a trivial amount has been conducted by universities and nonprofit organizations.   Federal policy towards industry in such areas as permitted rates of amortization,[10] allowance of research as an overhead expense, taxes on production devices, taxes involving R & D expenditures, and patent policy involving cartels and monopolies affects the health of the R & D system just as much as direct Federal expenditures on R & D.

Factors Affecting the Management of R & D

The effects of the increase in the absolute amount of research and development and its increased importance have a feedback to the management of R & D in six significant aspects:

1. The first is the short lifetime of consumer products, weapons systems, and the mechanisms of production.   For example, since the beginning of modern science several hundred years ago, the lifetime

[10] *The Army Production Base,* Volumes I and II, ORO-T-380, Operations Research Office, The Johns Hopkins University, January 1960.

of weapons systems has decreased continuously until today it is only 5 or 6 years. This is illustrated by Figure 7 which shows the decrease in the useful lifetime of weapons systems. Up to 20 or 30 years ago, the lifetime of weapons or weapons systems was at least as long as a man's professional life. There was time to develop doctrine, tactics, and strategy, and to educate and train military personnel in a weapon's use. The important weapons system was used in several and perhaps many wars before it became obsolete, and a professional military man was the best authority on strategy and tactics involving its use. Today it appears that very many, if not most, weapons systems will become obsolete without ever being employed. Since the prospect is that most weapons will not be used in combat during their limited spans of life, the professional military man cannot refer authoritatively to practical experience on which his stature and status depended in the past. He must become a theoretician, a role for which he is not trained, and he competes at a grave disadvantage with the superior well-trained civilian theoreticians on war. Practical-minded militarists of the last decade tended to regard weapons with short lifetimes as "inefficient" and they hoped for the efficiency and standardization and stability of the long lifetime product. Many conservative officers regret seeing this ideal receding ever farther from the realm of possibility.

Liberal and far-sighted military leaders, notably Generals Gavin and Taylor, regarded the roles of military personnel and civilian sci-

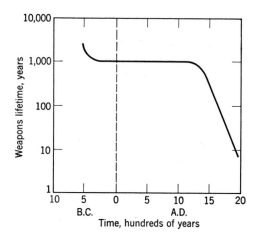

FIGURE 7.   Lifetime of weapons.

entists as one of a partnership with appreciable sharing of responsibility and authority in R & D. Their personal defeat was accompanied by a defeat of their ideas with respect to the sharing of authority in weapons systems development. As a result, by 1962, the increase in civilian control over development at the Department of Defense level was accompanied by an opposing purge of civilians within the three services. For example, each of the operations research groups of the three services deeply involved in R & D management had maintained scientific and ethical standards of very high quality. By 1962 each group had been severely disciplined. When this proved to be unacceptable to the existing managements (Johns Hopkins University for ORO and the Massachusetts Institute of Technology for OEG), the contracts were transferred to non-University management. At the same time, former research leaders returned to teaching and scientific research work. The policy to establish firmer military control was furthered by a vigorous postgraduate education of military officers in science and technology, and by a great increase in detailed project supervision by officers unskilled in R & D. (In one project at ORO, about nine officers supervised one junior researcher!) The lack of clarity in R & D relationships that have ensued resulted in a high turnover rate in both civilian and military managers. For civilians this was because of the unprofessional managerial climate and relationships, and for scientifically trained officers because of a combination of adverse career policy procedures and loss of high-caliber scientists of the officer corps to superior opportunities in industry.

It has been common practice to have average officer tenures on a project for as little time as 6 to 9 months. Under these circumstances, as is discussed under "Examples of Factors that Affect R & D Efficiency: Inflation, Tenure, and Technical Efficiency." (p. 21), officer personnel are in a training status only and make no contributions to the R & D effort, but rather constitute a severe drain. The stresses related to R & D management in Defense has thus resulted in a chaotic and degraded management situation with a serious reduction in R & D efficiency. Furthermore, this situation has had adverse effects on the performance of military R & D in industry.

The similar short lifetime of consumers' products, has also been revolutionary in the last several decades. In a great number of companies and industries, *half* of the consumers' products 5 to 10 years from now will be products not yet in existence.[11] Ninety percent of the prescriptions written by medical doctors today could not have been written 10 years ago. (Quotation from Dean George Packer

[11] See footnote 6.

Berry of the Harvard Medical School in talk to Southern California Industry, Education Conference, Lake Arrowhead, July 1957.)

To summarize: In military affairs the unstable and short lifetime of weapons systems has produced an even more severe instability in tactics and strategy. The resulting military and national dilemmas, as is well known, are unsolved. The nature of these dilemmas is inadequately studied. In industry and agriculture an equivalent effect has occurred. The increase in productivity through automation has resulted in consumer product instability which, in turn, has produced instability in labor employment, in capital investment, and in urban growth and transportation—in fact, in our entire economy. In agriculture, applied R & D has increased and continues to increase per capita productivity *on the farm* so fast that the agricultural system is not able to adapt fast enough sociologically; on the other hand, government controls and subsidies for agriculture have also been unable to reduce agricultural instability and to prevent satisfactorily serious difficulties in the agricultural-business system. Since the agricultural-business system involves over 40 percent of our GNP,[12] a far better understanding of the agricultural-business *system* is certainly required. In no sense can this problem be considered as only a "farm" problem that is sociological in nature. It is a big systems problem the solution of which is not yet known. To treat it as a farm problem alone could do great damage to the entire U. S. economy.

2. The second problem is that of increased choice resulting from organized R & D. As an example, Figure 8 indicates the number of technical choices in a particular military product situation as a function of time.[13] Many thousands of technical alternatives are now available from which products can be chosen for development, where once there were only two or three. Actually, over such a wide range, the military or commercial value of many of the choices is not too different. Many product developments which are, or could be, technical successes represent only marginal operational improvements. Nevertheless, they require approximately the same effort as it takes to bring a successful new product into practical being and usefulness. The combination of a surplus of technical choices with only a small prospect of operational advantage in any particular case results in a situation in which individual scientists or engineers, and lower and middle management, have no firm intuitive or pragmatic basis for

[12] John H. Davis and Ray A. Goldberg, *A Concept of Agribusiness,* Harvard University Press, Cambridge, Mass., 1957.

[13] Ellis A. Johnson, "Crisis in Science and Technology," *Operations Research,* Vol. 6, No. 1, Jan.–Feb. 1958, p. 18.

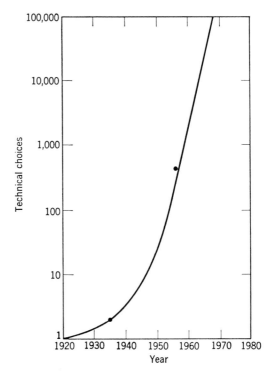

FIGURE 8.   Increase in technical choices.

judgment as to the usefulness of a prospective technically successful product.   Most newly proposed consumer products and[14] most newly proposed military products are failures.   Thus the decision regarding which one or which set of alternatives should receive R & D support is made especially difficult.   This has been well covered by Hitch and McKean[15] and by Johnson.[16]   At the lower levels of management there is the increasingly difficult problem of how to make particular devices compatible with the higher system into which they must fit— whether this is a military combat system, consumer product system, or an industrial production system.   At the higher levels of the Federal Government there is the question of whether particular devices whose development is supported by Federal funds are of the kinds that *ought* to be developed in order to increase further the over-all

[14] See footnote 6.
[15] Charles J. Hitch and Roland N. McKean, *The Economics of Defense in the Nuclear Age,* Harvard University Press, Cambridge, Mass., 1960.
[16] See footnote 13.

effectiveness of the U. S., considered as an economic-sociological system. With respect to patents, the multitude of technical choices, together with the present impossibility of reliably retrieving patent information, decreases the value of any particular patent as well as making it difficult to establish the validity of a patent. As a result the value of the patent system is in question.

To summarize: the effect of a large number of technical alternatives imposes a greatly increased need to consider the interrelations within the over-all national, military, economic, and business systems —i.e., it requires big-systems analysis—and tends to transfer more responsibility to upper levels of management in the choice of projects worthy of major R & D support. The direct consequence is an urgent need for highly qualified technical talent at the upper levels of management. Also, the value of the patent system as an economic incentive is jeopardized and needs re-examination.

3. A third problem is the relation between the short lifetime of the products of research, the large number of technical alternatives, and the long lead times required to bring these products into existence. Lead time is commonly defined as the time from the initial concept of an idea to actual full-scale routine operational use, but it is doubtful that the idea of lead time so comprehensively defined is a useful one. When inventions were simple and product improvement could bear a good fraction of the brunt of complete development, lead times were quite short, often 1 to 3 years. Today, complicated interactions between many individual devices or products of a complete system increase the need to explore, both in basic and applied research, areas that show promise but are not certain, and to provide for the development of components well ahead of time so that they can be tested for reliability and effectiveness (transistors are an example). As a result, lead times often are as long as 10–15 years and occasionally 20–40 years.[17]

[17] The Robertson Committee in 1955–1957 determined the average lead time on manned aircraft weapons systems to be 11 years. (Unclassified summary report of the Ad Hoc Study Group on Manned Aircraft Weapons System, Secretary of Defense release, February 21, 1957.)

David Novick testified before a Congressional Committee on the more than 40-year lead time in the history of the lowly zipper. One was displayed at the Columbian Exposition in 1893, and the patents for it were granted along the way, but not until 1940 did the zipper enter full-scale operational use. (Hearings on Federal Expenditure Policy for Economic Growth and Stability before the Subcommittee on Fiscal Policy of the Joint Economic Committee, November 18–27, 1957.)

Neil P. Ruzic reported in the June–July 1961 issue of *Industrial Research* on "The English Channel Tunnel; 159 Years of Research."

This again is a problem of management of R & D. A better managed R & D program, especially military R & D, would have a better balance in the amount of effort spent in basic and applied research and in component development; the areas to be explored would be based appreciably on long-range planning as high-risk, high-profit areas of capital investment. Hence, information would be more quickly available for rapid end-item product and systems development as well as for system components. Under these circumstances management innovation would be more efficient and end-item development, including systems, could be done in a relatively short time, perhaps in less than 5 years, with fewer models. The capital investment, therefore, in a balanced portfolio of basic and applied research, component development, end-item development, and systems development, i.e., their parallel development instead of series development, would lead to a rate of innovation perhaps two or three times faster than at present. This would certainly correspond to a very much higher "efficiency" in the performance of R & D. To repeat, as it is now, too many U. S. *development* efforts result in products that are technical successes but military or commercial failures.

To summarize: present U. S. lead times in R & D, now twice as long as for the USSR and four times as long as U. S. lead time in World War II, can be shortened by a better balance between basic and applied research, and component and end-item development. An increase in basic and applied research and component development is suggested as well as an increase in systems research. A reduction in lead times equals increased effectiveness of R & D.

4. The fourth problem, relatively new in this decade, lies in the neglect of great areas of R & D that require the integration of basic and applied research;[18,19] areas that single companies cannot afford to tackle or that are not immediately required for a particular end-item device but without which we are limited in long-range programming of R & D. For example, we need to understand in great detail the over-all effects of radiation received through ingestion of radioactive material and the possibility of preventitive and therapeutic measures. The design and practicality of nuclear developments are critically dependent on the chosen standards of radiation tolerance. Within some decades nuclear devices will provide the main

[18] See footnote 1.
[19] *Proceedings of the Army—ORO Conference on Basic and Applied Research and Component Development*, (U), The Johns Hopkins University Operations Research Office, Bethesda, Maryland, Vol. XI.

sources of energy for human use, including mobile power units. Quite apart from military events, we will be living in an environment in which accidents related to nonmilitary nuclear devices may subject us to the daily possibility of excess radiation as well as to occasional disasters. This problem cannot be solved in a piecemeal fashion. Problems like that of radioactive ingestion need multidisciplinary cooperation with a vengeance. The professions involved are physics, geophysics, biochemistry, biophysics, soil physics and chemistry, plant nutrition and pathology, animal nutrition and pathology, human nutrition and pathology, medicine, engineering, economics, psychology, sociology, law, etc. One might as well list most of the learned professions!

We need to increase the support of pioneering laboratories such as the Oak Ridge National Laboratory. We need an Institute of Radiation Medicine in conjunction with a research hospital to establish, in cooperation with existing laboratories, the acceptable radiation doses, methods of radiation therapy, and national safety regulations on an over-all systems basis.

With respect to the need and success of the "Institute" approach, an excellent example of a situation where the action has been successfully taken with great importance to the U. S.—including all of industry and governmental agencies—is the exploitation of knowledge that has resulted from the progress in physics of the solid state, physical chemistry, and chemistry in the development of new materials. In a $20,000,000 a year program, twelve such Institutes have been established at Universities. It has been proved possible to develop new synthetic materials with very superior qualities and low costs which do not necessarily exist in nature in commercial quantities, if at all, and often completely displace materials found in nature.[20] A continuing and even more intensive development of new materials will have a growing and tremendous effect on the U. S. economy, making us economically and strategically stronger. In this particular case a speedup in materials development has been provided by the "Institute" mechanism, as had long been proposed by von Hippel[21] and, more recently, by the President's Scientific Advisory Committee.[22] Many other neglected technical areas require

[20] Lawrence Lessig, "The Mighty Mix of New Materials," *Fortune* (May 1962).

[21] A. von Hippel, "Modern Materials Research," *Proceedings of the Army-ORO Conference on Basic and Applied Research and Component Development,* (U), The Johns Hopkins University Operations Research Office, Bethesda, Maryland, Vol. VII, p. 4.

[22] See reference 1.

the establishments of such technical institutes, particularly in meteorology and weather control and in handling information. This is also especially desirable in the behavioral sciences and in the areas involving technical aid, education, and the general area of peace technology.

To summarize: multicustomer-multidisciplinary problems require the establishment of National Institutes to carry out applied research of very broad scope involving a number of scientific disciplines; this is of critical importance to business, industry, and the economy as a whole where such applied research cannot be supported by individual companies. As suggested by the President's Science Advisory Committee, such Institutes should continue to be associated with Universities.

5. The fifth problem, and one of increasing importance, is that of secrecy. Especially within the Department of Defense we need a more sophisticated understanding of the communications requirements of development organizations, and the recognition of the reduced rate of "local" technical progress that results from excessive secrecy. The secrecy policy of the Government in military work (this also applies in part to industry and to nonmilitary agencies of the Government) hampers the effective use of R & D.[23]   Much work in the military establishment is repeated unwittingly and undesirably because of the deliberately erected communications barriers *within* the Department of Defense, where we have not only maintained but actually intensified interagency secrecy for reasons of interagency competition. Not only are some kinds of technical communications between the Army, Air Force, and Navy prohibited, technical communications to the Department of Defense by the three services are often prohibited as well. These "need to know" policies in many cases have been established by military personnel who mistakenly ascribe *all* USSR progress to espionage.[24]   We spread unnecessary secrecy to other departments of the Government in spite of our slow progress (compared to our potential). It is doubtful if there are any worthwhile secrets of a crucial nature to "keep," either secrets of nature or of invention. We must make a better compromise between the great need for improved technical communications and the deleterious effects of secrecy until *our* rate of technical progress so far exceeds that of

---

[23] *Secrecy and Science*, Hearing before the Subcommittee on Constitutional Rights, U. S. Senate, 86th Congress, U. S. Government Printing Office, 1959.

[24] Lt. Gen. Arthur G. Trudeau, *Industrial Security*, Vol. 2, No. 4, (October 1958) pp. 14, 24–27.

our competitors that we again need not fear that they will "catch up." We must make sure from now on that the use of our R & D resources is not limited by the compartmentation and inefficiency currently forced on the R & D system by unwarranted and unnecessary secrecy.

In summary: the lack of professional competence of the majority of United States R & D military managers and their short tenures of duty (see p. 30 for effect of tenure) and the interagency competition between the three military services have resulted in policies that prohibit technical exchange between the services in many significant areas of development. Very little significant exchange of technical information with U. S. allies is permitted. Because military development agencies are usually commanded by technically unqualified and transient military personnel, much of the Federal R & D effort is low in effectiveness and quality. One half of the free-world capability in military R & D is almost unused because of the rigid and timid refusal of the U. S. to help allies even in obsolescent weapons systems. The present policy of excessive secrecy is sterile and harmful since, in some respects, the USSR is ahead of the U. S. in weapons development.

6. The dilemma in the role of R & D groups in connection with the large systems of industry, military establishments, and government in general is, in large part, one of complexity and interdependence of factors within the systems. Figure 9 illustrates the many feedback interactions in the very big system concerned with *military* competition with the Soviet Union. (This is only one subsystem of our overall national system.)[25] No adequate logic or plan has as yet been formulated to deal with the complicated feedbacks of this particular kind of situation nor has any adequate study program been adopted to comprehend the problems. A pertinent study could be made only at the Presidential or National Security Council level, and attempts during the last 15 years to initiate one have always been defeated or died at the onset.[26] Therefore, the policies and procedures that could be

[25] D. P. Eckman (Ed.), *Systems: Research and Design Proceedings of the First Systems Symposium at Case Institute of Technology,* John Wiley & Sons, New York, 1961, Chapter 4.

[26] The last time this problem was identified for study and partially covered was under the leadership of Nelson Rockefeller in the Quantico I and Quantico II studies. The approach, however, was rejected by Dwight D. Eisenhower. The Rockefeller brothers continued the study under private auspices but this was not an adequate substitute, partly because of lack of access to classified information and partly because the effort was too small.

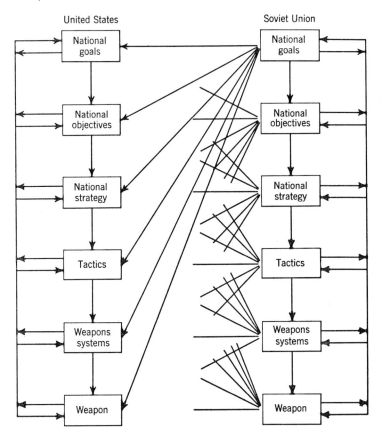

FIGURE 9.   Interaction of United States-Soviet Union systems.

used to develop the most effective technical system to meet our existing worldwide competition are not known.   Even without an integrated plan, the national goals, objectives, strategy, and tactics that
have been adopted on an intuitive basis should be more explicitly described and understood at all levels, including the relatively low working level of research organizations.   Work at the research level must
ultimately produce the actual devices that will further the adopted
goals.   Although most of the key decisions must be made at the high
organizational levels, there must be a continuous flow of information
from the research level.   Many potential devices that could help determine practical objectives, strategies, and tactics cannot be foreseen by the top management of the Government.   This is equally true
for very large industrial corporations.

Since our national situation is one of extremely rapid innovation (whether we like it or not), it is also necessary to consider the possibilities of the long- and intermediate-range futures and the "big systems" that might be possible and desirable at a later time. These considerations affect and are affected by lead-times in R & D. We have to know and understand the competitions, difficulties, and feedbacks of interactions involved in big systems and rapid innovation. Otherwise we may develop many devices that prove to be useless upon completion, or, by the same token, we may *not* initiate actions involving long lead times, thus running the risk of losing the most favorable future our country might achieve. An example of *inaction* has been our slowness in missile development; and an example of *action* was our development of nuclear devices. Another example of inaction is our failure to support education for science, and another example of action is the establishment of the National Science Foundation.

In summary: it is essential that more adequate long-range "big" systems analyses be conducted at the higher levels of Government, and that the results be fully explained to lower levels of R & D management and execution.

EXAMPLES OF FACTORS THAT AFFECT R & D EFFICIENCY: INFLATION, TENURE, AND TECHNICAL EFFICIENCY

The need for superior governmental policies can be illustrated by specific factors that greatly affect the efficiency of development in a particular organization, but which depend on national policies or actions. The first is the effect of R & D inflation in shortening tenure and the resulting reduction in technical efficiency. The inflation results from restrictions on the way in which Federal funds can be spent and from a shortage of personnel. The need for research personnel versus the supply of personnel is beginning to diverge. This is illustrated by Figure 10, which shows the estimate of Harrison Brown et al.[27] on the need as a function of time. The need is based on the values assigned to the use of technical personnel in industry and government. The effect of this divergence between need and supply has resulted in an inflation of R & D costs as shown in Figure 11, which plots a cost-of-research index versus time based on about an 8-percent sample of the U. S. technical labor force.[28] Participants

[27] Harrison Brown, James Bonner, John Weir, *The Next Hundred Years,* The Viking Press, New York, 1957, p. 120.
[28] Ellis A. Johnson and Helen S. Milton, "A Proposed Cost-of-Research Index," *IRE Transactions,* Vol. EM-8, No. 4, Dec. 1961.

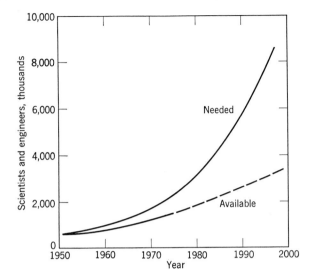

FIGURE 10.   Projected manpower needs.

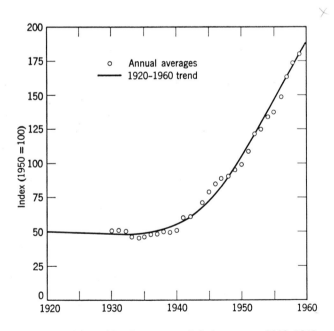

FIGURE 11.   Index of R & D cost per technical man-year, 1920–1960.

included the General Electric Company, the Bell Telephone Laboratories, Raytheon, etc. One of the major participants of the Government was the Bureau of Standards, and the Carnegie Institution of Washington represented the foundations.

Figure 12 presents a breakdown of the costs of R & D.[29] It is obvious that inflation in salaries is greater than the average of the in-

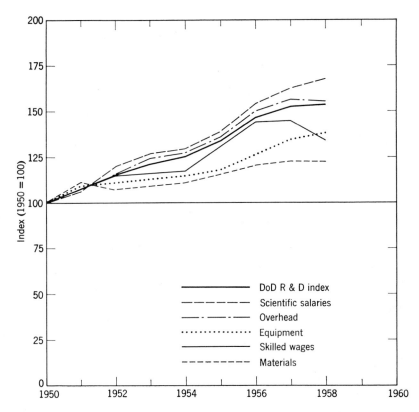

FIGURE 12. Department of Defense (DoD) composite R & D cost index and components, 1950–1958.

dex and of other costs such as materials. The actual inflation differs rather widely from industry to industry and from profession to profession, as illustrated in Figure 13. One reason is that not all kinds of activities have an equal urgency with respect to innovation. Cur-

[29] Committee on Government Operations, House Report No. 2552, *Research and Development,* 85th Congress, Second Session, 1958, p. 107.

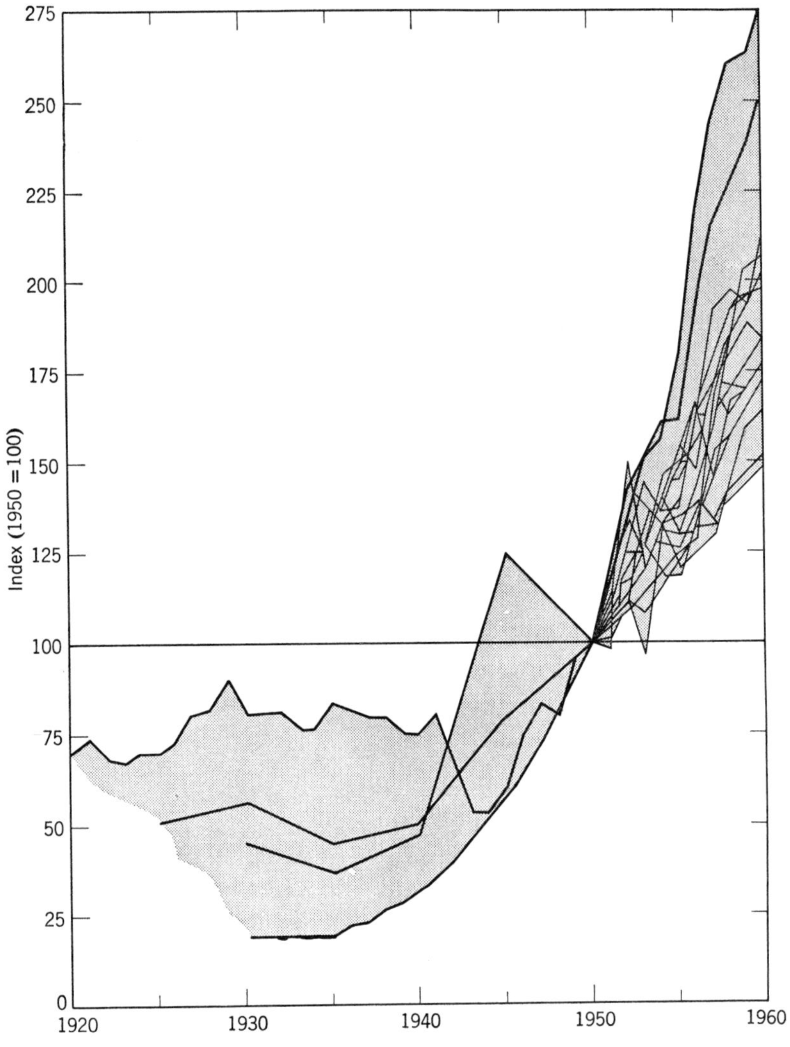

FIGURE 13. Indexes of R & D cost per technical man-year for 17 organizations, 1920–1960.

rently, physicists and mathematicians are in much greater demand than are economists or psychologists. Thus an average index cannot be applied in a "meat-axe" way. There is no question as to the high rate of inflation in R & D salaries compared to other professional salaries in the U. S.

In Figure 14 the inflation index is applied to R & D dollar expenditures to identify the relative volume of R & D effort. Of national funds spent since 1950 only about one-half has gone to an increase in effort, the other half has gone toward an increase in cost. Figure 15 shows the absolute increases in the U. S. and the Soviet technical labor forces. A comparison of Figures 15 and 16 leads to the conclusion that the increase in the technical labor force has been only slightly greater percentagewise than the "useful" increase in R & D funds. One must conclude that the number of people in the technical labor force is a much better measure of the R & D effort than the dollar budget because of the distorting effect of inflation on a single "dollar" comparison.

With respect to the competition between the U. S. and the Soviet Union, for each country the ratio of the technical labor forces to the total labor force, Figure 16, is probably a better measure as a forecast of the two economies. Even in a rapidly innovating world, most technical personnel must work as an integral part of the pro-

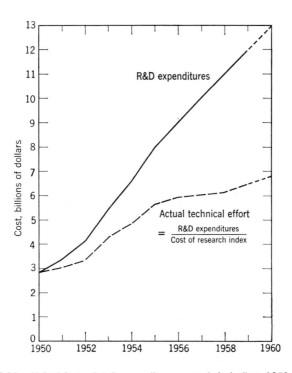

FIGURE 14.   United States R & D expenditures vs. technical effort, 1950–1960.

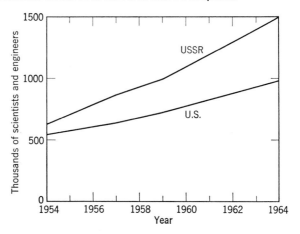

FIGURE 15.   Scientists and engineers employed in scientific-technical fields, U. S. and USSR.

duction and management system rather than as R & D "innovators." Thus the effect of the technical labor force occurs in two steps: the first step, using a relatively small part of the technical labor force, is concerned with the process of innovation; the second step, using larger parts of the technical labor force, is concerned with adapting and employing technical innovations as a part of the productive machinery. The technical labor required for this second step presumably needs to be proportional to the total labor force. An increase in per capita productivity would depend primarily on the tech-

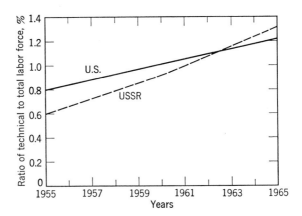

FIGURE 16.   Ratios of scientists and engineers to total labor force in the U. S. and USSR.

nical-to-total labor force ratio, whereas the first step would probably depend in a critical way on the absolute number of technical personnel used for science and the development of innovations, and the effect of the fraction used for this first step on the technical-to-total labor force ratio essential for the second step. Thus both of the U. S. and USSR economies, starved for technical personnel, must make difficult choices between their use of technical personnel, first, to generate innovations and, second, to apply these new innovations in the productive systems, as well as maintaining an increasing overall productivity at the same time. The balance between these two uses of technical personnel is hard to achieve, since we have no pragmatic guides from experience in this novel situation and none from philosophical or management theory. The relatively slow improvement in most of the Soviet productive machinery noted by Saulnier[30] may well be associated with this dilemma. It should be carefully noted that the actual appearance of both innovations and increases in productivity have lag times of the order of 5–10 years after technical employment begins. Thus the possible 1963 advantage of the USSR in the labor force ratios will not have great effects on the USSR economy until about 1975, and then only if other concurrent economic and sociological problems are simultaneously solved.

Nevertheless, the predicted existence of a greater Soviet technical labor force ratio provides the USSR with the possibility of an unusual economic and military advantage in the forthcoming decades. Thus, in spite of its present advantage in technical-to-total labor force ratio, the U. S. has no reason to be overly optimistic, since an early superiority on the part of the Soviet Union is forecast unless we take long-range action with respect to our educational system to increase the number of scientific and engineering personnel. Again we must emphasize that recognition of the importance of R & D to the entire nation has not yet been accompanied by action in the educational areas.

The factor of limited personnel is related to one of the critical effects of inflation not yet adequately measured. This is the effect of salary inflation on the tenure of employment and, thereby, on R & D productivity. Inflation tends to reduce the tenure of employment since organizations are prone to be quite conservative in raising salaries of personnel already in their employ, even at a time of rapidly rising salaries. However, the same organizations attempt to attract outside superior research personnel.

[30] Raymond J. Saulnier, "An Economist's View of the World," *Fortune,* May 1962, p. 29.

Thus, in most companies, there tends to be discrimination directed against existing employees in favor of new employees. The strategy for the individual, then, if he desires an advance in salary is to change jobs, especially if he is young. The result has been a considerable increase in job-hopping in the U. S. in recent years, with consequent reduction in the average tenure of personnel. The effect of this on the efficiency of R & D organizations has indeed been serious.

Tenure rates vary largely in conjunction with the shortages in particular professions. Figure 17 shows the average turnover rates in several of the scientific professions in the U. S. in 1955. The high turnover rate for mathematicians undoubtedly has resulted in part from the current popularity of computer use.

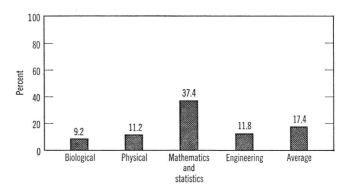

FIGURE 17. Annual separation rates in government scientific and engineering categories, 1955.

The rate of job-hopping and the length of tenure are especially critical to R & D efficiency if the average tenure falls too low. The results and hypotheses that follow are derived from a study of about 500 technical personnel over a 12-year period.

Figure 18 is applicable to both the individual and the group. It relates the research productivity of the individual as a function of the time he has been at work on a particular research subject. This exemplifies the situation with respect to new research accomplishment faced by the individual *after* he changes jobs, especially when this involves a change in organization. As a first approximation, little or no R & D productivity can be expected for 1½ to 2 years after a job change, followed by increasing productivity up to and for perhaps more than 10 years. Since most jobs may not last much longer than

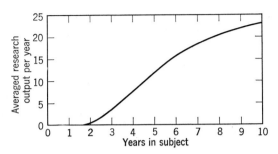

FIGURE 18.   Individual research productivity.

10 years in these days of rapid innovation, extrapolation beyond 7 to 10 years is futile and of little value.   There would, of course, be some carry-over to a new job if the new job of the individual or group were reasonably similar.

From this empirical curve we conclude that individuals who stay with an organization or group for 2 years or less produce a limited amount of finished work, and the initial period of employment must be regarded primarily as capital investment and orientation.   From 2 years on, the average productivity over the period of employment increases, reaching a maximum for the particular individual between the fifth and seventh year.   Figure 19 is a curve of predicted accumulated productivity as a function of the time of employment, and Figure 20 gives the predicted average productivity versus tenure.   We are now able to apply the data from the last few figures to calculate a

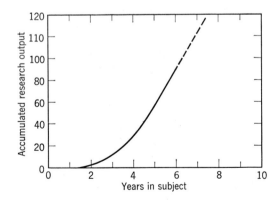

FIGURE 19.   Accumulated research productivity.

hypothetical efficiency of various organizations based on their turn-over rate. This has been done by using the data provided to a Congressional Committee on R & D[31] by the Army, Navy, and Air Force. The data are summarized in Figures 21 and 22.

By assuming a fairly uniform tenure, which is indeed a crude approximation, we can calculate the efficiency of the three services in their contracting. The calculated relative efficiency is 69 percent for the Air Force, 65 percent for the Navy, and 50 percent for the Army. For this particular period, the Air Force was about 40 percent more effective than the Army, and about 10 percent more effective than the Navy.

Exactly the same considerations apply to the productivity of an entire organization as a function of the "tenure" of the organization

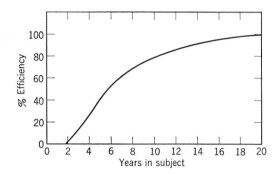

FIGURE 20.   Average research productivity.

in a particular area of development. An organizational tenure of much less than 10 years in a very complicated area of scientific appli-cation is increasingly inefficient as tenure is reduced. Organizational effectiveness only begins to reach a reasonable level in about 5 years. This implies need for long-term contracts for development tasks.

To summarize: an increasing shortage in technical personnel in the U. S. has led to a runaway inflation in technical salaries; salary infla-tion, in turn, has led to a reduction in tenure of technical employment, and reduced tenure has, in turn, reduced the productivity of technical personnel. The effect of too rapidly rising technical salaries is thus

[31] House Subcommittee on Manpower Utilization of the Committee on Post Office and Civil Service, 86th Congress, 2nd Session, *Personnel Procurement Costs of Selected Defense Contractors for Recruitment of Engineers and Scientists, Fiscal Year, 1959,* September 1960, pp. 3–5.

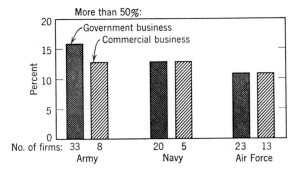

FIGURE 21.   Median separation rates of 102 private industry firms, 1959.

to *reduce* the total amount of technical accomplishments in the U. S. as a whole as compared to the potential. Since salary inflation is due largely to regulations restricting the ways in which Federal technical budgets can be spent, the amount of these Federal funds *spent on an excess of salaries* has had exactly the opposite effect from that intended; i.e., over-all U. S. accomplishments have been reduced rather than increased, although certain highly valued Federal projects have benefited. The situation is far worse today than in 1955, but even then mathematicians and statisticians were operating at about 20 percent efficiency. No wonder our superior technical resources produce meager results compared to this potential. We actually need higher Federal expenditures for R & D, but above all such expenditures *must* be accompanied by constraints and incentives that provide better balance in the ways the funds are spent. The implied long-range remedy is to increase rapidly the size of the technical labor force, and one of the partial short-range remedies is to modify Federal

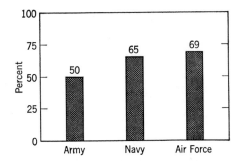

FIGURE 22.   "Military" contractor efficiency, 1959.

regulations to permit higher expenditures, at Government cost, in facilities, scientific and technical communications, increased tenure of both technical employment and technical contracts, and increased incentives for high performance. In Federal contracts especially, the value of tenure and stability in increasing performance should be recognized.

The shortage of scientific personnel can be alleviated to some extent by the conversion of graduates from the liberal arts to scientific research. Many of these graduates have an excellent background in mathematics, or are willing and able to obtain it. Some have been unusually successful in their conversion and represent a valuable addition to the technical labor force, thus reducing the effects of inflation. I believe that a deliberate program of conversion could increase our technical labor force by perhaps 5–20 percent, and thus relieve a fraction of the present inflationary pressure.

Research Productivity of the Group

The project group level has tended to become the basic unit in research, slowly replacing the individual scientists or inventor. Figure 23 indicates that R & D has more and more become a team activity in

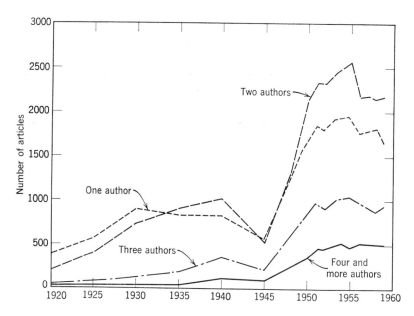

FIGURE 23. Trend in authorship pattern, 1920–1959. (Survey of 10 scientific journals.)

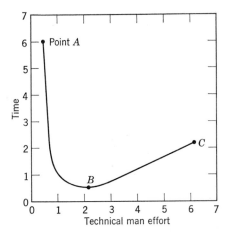

FIGURE 24.   Research effort vs. time for accomplishment.

the U. S. even in basic research.[32]   A similar teamwork situation is found in a survey of patent applications[33] and is most prominent in the development areas.   It is required in the synthesis of the many factors that pertain to complicated R & D problems.   In these areas each member explores one or more factors and, with other members, makes a creative discovery by joint effort.   Although a superior person might make such a discovery, it would be extremely unlikely since the extensive literature search and experimentation required may amount to more work than could possibly be achieved by one man.   The shape of the curve in Figure 24 represents the relationship between the size of the group and time of accomplishment of a research task.   A minimum time of R & D accomplishment occurs at some optimum group size.   Too large a group will take longer because too much increase in size appears to promote excessive communications among the members.   This is shown in Figure 25, in which the numbers of communication links as a function of group size are given. It can be seen that, when the group is unstructured and exceeds many more than six people, the possible number of communication links available become so extremely large that both communications and research progress tend to bog down.   A group of 12 people, for ex-

[32] Helen S. Milton and Henrietta H. Green, "The Group vs the Individual in Research," ORO-TP-4, Operations Research Office, The Johns Hopkins University, Bethesda, Maryland, 1960.

[33] A. B. Bakalar, "Hidden Resources," *Journal, Patent Office Society,* Vol. 41, No. 9, p. 591.

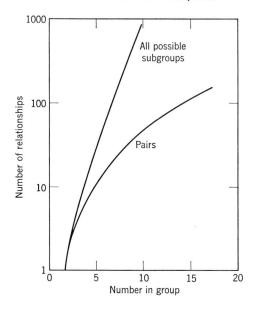

FIGURE 25.   Group size and communication links.

ample, might double the time and increase the total cost of doing a small research project by as much as seven times above the cost of a group of six people.   On the other hand, too small a group is unable to keep up with competitive progress.   Thus, the total research accomplishment of a group of three people might cost as much as four to five times that of a group of six.   Indeed the optimum "working" R & D group size, with existing techniques of management, lies somewhere between four and seven people, and very complicated problems requiring many people are more feasibly split up into a "team of teams" so that the segments can be handled by subgroups of similar size.

Government contracting procedures and the desire for empire building on the part of young administrators tend to increase group size well above the optimum.   Cost-plus-fixed-fee contracts which theoretically should work well, in practice tend to provide an incentive for too large groups, since to maximize profit requires spending the maximum amount of money, and this can be accomplished most easily by using an excess number of personnel.   Thus, contractual arrangements that provide particular kinds of incentives with respect to optimum group size could have an important effect.

To summarize: optimum group size and therefore technical efficiency is affected by Federal contract provisions. Revision of present contract incentives appears desirable.

Communications and Facilities

The contracting regulations of the Government make it almost impossible to provide and spend *adequate* funds specifically for facilities, libraries, communications (especially communications of an unusual and pioneering nature), frequent attendance at technical meetings and symposia, and especially for the use of very large study groups to achieve major syntheses on big systems problems. In many cases, additional funds spent in these areas, particularly in communications, might increase effectiveness by as much as 50–100 percent. Expenditures of funds for rapid data storage and retrieval, and thus better coordination of technical information, is very important and is relatively neglected.

An estimate summarizing the percentage improvements in the overall accomplishments of U. S. technology dependent on Federal policy are given in Table 1. Not all of these have been discussed in detail

TABLE 1

Possible Percentage Improvements in U. S. Research and Development

1. Control of inflation	20– 50
2. Optimizing group size	50–100
3. Optimizing communications	50–100
4. Improved facilities	10– 30
5. Conversion of liberal arts graduates	5– 20
6. Special opportunities for young scientists	50–100

here, but can be found elsewhere.[34, 35] Not all of the six factors considered are independent. As a crude estimate, an over-all improvement in the productivity of the U. S. technical labor force in the range of 100–300 percent appears reasonable and possible.

POSSIBLE ACTIONS TO IMPROVE U. S. TECHNOLOGY

This chapter has primarily been a review of our present competitive situation in the application of science to technology. It is clear that

[34] Ellis A. Johnson, "Mobilizing Young Brainpower," *Proceedings Military-Industrial Conference*, Chicago, Illinois, March 14–17, 1957.

[35] See footnote 13.

a serious national problem exists, and that its solution cannot be achieved solely by individual action of separate agencies or industries. It is also suggested that the solutions are far too complicated for the limited analysis possible to any individual, but that formal action at the level of the President is indicated.

There is no question about the responsibility of the Federal Government to encourage innovation, and thus R & D. This was recognized by the Founding Fathers in the establishment of the Patent Office. Other actions of the Government such as favorable tax regulations by the Treasury Department, direct support of research and its application in the several departments and agencies, and the budgetary consideration of the over-all impacts of R & D by the Bureau of the Budget have the same effect, are of the same nature, and should be considered in concert.

Backward departments spend as little as 0.03 percent on R & D (or less); forward-looking departments as much as 30–70 percent. There appears to be no rationale in the distribution of R & D effort by departments or agencies; many critical problems which long ago deserved R & D effort are handled on an *ad hoc* crisis basis when it is quite late (arms control, economically distressed areas of the U. S., and education are typical examples).

Discussion in this chapter has suggested that the faults have been primarily those of omission. The failures involve primarily multidepartment, multiindustry and multiagency problem areas (including big system analysis) of a multidisciplinary nature which no industry or single Federal agency could solve by itself or by appeal to an existing organization. Problems such as R & D inflation, the debilitating effects of excessive secrecy, and the lack of coordination of information within the Government require action at the highest level of policy by both the Congress and the President.

Thus the interests of the entire nation are involved in this question. The solution must be reasonably acceptable to five groupings of the American society: the public; the research community; executives in industry and government; systems groups such as the Government regulating agencies, labor unions, industrial associations; and the operating agencies of the local, State and Federal Governments and individual companies and enterprises (such as those in agriculture). These groups, all greatly affected by R & D, hold some values in common, but many of their values and goals are in conflict (as in automation); thus the groups have difficulty over agreement in very many of the aspects of the control of R & D, including the amount and allocation of funds. None of the existing agencies of Science or of the Federal Government have by themselves either the authority, scope, or impartiality to solve this problem. This includes the new Office of Science and Technology which has too low a status and authority and is not of Cabinet rank. The notable and distinguished groups especially concerned and interested besides the Congress, the President and Federal and State Departments and Agencies are the National Academy of Science (with the National Research Council), the American Association for the Advancement of Science, the Bureau of the Budget, the President's Science Advisory Committee, the Federal Science Council, the National Science Foundation, and the new Office of Science and Technology.

This situation has been widely discussed by scientists[36], [37], [38] and the Senate Committee on Government Operations.[39]

In a similar situation, when the force of circumstances required Government support of basic research in the U. S. in order to survive at an adequate level, a Presidential study was made under the leadership of Vannevar Bush (at the President's request). The proposer of the National Science Foundation, Vannevar Bush, as well as its many proponents (and opponents) feared for the freedom of basic research in our country because of the danger of too tight and too bureaucratic control if chiefly Government funds were to be used to support research. Some of these fears proved to have been justified. Still, the present high status of basic research in the U. S. testifies to the wisdom of the policies actually adopted and applied in this area.

Force of circumstance now requires us to consider additional actions, designed with equal care to protect our traditional freedoms, especially in our free enterprise system which might remedy our deficiences in the *application* of research to technology.

The establishment of a Congressional Commission as proposed by Senators McClellan, Humphrey, Mundt, Cotton, and Yarborough appears a most desirable step to study and recommend the best way to strengthen U. S. technology and to include the possibility of a Department of Science, which is favored by many. At the same time there should be established without delay committees within the Government, within each professional society, within the AAAS, and

[36] Don K. Price, "The Scientific Establishment," *Science,* Vol. 136, No. 3522, June 29, 1962.

[37] W. S. Sayre, "Scientists and American Science Policy," *Science,* Vol. 133, No. 3456, March 24, 1961.

[38] "New Office of Science & Technology . . . " Comment by D. S. Greenberg, *Science,* Vol. 136, No. 3510, April 6, 1962, p. 32.

[39] "Commission on Science and Technology," Senators McClellan and Humphrey, Congressional Record, pp. 1157–1159, January 31, 1962, Vol. 108, No. 14.

within the National Academy of Science to study the same problem with the view that these studies would be used at an early date by the Congressional Commission.

To bolster our deficient defense research, the immediate establishment of a "Division of Defense Research" as originally recommended by Bush in his report to the President (*Science, The Endless Frontier*) is proposed; or possibly the establishment of an independent civilian agency operated by civilians "independently of the military establishment," i.e., devoid of military control, to help achieve again the brilliantly successful program of development of weapons and devices of warfare of the World War II Office of Scientific Research and Development (OSRD). Such competition would indeed stimulate and improve the R & D quality of the three Service agencies and of the Department of Defense. This kind of healthy and independent internal competition of the quality previously provided by OSRD is needed because information—providing a competitive incentive—on the results and details of superior military developments by our external competitor, the USSR, come to us too late and too inaccurately.

APPENDIX U. S. VERSUS USSR LEAD TIMES

This appendix provides the code used in Figure 1 and refers to the footnotes in the section entitled "The Nature of the Problem."

First A-Bomb Test
U. S.—July 16, 1945.[1]
USSR—August 29, 1949.[1,2]

First H-Bomb Test
U. S.—November 1, 1952.[1,3]
USSR—August 12, 1953.[1]

Fission Explosion 30–40 KT
U. S.—April 18, 1953.[1]
USSR—August 31, 1953.[1]

Ground Weapons Atomic Munitions
U. S.—March 17–June 4, 1953. First test shot from 280-mm gun.[1]
USSR—April, 1954. Small caliber atomic weapons used in Army maneuvers.[4]

Atomic Submarine
U. S.—April 22, 1955. Nautilus operational.[5]
USSR—Possibly 1957.[6] No verified information as of 1959.[7]

Intercontinental Jet Bomber
U. S.—1955.[8]
USSR—1955.[8]

A-Bomb Stockpile, 4,000–5,000
U. S.—1954–1955.[9,10]
USSR—1958–1960 estimated.[11]

H-Bomb Air Dropped
    U. S.—May 21, 1956.[1]
    USSR—November 23, 1955.[1]
Motor Tested for IRBM
    U. S.—Late 1956, early 1957.[12]
    USSR—1950–1951.[13]
IRBM Tests
    U. S.—1957.[14]
    USSR—Mid-1955.[15]
Satellite
    U. S.—January 31, 1958, Explorer.[16]
    USSR—October 4, 1957, Sputnik I.[17]
IRBM Operational
    U. S.—Late 1958.[18]
    USSR—1957.[19]
ICBM—5,000-mile Test
    U. S.—November 28, 1958.[20]
    USSR—August 1957.[21]
Atomic Surface Ships Launched
    U. S.—July 21, 1959.[22]
    USSR—April 21, 1957.[23]
5,000-mile ICBMs Operational
    U. S.—1959–1960.[24]
    USSR—1958–1959.[25]
Submarine FBM Launchers
    U. S.—Estimated 1960.[26]
    USSR—1956–1957.[27]
FBM (Fleet Ballistic Missile) for Submarines
    U. S.—Estimated 1960.[28]
    USSR—1958–1959.[29]

REFERENCES

1. U. S. Joint Committee on Atomic Energy, Special Committee on Radiation (85th Congress, 1st Session), *The Nature of Radioactive Fallout and its Effect on Man*, Hearings, U. S. Govt. Printing Office, Washington, D. C., 1957, part 2, pp. 2063–2065.
2. Statement by President Truman, September 23, 1949, *The Washington* (D. C.) *Post and Times Herald,* September, 24 1949; Atomic Energy Commission, Public Information Service, unclassified memorandum, July 21, 1959.
3. *The Washington* (D. C.) *Post and Times Herald,* October 31, 1957, identified specific date. Hearings (Ref. 1) identified "Fall of 1952."
4. "The Arms Race," *Bulletin of the Atomic Scientists,* June 1954, p. 236.
5. *Jane's Fighting Ships,* 1955–1956, McGraw-Hill Book Co., New York 1956, p. 425.
6. "Probably Three Atomic Submarines," quoted from 1958 issue of Swedish Naval Yearbook in the *Military Review,* March 1958, p. 72.

7. Baldwin, Hanson W., *The New York Times,* April 7, 1959; *Missiles and Rockets,* July 27, 1959, p. 7.

8. *Aviation Age,* April 1958, p. 8.

9. Based on estimates of Lapp, Alsop, and P. M. S. Blackett (British), Ref. 4.

10. Statement of Prof. Cecil F. Powell (British) in *The New York Times,* February 27, 1955.

11. Estimates for earlier dates: *The Chicago Sun Times,* October 14, 1950; *American Legion Bulletin* quoted in the *New York Journal-American,* April 22, 1954; see also Refs. 4 and Ref. 10.

12. "Thor Engine Reaches Production Test," *Missiles and Rockets,* July 7, 1958, p. 23; U. S. Congress, House Committee on Government Operations (86th Congress, 1st Session) *Organization and Management of Missile Programs,* U. S. Govt. Printing Office, Washington, D. C., 1959 (House Report No. 1181) p. 14.

13. *Aviation Week,* November 18, 1957, p. 27.

14. For Jupiter: *Army Times,* June 28, 1958; *The St. Louis Post-Dispatch,* February 23, 1958; U. S. Congress House Committee on Appropriations, *Dept. of Defense: The Ballistic Missile Program,* Hearings, U. S. Government Printing Office, Washington, D. C., 1957, p. 74. For Thor: *Aviation Week,* March 3, 1958, p. 92; *U. S. News and World Report,* December 27, 1957, p. 31.

15. Stockwell, Richard, E., "An Evaluation of Russia's Missile Program," *Automotive Industries,* January 1, 1958, p. 104; *Aviation Week,* September 2, 1957, p. 27; *ibid.,* September 16, 1957, p. 73; *ibid.,* March 3, 1958, p. 92; Shepley, James, R., "Life-and-Death Debate Over Missile Program," *Life,* March 9, 1959, pp. 119–120.

16. *The Washington Post and Times Herald,* February 1, 1958.

17. *Ibid.,* October 5, 1957.

18. *Missiles and Rockets,* September 15, 1958, p. 30; *U. S. News and World Report,* December 27, 1957, p. 31; U. S. Library of Congress, Legislative Reference Service, *The United States Guided Missile Program.* Prepared for the Preparedness Investigation Subcommittee of the Senate Committee on Armed Services (86th Congress, 1st Session) by Charles H. Donnelly, U. S. Government Printing Office, Washington, D. C., 1959, Table, p. 61.

19. *Aviation Age,* April 1958, p. 8; *Aviation Week,* September 1957, p. 73; Barnett, David, *The Washington Evening Star,* November 10, 1957.

20. Reference 18, *The United States Guided Missile Program,* pp. 82–83.

21. *Aviation Age,* April 1958, p. 8; *Aviation Week,* September 2, 1957, p. 27; *ibid.,* September 16, 1957; Baldwin, Hanson, W., *The New York Times,* April 6, 1958; *Jane's All the World's Aircraft, 1958–1959,* McGraw-Hill Book Company, New York, 1959, p. 403; Shepley, James, R., Ref. 15; Albright, Robert C., *The Washington Post and Times Herald,* October 31, 1957.

22. *The Washington Post and Times Herald,* July 21, 1959. (Launching of nuclear-powered merchant vessel, July 21, 1959.)

23. *Jane's Fighting Ships, 1957–1958,* McGraw-Hill Book Company, New York, 1958, p. 351; *U. S. News and World Report,* October 19, 1956, p. 10.

24. Parke, Richard, H., *The New York Times,* June 10, 1959: Phillips, Thomas, R., "Mr. McElroy's Maginot Line," *The Reporter,* February 19, 1959, p. 25.

25. *Missiles and Rockets,* May 1957, p. 63.

26. Defense Secretary McElroy tells Senate Preparedness Investigating Subcommittee that Polaris missiles will be combat ready in 1960, *The Washington Evening Star*, February 8, 1959; *ibid.*, June 30, 1959.

27. *Military Review*, November 1956, p. 80 (CH-18, i.e., Comet II is not to be confused with the family of Comet 1, 2, 3, and 4 described in this reference); see also Lee, Asher (Ed.), *The Soviet Air and Rocket Forces*, Praeger, New York, 1959, p. 157; Baar, James, "Soviet Subs Bigger Threat Than ICBMS," *Missiles and Rockets*, August 10, 1959, p. 32; *Aviation Age*, April 1958, p. 96; *Military Review*, April 1959, pp. 95, 96, 105; *Missiles and Rockets*, July 20, 1959, p. 176.

28. *The New York Times*, July 29, 1959 (article on first Atlas intercontinental ballistic missiles to be installed for combat by September 1st, 1959); The *Washington Evening Star*, September 27, 1958 (Defense Secretary McElroy indicated that the Air Force's ICBM should be operational by early 1960); Prima, L. Edgar, *ibid.*, May 16, 1959.

29. *Aviation Age*, April 1958, pp. 20, 94–95; *Aviation Week*, March 3, 1958, p. 259: Baldwin, Hanson, W., *The New York Times*, March 25, 1959: "Technical Management Intelligence," *Space/Aeronautics*, February 1959, pp. 23–24; *Statement* of General A. W. Betts and *Comment* of General T. R. Phillips, Testimony in U. S. Congress, Senate Committee on Aeronautical and Space Sciences (86th Congress, 1st Session), *Investigation of Governmental Organization for Space Activities*, Hearings, U. S. Government Printing Office, Washington, D. C., 1959, p. 540.

2
.

Measurements of Scientific Research and Development and Related Activities, *Jacob Perlman*[1]

The acceleration of progress in science and technology in recent years has focused attention on the various activities involved in this field. These scientific efforts may be viewed as comprising two major areas. The first consists of scientific research and development and certain related activities. The second is composed of the education and training of scientists and engineers and technical supporting personnel.

This chapter is confined to the first area—scientific research and development (R & D) and related activities. However, a considerable volume of data dealing with the second area is available. This information on the education and training of scientists and engineers and technical supporting personnel has been compiled by the following: the Office of Education, Department of Health, Education, and Welfare; the National Science Foundation; the National Academy of Sciences—National Research Council; and other private and public agencies.

There are many conceptual problems involved in defining scientific R & D and related activities, as later discussion will indicate. The core activity, R & D, includes the planning and administration as well

[1] Mr. Perlman is Head, Office of Economic and Statistical Studies, National Science Foundation. The opinions expressed here represent the author's personal views and conclusions and are not necessarily those of the National Science Foundation. Acknowledgment is made to Kathryn S. Arnow, who was assisted by Olive Q. Baker, and to other members of the staff of the Office for cooperation in the preparation of this chapter.

as the actual performance of work. The related or associated activities consist of the dissemination of scientific information and two scientific activities of a general service nature—testing and standardization and the collection of scientific data.

Viewed from the standpoint of the allocation of dollar and manpower resources, scientific R & D and related activities loom today as an important segment of the national economy. In 1960–1961, the latest year for which estimates are available, the current operating funds used for performance of scientific R & D alone amounted to $14 billion, or 2.8 percent of the gross national product (GNP). There are no accurate national figures available on the smaller dollar outlays for R & D capital items, nor for the dissemination of scientific information, testing and standardization, and scientific data collection, but it is quite likely that the addition of these would lead to a total annual figure of no less than $16 billion.

With respect to manpower allocation, the data are similarly striking. Thus, in 1960, the latest year for which estimates are available, the full-time equivalent number of scientists and engineers engaged in R & D alone amounted to 387,000, or one-third of the estimated total number of scientists and engineers in the country. To these R & D scientists and engineers must be added an undetermined number of skilled technicians and other supporting personnel also engaged in R & D as well as the personnel employed in dissemination of scientific information, testing and standardization, and scientific data collection. The total engaged in R & D and related scientific activities is thus an impressive component of the nation's labor force.

Indeed, scientific activities can no longer be regarded as playing a subordinate role in the economy. On the contrary, some economists have begun to look upon this complex as a distinct, horizontal "industry of discovery," cutting across many other vertical industrial activities and possessing characteristics of its own. This new industry occupies a strategic place with respect to both national defense and the stabilization and growth of the economy.

In recognition of the significance of scientific R & D and related activities, the National Science Foundation has developed a broad system of measurement in this area. The system provides the basis for analyzing many problems associated with R & D and aids in the necessary decision making and policy formulation.

This chapter describes this program of measurements, both actual and proposed, pointing out the difficulties encountered in the collection of data, the limitations of the information obtained, and the various uses for the figures. The discussion deals primarily with scientific R & D and, secondarily, with the dissemination of scientific information. Testing and standardization and scientific data collection are not treated in detail because these activities have not yet been brought under the regular coverage of the National Science Foundation survey program.

OVER-ALL ASPECTS OF THE NATIONAL SCIENCE FOUNDATION PROGRAM

The National Science Foundation, which was established in 1950, began, not long afterwards, to develop a framework of comprehensive surveys of scientific R & D and related activities on a systematic and recurring basis. Earlier, in the 1930's and 1940's, various public groups had shown interest in R & D trends, but their statistical inquiries were necessarily limited in nature.

The Foundation's first over-all surveys, for the year 1953–1954, covered many aspects of scientific activities in the major parts or sectors of the economy—Government, industry, colleges and universities, and other nonprofit institutions. Although this effort was exploratory in nature, the resulting data were sufficiently accurate to serve as the basis for later comparisons and time series.

Since 1953–1954, the Foundation has gradually expanded the survey programs to achieve more intensive as well as extensive coverage of scientific R & D and related activities. At the same time, improvements have been made in the accuracy and validity of the data. This growth and improvement have been systematic, giving full recognition to the scope of the subject and the need for a continuing flow of information on a periodic basis.

The measurement of the volume of scientific R & D and related activities must be undertaken from the standpoint of both the input of human and material resources into these activities and the output in the form of the results of the activities. Thus far, the Foundation's survey program has concentrated on inputs. Measuring the output of scientific activities is a task of far greater conceptual and statistical intricacy, but an approach to this aspect is now being planned. Ultimately, when statistics on input and output are available together, it should be possible to undertake analytical studies of the efficiency of resource allocation to scientific R & D and related activities.

The dollar and manpower inputs into R & D are the central concern of the Foundation's program of measurement today. Most of the discussion which follows will therefore center on R & D statistics. A later section will deal with data on scientific information activities, which are also of critical importance.

In working with dollar inputs, a distinction must be made between current expenditures for the conduct of R & D and capital expenditures for R & D equipment and facilities. Dollar allocations for current operation are larger than those for capital items but both inputs are obviously indispensable. The survey program of the Foundation has covered both, but the collection of data on R & D capital expenditures has encountered particular difficulty.

With respect to current operations of research and development, the surveys have included both dollar and manpower[2] figures, these being different but complementary measures of the volume of activity. Lastly, all fund figures collected have been in terms of current dollars. An index of R & D costs is now being developed for the purpose of converting R & D expenditures into constant dollars.

In building the program of R & D surveys, it has been necessary to bear in mind the diverse purposes to which the data will be put. These include serving as a basis for detailed analytical studies, providing a background for decision making in the area of science policy, and casting light on the role of science in the economy as a whole. This wide range of uses, together with the relative newness of the survey program, has led the Foundation to follow a grass-roots approach of wide formal and informal consultation with survey respondents and persons interested in using the figures. Such contacts have resulted in important contributions to the development of statistical methods and techniques, in improvements in the accuracy and validity of the data, and in a lightening of the burden of the reporting process.

CONCEPTUAL FRAMEWORK OF R & D SURVEY PROGRAM

No statistical inquiry is free of problems of concept and definition. Such difficulties loom particularly large in surveys of R & D because of the comparative newness of the survey program and the abstract and dynamic nature of many of the activities covered. Indeed, there is hardly a survey category from "basic research" to "scientist and engineer" which cannot stimulate conceptual debate among representatives of the scientific community.

For this reason, the National Science Foundation has followed a pragmatic approach to concepts and definitions. Emphasis has been placed on the subject categories of greatest significance to the study

[2] The responsibility for compiling data on scientific manpower is shared by the Foundation's Office of Economic and Statistical Studies and Division of Scientific Personnel and Education, the former being interested in the manpower data as a complement to dollar measures of R & D and the latter being concerned with all the aspects of the scientific manpower problem.

of R & D inputs. For each of these categories, there has been a review of the range of possible concepts and definitions. Decisions on official definitions have been reached after this review and with the benefit of the consultation mentioned previously. On a continuing basis, it is the Foundation's policy to keep aware of areas where concepts, definitions, and terminology require re-examination; administrative machinery has been set up to take cognizance of these matters.

Three major categories of concepts and definitions underlie the entire present survey program. These refer, first, to the activities which are being surveyed—R & D, scientific information, etc.; second, to the groups which carry on the activities—the sectors of the economy; and third, to the measures of input applied to the activities— funds expended and personnel employed. These categories can each be briefly summarized.

R & D and Related Activities

In the Foundation surveys, R & D is regarded as a composite of basic research, applied research, and development. As far as possible, an attempt is made to obtain information on each of these component activities, separately, on the basis of definitions that will yield comparable and homogeneous data from diverse sources.

Research, as a category, is defined as "systematic intensive study directed toward fuller scientific knowledge of the subject studied." Within this generalization the distinction between basic and applied research is made principally in terms of motivation, i.e., basic research is conceived of as primarily concerned with achieving "fuller understanding," whereas applied research has a "practical" objective in view. Development, as a separate activity, is defined as

the systematic use of scientific knowledge directed toward the production of useful materials, devices, systems, or methods, including design and development of prototypes and processes.

To assist industry respondents in drawing a line, for reporting purposes, between development and production, the survey instructions further point out:

If the primary objective is to make further improvements on the product or process, then the work comes within the definition of research and development. If, on the other hand, the product or process is substantially "set," and the primary objective is to develop markets or to do preproduction planning, or to get the production process going smoothly, then the work is no longer research and development.

In the abstract, R & D includes a great variety of activities; among them are the collection of masses of scientific data and the devising and use of many types of scientific tests. Furthermore, R & D draws constantly on existing scientific knowledge and leads to the production of new scientific information. As a practical matter, each of these three activities—data collection, testing and standardization, and scientific information—may be carried on as an integral part of a given organization's R & D activity, or it may be conducted on a separate basis, perhaps as the principal activity of another organization. In any event, whether or not these activities are an integral part of a particular respondent's R & D operation, they are classified as separate scientific activities, under National Science Foundation definitions, when they are separately identifiable. As noted earlier, scientific information is the only one of the three related scientific activities now covered in the survey program. Nonetheless, the definitions of all three are cited here in order to round out the picture of R & D and related scientific activities.

Scientific information (discussed in more detail in the following) is regarded as comprising all aspects of communication among scientists, including but not limited to the publication; dissemination; organization; translation of information resulting from or required in scientific activities; and travel, scientific conferences, and symposia organized to further the exchange of information.

Testing and standardization, as a separate scientific activity, includes such matters as the establishment of standards, calibration of secondary standards, and nonroutine quality testing when these are separately identifiable. The collection of general-purpose scientific data covers such activities as geological and geophysical exploration and mapping and the collection of statistics on population.

A wide range of scientific fields is covered in the surveys of R & D: the physical sciences—astronomy, chemistry, earth sciences, mathematics, physics, and engineering; and the life sciences—biological, medical, and agricultural. The physical and life sciences together make up the natural sciences. The social sciences are presently covered in the Federal sector and in certain nonprofit organizations, but they are excluded from the industry sector pending a study of the nature of industrial social science research.

The Four Sectors

Earlier discussion has implied that the national totals of dollars and manpower resources allocated to R & D are aggregates built up from detailed data obtained in the regularly recurring statistical surveys of this activity in four broad sectors of the economy—the Federal Government, industry, colleges and universities, and other nonprofit institutions.   This conventional method of grouping the numerous organizations in the R & D community takes account of the broad legal and functional characteristics of these entities rather than their particular research role.   Respondents are classified, on a legal basis, as either public or nonpublic in nature, with the Federal Government representing the public portion, and the remaining three sectors representing the private portion of the economy.   In turn, the latter is subdivided into the profit sector—namely, industry—and the two nonprofit sectors—colleges and universities and other nonprofit institutions.

The Federal Government is the predominant governmental level in terms of support and performance of R & D.   Nonetheless, state and local government units may eventually be included in the public sector as problems of surveying them on a regular basis are solved. Their present omission does not represent a significant quantitative gap, since, with one important exception, their R & D expenditures are relatively small.[3]   This exception is the research outlays of the publicly controlled institutions of higher education which are covered in the surveys but are entered with data for the colleges and universities sector.   This is done because the educational function of the state and local colleges is regarded as more important for sectoring analysis than their public status.

The range and variety of R & D organizations covered in the intramural operations of the Federal Government sector are considerable. The sector does not include, however, the fifty or so Federal contract research centers, such as Oak Ridge National Laboratory and Lincoln Laboratory, which are supported wholly or predominantly by Federal agencies but are operated under contract by an industrial, university, or independent nonprofit organization.   Each of these centers is included in the same sector as its administering organization.

Companies engaged in manufacturing and nonmanufacturing compose the industry sector, together with those Federal contract research centers such as the Space Technology Laboratory (Air Force), which are administered by industrial firms.

---

[3] The scientific activities expenditures of the governments of six representative states were surveyed for fiscal year 1954 under the auspices of the National Science Foundation and reported in National Science Foundation, *Scientific Activities in Six State Governments. Summary Report of a Survey, Fiscal Year 1954*, Washington 25, D. C., Supt. of Documents, U. S. Government Printing Office, 1958.

The first of the two nonprofit sectors, colleges and universities, is composed of all institutions of higher education, both public and private. For analytical purposes, the component parts of these institutions are classified in three major organizational categories: (1) Colleges and universities proper, consisting of colleges of liberal arts, schools of arts and sciences, professional schools such as medicine and engineering, and affiliated research institutions, hospitals, and similar organizations; (2) agricultural experiment stations and associated schools of agriculture; and (3) Federal contract research centers, such as Ames Laboratory (Atomic Energy Commission), which are administered by educational institutions.

The other nonprofit sector, probably the most diverse in its composition, consists of private philanthropic foundations, voluntary health agencies, nonprofit research institutes, professional societies, museums, zoological and botanical gardens, arboretums, and Federal contract research centers, such as The RAND Corporation, which are independently administered. Some of the museums, zoos, and similar institutions are closely related to units of local government whereas others are more independent, but this possible difference in legal nature does not appear important enough to justify departing from a functional grouping of such organizations. On the other hand, certain large nonprofit research institutes are rather highly oriented to the research problems of industry, but it has seemed more useful for survey and analytical purposes to group them, on the basis of their legal nature, together with other nonprofit research organizations having programs of a more diversified nature.

Nature of Dollar and Manpower Measurements

The Foundation is interested in data on both funds and personnel as complementary measures of R & D input. The major focus in measuring dollar input has been the current operating costs of the components of R & D. A full cost concept is employed here, covering both direct and indirect costs of conducting, planning, and administering R & D, including depreciation of R & D plant.

Respondents in all sectors furnish data on current operating costs for R & D as a whole and for basic research, applied research, and development. Basic research expenditures are categorized by field.

Information on capital investment in R & D is also obtained in the Foundation surveys, but a national total on capital outlays covering all four sectors is not yet available. As later discussion will indicate, problems of concept and survey methodology have made it necessary to proceed rather slowly with some sector surveys of capital expenditures.

The employed scientist and engineer, as a unit of input measurement, are sometimes described as less elusive than dollar data because the latter are subject to the distortion of price fluctuations. Yet, simple headcounts of persons employed are not an accurate indication of the manpower input into R & D activity. This is because scientists and engineers, wherever employed, but particularly in colleges and universities, tend to divide their time among R & D, teaching, consultation, production, scientific information, and other activities. Because of this, the survey data on R & D scientists and engineers are collected in such a way as to make it possible to estimate the "full-time equivalent" of the numbers of scientists and engineers employed part time in research and development. Through alloting fractional weight to persons employed on a part-time basis, full-time equivalent provides a common unit by which fulltime employees and part-time employees are made additive. This method takes no account, of course, of the different levels of competence or utilization of personnel.

Since many R & D scientists range over a wide variety of work, the surveys require only that personnel be classified as to employment in R & D with no allocation among the basic, applied, and development components. Special estimates on scientists and engineers engaged in basic research,[4] published in 1961, were based on the best judgment of the Foundation's staff, relying on clues from the surveys and general knowledge of the field.

There is considerable looseness in many public discussions of numbers of employed chemists, mathematicians, and the like, because of a failure to recognize that there may be a difference between the discipline in which a scientist has been trained and that in which he is employed. The inquiries in the Foundation surveys are answered by employers, and they therefore furnish information on the fields in which scientists and engineers are employed, i.e., their occupational rather than training specialties. Conceptually, this makes good sense for survey purposes, since it is for work in these fields that the corresponding dollars are expended.

Deliberate use has been made here of the phrase "employed as" in order to avoid the implication that the surveys also include the relatively small number of nonsalaried persons engaged in research, par-

⁴ These special estimates of scientists and engineers engaged in basic research in 1960–61 appeared in the National Science Foundation report, *Investing in Scientific Progress, 1961–1970,* NSF 61-27, Washington, D. C., 1961.

ticularly in colleges and universities, who are not on the payroll of the reporting institution. The most important of these are graduate students supported by fellowships rather than salaries.

SECTOR SURVEY PROGRAMS

Each of the four sectors described above is characterized by its own particular role in R & D activity. The Federal Government predominates as a source of R & D funds, while industry overshadows all other sectors in R & D performance as measured by dollar volume and in the employment of professional scientific personnel. The colleges and universities, with their inherent capabilities in basic research, use the largest volume of funds of any sector in performance in this area. The other nonprofit institutions, with considerable freedom in their chosen avenues of research, direct their funds along many lines of scientific endeavor.

Federal Government

The initial National Science Foundation survey of R & D took place in the Federal Government sector and covered fiscal years 1951 and 1952. The study, which was reported in the first issue of the annual publication, *Federal Funds for Science*,[5] covered nonprofit organizations as recipients of Federal funds. The nonprofit organizations were considered a logical area in which to begin Federal surveys in the light of both the Foundation's special concern with nonprofit institutions and the growing "research partnership" between these institutions—particularly the colleges and universities—and the Federal Government.

All the Federal agencies entering into financial transactions with nonprofit institutions were circularized by questionnaire for *Federal Funds for Science, I.* Data on funds for the conduct of R & D were collected for fiscal years 1951 and 1952 by: (1) character of work—basic, applied, and development; and (2) field of science—life, physical, and social. Agencies were also asked to report their obligations for R & D plant.

The survey responses indicated that about 98 percent of the R & D funds flowing to nonprofit institutions came from four agencies, the Department of Defense, Atomic Energy Commission, the Federal

[5] National Science Foundation, *Federal Funds for Science, I. Federal Funds for Scientific Research and Development at Nonprofit Institutions, 1950–51 and 1951–52*, Washington D. C., Supt. of Documents, U. S. Government Printing Office, 1953.

Security Agency (later absorbed in the Department of Health, Education, and Welfare), and the Department of Agriculture. Many different nonprofit institutions were carrying out R & D sponsored by the Government, but the greatest concentration of research performance, as measured by reported dollar volume, was in the large universities. In fact, the community's dependence on the colleges and universities as uniquely qualified research institutions was well-documented by this survey. At the same time, the impact of Government-sponsored research upon the colleges and universities was quantitatively explored for the first time.

The annual Federal surveys following this initial effort were on a broader basis, covering Federal Government obligations for R & D performed in all sectors of the economy. In addition, when the first bench-mark surveys for the other three sectors of the economy were launched, for 1953–1954, a special parallel inquiry was conducted in the Federal Government. The scope of this Federal survey extended beyond R & D expenditures, as covered in *Federal Funds for Science* and in the other three-sector surveys, to include related scientific activities such as scientific data collection, the dissemination of scientific information, and the testing and standardization of materials and products as well as the training of scientific manpower. Data were also requested on obligations for R & D plant.[6]

For each of the above activities and for R & D plant, each reporting Federal agency provided data on funds obligated for intramural use and on funds provided to industry, colleges and universities, and other nonprofit institutions. As in the survey covering fiscal years 1951 and 1952, data on R & D were classified by character of research (basic, applied, and development) and field of science including social science. Thirty-eight departments and agencies of the Federal Government reported obligating $2.6 billion for scientific activities (including training) and for R & D plant in the fiscal year 1954. Funds for the performance of research and development accounted for 80 percent of the total.

The annual Federal inquiries which followed the special broad survey of fiscal years 1953 and 1954 concentrated on R & D proper, i.e., on current operating costs plus expenditures for R & D plant. Within this context, however, there was a continuing increase in depth of detail and analysis. As events in the late 1950's and early 1960's led to increased interest in Federal science activities, the

---

[6] National Science Foundation, *Funds for Scientific Activities in the Federal Government, Fiscal Years 1953 and 1954,* Washington D. C., Supt. of Documents, U. S. Government Printing Office, 1958.

Federal survey moved toward including again the associated or related scientific activities. *Federal Funds for Science, X*[7] presented data on Federal support of scientific and technical information. Data on training and education of scientific personnel are scheduled for coverage in the 1962 survey.

The Federal survey data show that in recent years the Government, as the primary source of funds for R & D, has provided over 60 percent of the national total. Federal Government agencies use about 15 percent of the national total of R & D funds for performance in their own laboratories, but they provide over half of all funds used by each of the other sectors in the performance of research and development.

An estimated $9.5 billion of Federal funds were obligated for R & D for fiscal year 1962, with about $2.2 billion of the total allocated for intramural use. Obligations for R & D plant raised the total to $10.5 billion. Twenty-five agencies were involved in this effort, with four agencies—the Department of Defense, National Aeronautics and Space Administration (NASA), Atomic Energy Commission, and the Department of Health, Education, and Welfare—accounting for over 90 percent of total funds. The ascendancy of a relatively new agency, NASA, as a prime supporter of R & D reflects the recent acceleration in aero-space research, as measured by funds obligated.

In the decade covered by the Federal surveys, there have been opportunities to improve the methodology used, as well as to develop a better understanding with respondents concerning various aspects of the inquiry. The surveys are conducted by mail questionnaires sent to the individual agencies. The completed forms are carefully checked and analyzed by Foundation staff. When necessary, visits are made to respondents for clarification of instructions to insure uniform reporting. As a result, some agencies have adapted their record keeping to harmonize with the questionnaires and instructions. However, concepts and definitions continue to present problems, especially as to the separate identification of basic research. Also, in estimating the allocation of research funds among scientific fields, questions of categorization are raised by the new interdisciplinary groupings.

The Federal data on R & D expenditures and obligations are reported in *Federal Funds for Science* on the basis of a three-year cycle, following the procedure used in the Federal budget. Figures reported

[7] National Science Foundation, *Federal Funds for Science, X. The Federal Research and Development Budget, Fiscal Years 1960, 1961, and 1962,* Washington D. C., Supt. of Documents, U. S. Government Printing Office, 1961.

for the earliest year reflect transactions for a completed fiscal year and are thus the actual amounts for that year. Data for the middle and latest years, based on various stages of program planning, are estimates. Because of the budget context of the Federal survey data, they are furnished in terms of both obligations and expenditures. The nature of Federal accounting makes much more detail available for obligations than for expenditures. Obligations data, it should be borne in mind, are expressions of program plans in various stages of the three-year cycle rather than indicators of actual disbursements.

From the Foundation surveys the trend data for the 1950's as well as available estimates for the preceding decade make possible the tracing of the historical picture for the Federal sector since the fiscal year 1940. The long-term trend of aggregate expenditures for R & D and for R & D plant has, in general, been upward. In the fiscal year 1940, these expenditures amounted to an estimated $74,000,000. They may reach $10 billion for the fiscal year 1962, with every indication that growth will continue in future years.

The trend in Federal spending for R & D since 1940 has shown three major waves. The first dates roughly from 1940 through the period of peacetime readjustment following World War II. The second wave, extending from 1950 to 1955, was stimulated by growth in peacetime R & D endeavors and later by the new military requirements of the Korean conflict. The third wave, from 1956 through the present, has resulted from a variety of factors, including the reactions to Sputnik, the cold war, surging interest in certain civilian research efforts, and the man-in-space program. In the fiscal year 1961, an estimated 11 percent of the total Federal budget was earmarked for R & D and R & D plant; the same percentage is anticipated for the fiscal year 1962.

The measurement of manpower input in Federal Government R & D was first undertaken by the Foundation through a detailed scientific manpower study paralleling the special Federal funds survey for fiscal year 1954.[8] In recent years, Federal professional scientific personnel in R & D have been surveyed by the U. S. Civil Service Commission as part of the recurring white-collar worker surveys.[9]

The 1954 manpower study indicated that the Federal Government used the services of about 30,000 civilian scientists and engineers in

[8] National Science Foundation, *Scientific Manpower in the Federal Government, 1954*, Washington D. C., May 1957.

[9] National Science Foundation, *Scientists and Engineers in the Federal Government, October 1958*, Washington D. C., Supt. of Documents, U. S. Government Printing Office, 1961.

R & D activities in the natural and social sciences.   The number rose to approximately 42,000 in 1958 and to over 43,000 in 1960.   Some 35,000 of the latter were concentrated in the physical sciences, including engineering, as compared to 4,300 in the life sciences.   Scientists and engineers in the planning and administration of R & D were included in the totals.

Industry

The first National Science Foundation survey of industry's performance of R & D and employment of professional scientific manpower covered 1953, with several summary questions relating to 1954.[10] The inquiry was carried out in cooperation with the Bureau of Labor Statistics and was part of the nationwide group of surveys covering the bench mark year 1953–1954.   The industry schedule contained questions on the cost of R & D in the natural sciences, including engineering; sources of support, i.e., company-financed or Government-financed; the amount of basic research classified by field of science; and the volume of company-financed R & D contracted to outside organizations.   The number of R & D scientists and engineers employed by industry was also requested.   Various industrial organizations as well as the National Association of Manufacturers participated in the formulation of the survey questionnaire and instructions.

Simultaneously with the comprehensive industry survey of 1953, two small groups of industry-oriented organizations—trade associations and commercial laboratories—were covered separately.[11]   Although responsible for only a relatively small volume of R & D performed, they were considered part of the over-all industry picture.

The next comprehensive survey of industrial R & D was for 1956; since then this inquiry has been conducted on an annual basis.   An important innovation in the 1956 survey[12] was the classification of

[10] National Science Foundation, *Science and Engineering in American Industry. Final Report on a 1953–54 Survey*, Washington, D. C., Supt. of Documents, U. S. Government Printing Office, 1956.

[11] Maxwell Research Center, Syracuse University (prepared for the National Science Foundation), *Research and Development by Nonprofit Resarch Institutes and Commercial Laboratories, 1953*, Washington, D. C.: Supt. of Documents, U. S. Government Printing Office, 1956.   Battelle Memorial Institute (prepared for the National Science Foundation), *Research by Cooperative Organizations. A Survey of Scientific Research by Trade Associations, Professional and Technical Societies, and Other Cooperative Groups, 1953*, Washington D. C., Supt. of Documents, U. S. Government Printing Office, 1956.

[12] National Science Foundation, *Science and Engineering in American Industry. Report on a 1956 Survey*, Washington D. C., Supt. of Documents, U. S. Government Printing Office, 1959.

expenditures by basic research, applied research, and development. Commercial laboratories and engineering services as well as trade associations were made an integral part of the 1956 survey.

With the 1957 survey, the responsibility for the collection of industry expenditures data was transferred from the Bureau of Labor Statistics to the Bureau of the Census. This change was made primarily to enable the Foundation to relate data on R & D expenditures to other economic statistics, such as net sales and employment, also collected by the Bureau of the Census.

Beginning with the 1957 survey, statistics on annual R & D performance costs per R & D scientist or engineer have been derived annually from the survey data and tabulated according to industry and size of company. These serve as a useful tool in the interindustry and intercompany analysis of the cost structure of R & D programs. To obtain the personnel data for computing this cost ratio, the survey requests information on the number of scientists and engineers employed in R & D by the company.

The ratio of R & D funds to net sales, based on survey data, is frequently used to indicate the relative importance of R & D in a company or industry. A related ratio, also derived from the survey data, is that of R & D funds per employee by industry and by company-size groups. This is a particularly useful ratio in instances where employment provides a more satisfactory measure than net sales of the productive activities of various industries.

The 1958 industry[13] survey was expanded to include additional information. Expenditures data on R & D performed abroad for the benefit of American firms were requested. Furthermore, Federal contract research centers administered by industrial organizations (formerly covered only in the Federal Government survey) were included as performing units. Thus, with 1958, the industry survey covered the entire sector for the first time. A minor omission was the small industry-oriented organizations such as trade associations, which are estimated to account for less than 1 percent of the Nation's annual volume of industrial R & D performance.

Funds used in the performance of industrial R & D in the natural sciences amounted to $10.5 billion in 1960, according to the most recent survey.[14] This sum was three-fourths of the corresponding national

[13] National Science Foundation, *Funds for Research and Development in Industry, 1958,* Washington, D. C., Supt. of Documents, U. S. Government Printing Office, 1961.

[14] National Science Foundation, "Funds for Performance of Research and Development in American Industry, 1960. A Preliminary Report," *Reviews of*

total and larger than all expenditures for R & D performed throughout the nation 3 years earlier. The estimated level for 1961 was $11.0 billion.

Two industries most closely associated with defense R & D projects accounted for more than one-half (56 percent) of the $10.5 billion for industrial R & D in 1960. One of these industries, aircraft and parts, reported $3.5 billion, while the other, electrical equipment and communications, reported $2.4 billion. From a source standpoint, more than three-fourths of the $6.1 billion provided to industry for R & D by the Government was contracted to these two industries. Aircraft and parts reported receiving $3.0 billion of Federal funds while electrical equipment and communications reported $1.6 billion.

Federal contract research centers administered by industrial firms used $534,000,000 in the performance of R & D in 1960. Of this amount, 6 percent of $34,000,000 went into basic research activities.

Total industrial R & D expenditures increased nearly threefold during the eight-year Foundation survey period, 1953–1960. Federal Government sponsorship of industrial R & D performance expanded more than fourfold during this time, from $1.4 billion to $6.1 billion. The Federal Government financed 58 percent of industrial R & D performance in 1960, compared with 39 percent in 1953. R & D performance financed by company funds totaled $4.4 billion in 1960, double the comparable figure for 1953.

Funds for the performance of industrial basic research increased from $151,000,000 in 1953 to $382,000,000 in 1960. The volume of funds expended by industry on basic research has accounted for only 4 percent of the sector's total R & D expenditures over the period. On the other hand, industrial expenditures for the performance of basic research equal about 30 percent of basic research expenditures by the nation as a whole.

The National Science Foundation industry surveys have been conducted through mail questionnaires sent to a stratified random sample of companies in all manufacturing industries and those nonmanufacturing industries known to finance or perform research and development. All manufacturing companies employing 1,000 or more employees are covered, and smaller companies are included on a sample basis. Members of the Foundation and Census Bureau staffs personally visit industrial corporations to discuss reporting problems,

Data on Research & Development, No. 30, Washington, D. C., Supt. of Documents, U. S. Government Printing Office, September 1961.

when necessary. The response rate for industry as a whole has been exceedingly high, more than 95 percent; in the group of firms employing over 1,000 persons almost all firms respond.

As in other sectors, respondents in industry encounter conceptual problems. Certain firms have difficulty in distinguishing between basic and applied research or in clearly identifying the cutoff point at which development ends and production begins. A more specific problem area is the classification of geological and geophysical exploration. Although such exploration is specifically excluded from R & D in the industry survey definition, some authorities believe that it should be classified as R & D. A more general problem is that of achieving comparability of returns. Because of differences in accounting systems from firm to firm and differences in the points of view of respondents, inconsistencies may occur in reporting.

In the earlier surveys of industrial R & D conducted by the Bureau of Labor Statistics, information on the number of R & D scientists and engineers employed by industrial organizations was collected in detail in connection with the funds data. When the Census Bureau assumed the responsibility for the 1957 survey of industrial R & D expenditures, the Bureau of Labor Statistics, which had a continuing interest in studying manpower resources, retained responsibility for surveying all scientists and engineers as well as R & D scientists and engineers by industry and field.

Recent figures from these surveys indicate that the full-time equivalent[15] of R & D scientists and engineers employed by industrial organizations in the natural science was about 286,000 for 1960.[16] This compares with 164,000 in 1954, 240,000 in 1958, and 258,000 in 1959.

Also in the industry sector, the Foundation recently completed a special survey of the publication policies and practices of 174 manufacturing firms. A booklet, *Publication of Basic Research Findings in Industry, 1957–59*,[17] summarizes the inquiry. Surveyed companies were asked to provide information primarily on the administration of their publication policies, the number of basic research papers published, and the media through which such papers were dissemi-

---

[15] For an explanation of full-time equivalent, see p. 50.

[16] National Science Foundation, "Trends in Funds and Personnel for Research and Development, 1953–61," *Reviews of Data on Research & Development, No. 33*, Washington, D. C., Supt. of Documents, U. S. Government Printing Office, March 1962.

[17] National Science Foundation, Washington, D. C., Supt. of Documents, U. S. Government Printing Office, 1961.

nated. Firms not actively engaged in basic research or with relatively small basic research programs (funds of less than $50,000 for basic research performance in 1957) were not surveyed.

Colleges and Universities

The first Foundation survey of R & D at institutions of higher education covered colleges and universities and their associated institutions and agricultural experiment stations for the year 1953–54.[18] University officials cooperated with the Foundation in the formulation of the survey questionnaires and instructions designed to obtain R & D fiscal and manpower data. Information on Federal contract research centers administered by universities was already available from the concurrent Federal government bench-mark survey; these centers were later included in the university program.

The total R & D cost structure surveyed covered separately budgeted or "earmarked" research, associated indirect costs borne by both the sponsor and university, and departmental research, i.e., faculty research allied to the instructual function of the departments. Also surveyed were sources of support—Federal agencies, the universities' own funds, and other non-Federal institutions. Research expenditures were classified in terms of component, basic, or applied. Fields of science covered were the physical sciences including engineering, life sciences including psychology, and the social sciences. One hundred and ninety larger schools and their associated institutions, as well as 930 smaller colleges, both public and private, received the schedules.

The survey indicated that total R & D expenditures (current operating costs) for the entire college and university sector equaled almost $500,000,000 for 1953–1954. About one-half of this was spent at the colleges and universities proper, i.e., at schools of arts and sciences; at professional schools, such as medicine, engineering, dentistry, and public health; and at affiliated research institutes, hospitals, and like organizations. Over $75,000,000 were expended for research and development at the agricultural experiment stations, where the surveyed costs were limited to separately budgeted research.[19] Expenditures by Federal contract research centers administered by universities accounted for the remainder, approximately $130,000,000.

[18] National Science Foundation, *Scientific Research and Development in Colleges and Universities—Expenditures and Manpower, 1953–54*, Washington, D. C., Supt. of Documents, U. S. Government Printing Office, 1959.

[19] These are revised figures which differ somewhat from those shown in the survey report cited in footnote 17.

Important new information in the field of scientific manpower emerged from the survey's coverage of all professional scientific personnel, including those engaged in R & D at the schools. These were surveyed on a full-time equivalent basis as of April 1954. Supporting personnel, both professional and technical, were similarly covered for the larger schools. The number of full-time equivalent R & D scientists and engineers employed by the entire college and university complex was about 26,000 for 1954; supporting personnel numbered over 13,000. A census of college and university scientific faculty was also made, classifying the members by academic rank and traditional academic discipline.

The 1953–1954 university survey was a pioneering undertaking that resulted in valuable new knowledge and set the pattern for future surveys. However, because of the diversity of the items covered, it was a time-consuming task for the respondents as well as the Foundation. Some of the concepts used proved difficult for survey purposes. The schools found it especially onerous to ascertain their expenditures for departmental research. Here, man-hours and materials for research and for teaching were so intertwined that any separate allocation for research was at best an approximation. Since departmental research and associated indirect costs borne by the institutions represented only about 10 percent of all R & D at the colleges and universities, it was decided that in the next survey only separately budgeted R & D funds would be covered.

The interchange of ideas concerning the measurement of research and development, which took place between the Foundation and colleges and universities during the years following the 1953–1954 survey, laid the basis for the 1957–1958 inquiry. The latter covered operating expenditures for separately budgeted R & D, professional scientific manpower, and facilities. The data collection for this inquiry was handled by the Office of Education of the Department of Health, Education, and Welfare. Questionnaires were sent to 1,900 independent and autonomous institutions of higher education in the United States, including Hawaii, Pureto Rico, and Alaska. Of the 1,900 institutions contacted, about 350 reported R & D operating expenditures.

Reported separately budgeted operating expenditures for R & D in the natural and social sciences in colleges and universities amounted to about $740,000,000 in 1957–1958, as compared with about $410,000-000 in 1953–1954. It is significant that more than one-half of the "earmarked" R & D expenditures of colleges and universities in 1957–1958 were at the agricultural experiment stations and Federal contract research centers combined. Thus, approximately $330,000,000 were spent within colleges and universities proper, whereas in agricultural experiment stations, including schools of agriculture, the outlays were about $120,000,000, and in Federal contract research centers, about $290,000,000. Over the 4 years between the two surveys, Federal support of R & D at educational institutions rose from about $290,-000,000 to about $540,000,000.

For the university sector as a whole, 48 percent of the 1957–1958 funds were used for basic research, 34 percent for applied research, and 18 percent for development. Within the subsector groupings, basic research continued to hold the place of prominence at the colleges and universities proper, whereas applied R & D was dominant at agricultural experiment stations and the Federal contract research centers.

Almost 70,000 scientists and engineers engaged part-time or full-time in university research, represented 44 percent of all employed scientists and engineers at the schools in 1958. The life sciences were the field in which the highest percentage of the R & D scientists were working—some 47 percent. The physical sciences accounted for 26 percent, the engineering sciences for 17 percent, and the social sciences for 10 percent.

The coverage of R & D outlays was enlarged in the 1957–1958 college and university survey to include questions on the amount of funds spent on capital items such as new major equipment and laboratory facilities as well as on the modernization of older equipment and laboratory facilities. The schools reported spending $154,-000,000 for facilities and other capital items used for R & D purposes in the natural and social sciences, a sum equal to one-fifth of total current operating expenditures for R & D in 1957–1958.[20] Approximately three-fourths ($112,000,000) of the total spent on capital items came from the universities' own funds, state appropriations, and other non-Federal sources. The remaining one-fourth was supplied by the Federal Government.

By field of science, the funds for R & D facilities were distributed as follows: life sciences, 50 percent; physical sciences, 33 percent; engineering, 15 percent; and social sciences, 3 percent. This pattern resembled those for R & D expenditures and manpower.

Twelve colleges and universities accounted for more than one-half of the total of $154,000,000 for R & D capital items. The organiza-

[20] National Science Foundation, "Capital Expenditures for Research and Development in Colleges and Universities, Fiscal Year 1958 (A Preliminary Report)," *Reviews of Data on Research & Development,* No. 28, Washington, D. C., Supt. of Documents, U. S. Government Printing Office, 1961.

tional unit reporting by far the largest expenditures for R & D facilities represented colleges and universities proper, with almost three-fourths of the total.

Originally it was planned to place the survey of the college and university sector on an annual basis, as in the case of the Federal Government and industry sectors. However, because of the increased demand made upon the Foundation for more detailed special information on activities at institutions of higher learning, a many-sided annual survey became too formidable an undertaking. Accordingly, it was deemed more practical to cover this sector by successive inquiries dealing with broad segments of data, such as operating expenditures for R & D, outlays for facilities, and employment of personnel.

Currently, the Foundation with the assistance of the Office of Education of the Department of Health, Education, and Welfare is conducting a detailed survey of all scientific professional personnel, paid directly by the university, who were engaged in teaching, R & D, or other activities as of March 1, 1961. Agricultural experiment stations and Federal contract research centers are being covered, as well as colleges and universities proper and their associated institutions. These data are being collected on a full-time equivalent basis and span the natural and social sciences. Some 700 schools and associated institutions have received questionnaires. A survey of projected facility and apparatus needs in colleges and universities, 1963–1972, is also under way, and will be discussed later.

In addition to the over-all periodical surveys, the Foundation has occasionally been asked to conduct inquiries of a more specialized nature in the college and university sector. For example, the indirect cost of federally sponsored R & D conducted at colleges and universities has just been surveyed, on a comprehensive basis, for 1959–1960. Less detailed studies of this subject were made previously, in 1953–1954 and 1957–1958. In the latest survey, schedules were mailed to approximately 275 colleges and universities engaged in federally sponsored R & D. The Committee on Governmental Relations of the National Federation of College and University Business Officers Associations as well as many administrative officers of the schools assisted in the planning. A preliminary report on findings has been released.[21]

Despite the progress made in college and university surveys, in-

[21] National Science Foundation, "Indirect Costs of Research and Development in Colleges and Universities, Fiscal Year 1960," *Reviews of Data on Research & Development*, No. 32, Washington, D. C., Supt. of Documents, U. S. Government Printing Office, March 1962.

complete record keeping by a number of schools has made it difficult for the National Science Foundation to obtain data in the form desired. Universities often have old decentralized accounting systems which no longer meet their own internal needs or those of agencies that call on them for reports. In recent years, the schools themselves have become interested in having available up-to-date and accurate data concerning their activities. This has led many institutions to seek the assistance and advice of the Foundation in formulating a more orderly method of recording data on their scientific activities.

As a result, a cooperative case study has been set up by the Foundation to devise and test simplified and adequate systems of measuring and reporting the financial, manpower, facility, and other inputs in college and university activities. Seven institutions, under contract with the Foundation, are conducting a series of self-studies to establish such measurements. These schools are St. Louis University, the Universities of Arizona, Florida, and Pennsylvania; Rensselaer Polytechnic Institute; Michigan State University; and Texas Agricultural and Mechanical College. The National Institutes of Health, U. S. Department of Health, Education, and Welfare, also requires a continuing flow of accurate data on university resources and activities related to health and is, therefore, participating in the study as a cosponsoring agency.

Other Nonprofit Institutions

The other nonprofit sector, as indicated above, is composed of private philanthropic foundations, voluntary health agencies, independent nonprofit research institutes, professional and technical societies, science museums, zoological and botanical gardens, arboretums, and Federal contract research centers administered by independent organizations. These institutions are so diverse in nature that perhaps the only characteristic which they have in common is their nonprofit status.

In 1953–1954, the National Science Foundation undertook an exploratory survey of the R & D expenditures and manpower of this heterogeneous group, following procedures that would produce comparable and additive statistical data. The results of this inquiry afforded the first over-all glimpse of the R & D activity of the other nonprofit institutions.

Four separate surveys were conducted to cover the various component nonprofit organizations. The activities of the larger private foundations, numbering 77 and each having assets of about $10,000,000 or more, were analysed by the Russell Sage Foundation for the National Science Foundation.[22]   The 4,000 smaller foundations and most of the remaining organizations were surveyed directly by the National Science Foundation.[23]   However, some professional societies and similar cooperative groups as well as certain large nonprofit research institutes were treated as separate groups and studied by Battelle Memorial Institute and the Maxwell Research Center of Syracuse University respectively.[24]   The R & D data on the associated Federal contract research centers were obtained from the supporting Federal agencies.   Only the smaller foundations were surveyed on a sampling basis; all the remaining institutions were covered on the basis of those "known to be doing" scientific research.

For analytical purposes, the other nonprofit institutions were divided by the Foundation into two groups according to their primary function: (1) granting organizations or (2) performing organizations. Foundations and voluntary health agencies make up the first group, and the remaining organizations the second.

Funds expended by the other nonprofit institutions in performance of reasearch and development amounted to about $100,000,000 in 1953–1954; over one-half of the total was provided by the Federal Government.   As sources of funds, the other nonprofit institutions provided about $40,000,000 for the nation's R & D in the same period. Approximately 4,500 full-time equivalent R & D scientists and engineers were employed in this sector.

With the exploratory survey as a basis, another of similar scope was undertaken by the Foundation in 1957.   All the subsector groups were included in one survey, with minor variations in the form of the questionnaire sent to the organizations which were primarily granting and those which were primarily performing.   The Bureau of Labor Statistics was the collecting agency for the inquiry, which covered R & D expenditures and personnel.[25]   Information on both the natural and social sciences was requested from the philanthropic foundations and voluntary health agencies, but only data on the natural sciences were required of the independent nonprofit research institutes and other performing institutions.

[22] Andrews, F. Emerson, Russell Sage Foundation (prepared for the National Science Foundation), *Scientific Research Expenditures by the Larger Private Foundations.* Washington, D. C., Supt. of Documents, U. S. Government Printing Office, 1956.

[23] National Science Foundation, *Research Expenditures of Foundations and Other Nonprofit Institutions, 1953–54,* Washington, D. C. 1958.

[24] *Op. cit.*

[25] National Science Foundation, *Scientific Research and Development of Nonprofit Organizations—Expenditures and Manpower, 1957,* Washington, D. C., Supt. of Documents, U. S. Government Printing Office, 1961.

The returns from the 1957 survey showed that the foundations and health agencies continued to be very active as sources of support for R & D at colleges and universities and other nonprofit organizations. Total R & D outlays by both of these groups amounted to $94,600,000 in 1957. The foundations reported $71,500,000 of this total and the voluntary health agencies, $23,100,000. In keeping with the granting rather than performing character of their programs, both groups of institutions combined employed, intramurally, only about 600 R & D scientists and engineers on a full-time equivalent basis.

Of the organizations concerned primarily with the performance of research, the 46 independent nonprofit research institutes as a group used the largest volume of funds in the conduct of R & D. These institutes expended about $90,000,000 for this purpose, with about one-third, or slightly over $30,000,000, going for basic research. R & D scientists and engineers employed in the natural sciences in this group totaled some 3,900 full-time equivalents.

The Federal contract research centers administered by other nonprofit institutions expended about $25,000,000 on R & D in 1957. It is interesting to note that approximately three-fifths ($14,500,000 million) of this total represented basic research, in contrast to the much smaller emphasis on basic research at research centers administered by the industry and university sectors. The scientific skills of approximately 770 full-time equivalent R & D scientists and engineers were utilized in this undertaking.

The remaining institutions in the sector—the professional and technical societies, science museums, zoological and botanical gardens, and arboretums—have provided the scientific community with a service which far exceeds their R & D activities, as measured by R & D expenditures and scientific manpower employed. The professional and technical societies expended about $4,700,000 intramurally in the performance of research and development and employed about 170 full-time equivalent R & D scientists and engineers. They also provided $2,000,000 through contracts or grants for support of R & D at colleges and universities and elsewhere. An important additional contribution—particularly to the dissemination of scientific information—included their sponsorship of annual scientific meetings and the publication of scholarly journals.

The science museums, zoological gardens, and arboretums used about $1,800,000 in 1957 in the performance of research and employed about 175 full-time equivalent R & D scientists and engineers. A very high percentage of their research was basic—about 80 percent. These organizations have made notable contributions in such areas as taxonomy and the behavior patterns of plants and animals. They have also been the leaders in the field of visual interpretation and presentation in the natural sciences.

The 1957 survey, as pointed out, attempted to include the full range of the "other nonprofit" institutions. This approach proved cumbersome because of the heterogeneity of the organizations covered in one year. As a result, the subsector groups are now being studied separately, in turn. The survey of private philanthropic foundations covering 1960 has been completed, and a preliminary report of the finding is scheduled for early publication.[26] The nonprofit research institutes will be covered next.

NATIONAL TOTALS OF RESEARCH AND DEVELOPMENT

The national totals of $14 billion for research and development and $1.3 billion for basic research in 1960–1961 are aggregates based on the sector surveys that have been described. The discussion has indicated that information is obtained from subsector groups in their roles as performers of research, or users of funds, and as financers of research, or sources of funds. The aggregating of data must be accomplished in a manner which takes account of these complementary functions and the complex financing-performance division of labor among the organizations of the research community. As already noted, some organizations, such as philanthropic foundations, are primarily providers of R & D funds; other organizations, such as colleges and universities, are essentially performers of R & D, receiving a major portion of the financing from outside sources; still others, such as most Federal agencies, combine the two functions and are both providers of R & D funds and R & D performers. Voluntary health agencies represent another type, acting primarily as intermediaries which collect funds from many sources and distribute them to research organizations.

Not all the flows of funds implied by this situation can be represented in a two-dimensional tabular arrangement. But a simple four-square matrix does provide a good framework for entering information, at the sector level, on the expenditure of funds for performance of research during a given survey period and on the major through-transfers of funds which financed such performance. This approach minimizes the possibility of double counting.

Table 1 is such a matrix or transfer table for 1960–1961. The ar-

[26] National Science Foundation, "Scientific Research and Other Programs of a Selected Group of Private Philanthropic Foundations, 1960," *Reviews of Data on Research & Development,* Washington, D. C., Supt. of Documents, U. S. Government Printing Office, 1962.

TABLE 1

Intersectoral Transfers of Funds Used for Performance of R & D, 1960–1961[a] (Preliminary)

Major Sector	R & D Performers (Millions of Dollars)					Percent Distribution
	Federal Government	Industry	Colleges and Universities	Other Nonprofit Institutions	Total, by Source	
	(1)	(2)	(3)	(4)	(5)	(6)
Sources of R & D funds (1) Federal Government	$2,060	$6,130[b]	$890[b]	$140[b]	$9,220	65
(2) Industry	—	4,370	50	70	4,490	32
(3) Colleges and universities[c]	—	—	210	—	210	2
(4) Other nonprofit institutions[c]	—	—	50	70	120	1
(5) Total, by performer	2,060	10,500[b]	1,200[b]	280[b]	14,040	100
(6) Percent distribution	15	75	8	2	100	

[a] Data on sources of funds are based on reports by the performers.

[b] Includes funds from the Federal Government for research centers administered by organizations in this sector under contract with Federal agencies.

[c] Data include state and local government funds received by these institutions and used for research and development.

Source: National Science Foundation.

rangement of the data indicates that, both conceptually and statistically, the national total of expenditures for a given research activity —in this case R & D as a whole—can be viewed as an aggregate of sector funds provided, as in column 5 at the right, or as the sum of amounts spent in performance of R & D, as in row 5 at the bottom of the table.

This matrix is based on reports by respondents on the expenditures for their performance of R & D and on the original sources of these funds. The figure on Federal funds for intramural R & D is in terms of obligations; however, because expenditures data are not available for this item. State and local government funds received by colleges and universities and other nonprofit institutions are treated in the matrix as these sectors' own funds.

The performance totals in row 5 of Table 1 are primary information from respondents; the source estimates in column 5 are derived from this information via the matrix. This method provides an accurate total on *national input of funds into performance* during a given survey year. Such performance data can be related to estimates of personnel employed in R & D and to estimates of the dollar magnitude of other economic activities.

Obviously, a different matrix could be made up by the opposite procedure, using the amounts which the various sector organizations reported they allocated (as sources) to R & D, during a given survey year and information on the recipients to whom they gave these funds. In such a case, the primary data on the total spent in support of R & D by each sector would be entered in column 5, at the right of the table, with the distribution by recipients in columns 1–4. The performance totals in row 5 at the bottom would then be derived from the data on recipients. This approach would reflect more accurately the amounts of money *obligated or set in motion for, rather than consumed in, R & D* during the survey year. Although of interest, this approach would not meet the needs of most users of R & D data.

The predominant financing role of the Federal Government in R & D is shown in both absolute and relative terms in columns 5 and 6 respectively of Table 1. A similar situation with respect to basic research is reflected by the dollar and percent distributions in columns 5 and 6 of Table 2, which presents the intersectoral transfers of funds used for performance of basic research in 1960–1961. The data indicate that Federal funds accounted for almost two-thirds and three-fifths, respectively, of the R & D and basic research totals.

A different situation exists with respect to the use of funds in per-

TABLE 2

Intersectoral Transfers of Funds Used for Performance of Basic Research, 1960–1961ᵃ (Preliminary)

		Basic Research Performers (Millions of Dollars)					Percent Distri-bution
Major Sector		Federal Government	Industry	Colleges and Universities	Other Nonprofit Institutions	Total, by Source	
		(1)	(2)	(3)	(4)	(5)	(6)
Sources of basic research funds	(1) Federal Government	$245	$100ᵇ	$350ᵇ	$50ᵇ	$745	58
	(2) Industry	—	282	23	8	313	24
	(3) Colleges and universitiesᶜ	—	—	161	—	161	12
	(4) Other nonprofit institutionsᶜ	—	—	41	42	83	6
	(5) Total, by Performer	245	382ᵇ	575ᵇ	100ᵇ	1,302	100
(6) Percent distribution		19	29	44	8	100	

ᵃ Data on sources of funds are based on reports by the performers.

ᵇ Includes funds from the Federal Government for research centers administered by organizations in this sector under contract with Federal agencies.

ᶜ Data include state and local government funds received by these institutions and used for basic research.

Source: National Science Foundation.

formance.   Industrial laboratories reported three-quarters of the total
for R & D, and over one-half the basic research total was expended
by the colleges and universities and other nonprofit institutions.

The framework of the matrix implies 16 possible source-performer
transfers, including intrasectoral financing.   The entries indicate that

TABLE 3

Total Expenditures for R & D and for the Basic Research Portion, 1953–1954—
1960–1961

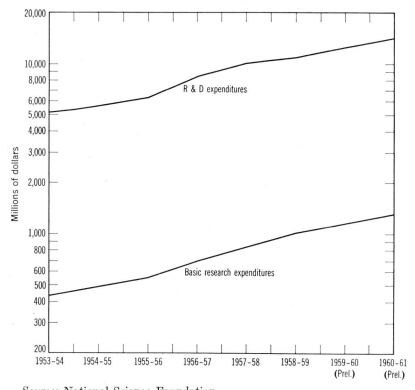

Source: National Science Foundation.

ten of these possibilities are actually major working relationships reflected by the surveys.   The remaining six involve sums below the
rounding level of $10,000,000.

The Foundation survey program also provides time series data for
1953–1954 through 1960–1961 on the major aspects of R & D and
basic research funds (see Table 3).   The annual data, presented in
Tables 4 and 6, indicate the sources of funds used by each sector in

TABLE 4

Time Series on Transfers of Funds Used for Performance of R & D, by Sector, Distributed by Source 1953-1954—1960-1961ᵃ
(Millions of Dollars)

Year	Total R & D	Federal Govt.		Industry			Colleges and Universities					Other Nonprofit Institutions			
		Total Funds Used	Source Federal	Total Funds Used	Sources Fed. Govt.	Sources Indus-try	Total Funds Used	Sources Fed. Govt.	Sources Indus-try	Sources Col. Univ.	ONP	Total Funds Used	Sources Fed. Govt.	Sources Indus-try	ONPᵇ
Performance 1953-54	5,150	970		3,630			450					100			
Source			970		1,430	2,200		280	20	130	20		60	20	20
Performance 1954-55	5,620	950		4,070ᶜ			480ᶜ					120ᶜ			
Source			950		1,750	2,320		300	20	140	20		70	25	25
Performance 1955-56	6,390	1,090		4,640ᶜ			530ᶜ					130ᶜ			
Source			1,090		2,180	2,460		330	20	155	25		70	30	30
Performance 1956-57	8,610	1,280		6,540			650ᶜ					140ᶜ			
Source			1,280		3,330	3,210		415	25	180	30		70	30	40
Performance 1957-58	10,030	1,440		7,660			780					150			
Source			1,440		4,330	3,330		530	30	190	30		80	30	40
Performance 1958-59	11,070	1,730		8,300			840ᶜ					200ᶜ			
Source			1,730		4,760	3,540		570	40	190	40		110	40	50
Performance 1959-60 (prel.)	12,620	1,830		9,550			1,000ᶜ					240ᶜ			
Source			1,830		5,610	3,940		720	40	200	40		130	50	60
Performance 1960-61 (prel.)	14,040	2,060		10,500			1,200ᶜ					280ᶜ			
Source			2,060		6,130	4,370		890	50	210	50		140	70	70

ᵃ Data on sources of funds are based on reports by the performers.
ᵇ State and local government funds spent for R & D by the colleges and universities and other nonprofit institutions are included with the respective sector's own funds.
ᶜ Estimates derived from related available information. No sector survey took place in this year.

Source: National Science Foundation, March 1962.

Note: Expenditures of Federal contract research centers administered by industry, colleges and universities, and other nonprofit institutions, are included in the totals of the respective sectors.

the performance of R & D and basic research respectively. Tables 5 and 7 sum up the amounts of money each sector was reported as furnishing (as a source) in each year.

These trend data invite much probing and analysis. Over the 8 years, funds used in the performance of R & D (in current dollars) have grown over 2½ times, from $5.2 billion to $14.0 billion, and that

TABLE 5

Sources of Funds Used for R & D, by Sector 1953–1954—
1960–1961ᵃ (Millions of Dollars)

Year	Total	Federal Government	Industry	Colleges and Universitiesᵇ	Other Nonprofit Institutionsᵇ
1953–54	$5,150	$2,740	$2,240	$130	$40
1954–55	5,620	3,070	2,365	140	45
1955–56	6,390	3,670	2,510	155	55
1956–57	8,610	5,095	3,265	180	70
1957–58	10,030	6,380	3,390	190	70
1958–59	11,070	7,170	3,620	190	90
1959–60 (prel.)	12,620	8,290	4,030	200	100
1960–61 (prel.)	14,040	9,220	4,490	210	120

ᵃ Data are based on reports by the performers.

ᵇ State and Local government funds spent for research and development by the colleges and universities and other nonprofit institutions are included with the respective sector's own funds.

Source: National Science Foundation, March 1962.

Note: With the exception of data for 1953–1954 and 1957–1958, the years in which surveys covered all sectors, data on sectors as sources of funds are estimates.

basic research funds have tripled from $.4 billion to $1.3 billion. On a cumulative basis, during the decade ending with 1960–1961 there was, in current dollars, a national investment of approximately $80 billion for R & D and about $7 billion for basic research. Over the years, basic research expenditures have ranged between 8 and 9 percent of total R & D.[27]

[27] National Science Foundation, "Trends in Funds and Personnel for Research and Development, 1953–61," *Reviews of Data on Research & Development,* No. 33, March 1962, pp. 1–2.

TABLE 6

Time Series on Transfers of Funds Used for Performance of Basic Research, by Sector, Distributed by Source 1953–1954—1960–1961ᵃ (Millions of Dollars)

Year	Total Basic Research	Federal Govt. Total Funds Used	Federal Govt. Source Federal Funds	Industry Total Funds Used	Industry Fed. Govt.	Industry Indus-try	Colleges and Universities Total Funds Used	Col. Univ. Fed. Govt.	Col. Univ. Indus-try	Col. and Univ.ᵇ	Col. Univ. ONP	Other Nonprofit Total Funds Used	Other Nonprofit Fed. Govt.	Other Nonprofit Indus-try	Other Nonprofit ONPᵇ
Performance 1953–54	432	47		151			208					26			
Source			47		19	132		119	11	62	16		10	4	12
Performance 1954–55	485	55		166ᶜ			230ᶜ					34ᶜ			
Source			55		NA	NA		129	11	70	20		15	4	15
Performance 1955–56	547	65		189ᶜ			250ᶜ					43ᶜ			
Source			65		NA	NA		144	11	75	20		20	5	18
Performance 1956–57	694	90		253			300ᶜ					51ᶜ			
Source			90		NA	NA		173	12	90	25		25	5	21
Performance 1957–58	834	111		271			392					60			
Source			111		41	230		240	14	111	27		30	5	25
Performance 1958–59	1,016	221		305			420ᶜ					70ᶜ			
Source			221		55	250		256	17	118	29		35	6	29
Performance 1959–60 (prel.)	1,150	220		345			500ᶜ					85ᶜ			
Source			220		79	266		305	20	140	35		42	7	36
Performance 1960–61 (prel.)	1,302	245		382			575ᶜ					100ᶜ			
Source			245		100	282		350	23	161	41		50	8	42

ᵃ Data on sources of funds are based on reports by the performers.
ᵇ State and local government funds spent for basic research by the colleges and universities and other nonprofit institutions are included with the respective sector's own funds.
ᶜ Estimates derived from related available information. No sector survey took place in this year.
NA—not available.
Source: National Science Foundation, March 1962.
Note: Expenditures of Federal contract research centers administered by industry, colleges and universities, and other nonprofit institutions are included in the totals of the respective sectors.

73

TABLE 7

Sources of Funds Used for Basic Research, by Sector 1953–1954—1960–1961[a]
(Millions of Dollars)

Year	Total	Federal Government	Industry	Colleges and Universities[b]	Other Nonprofit Institutions[b]
1953–54	$432	$195	$147	$62	$28
1954–55	485	NA	NA	NA	NA
1955–56	547	NA	NA	NA	NA
1956–57	694	NA	NA	NA	NA
1957–58	834	422	249	111	52
1958–59	1,016	565	275	118	58
1959–60 (prel.)	1,150	646	293	140	71
1960–61 (prel.)	1,302	745	313	161	83

[a] Data are based on reports by the performers.

[b] State and local government funds spent for basic research by the colleges and universities and other nonprofit institutions are included with the respective sector's own funds.

NA—not available.

Source: National Science Foundation, March 1962.

Note: With the exception of data for 1953–54 and 1957–58, the years in which surveys covered all sectors, data on sectors as sources of funds are estimates.

OTHER SOURCES OF R & D DATA

In addition to the comprehensive surveys sponsored by the National Science Foundation, there are two other annual surveys of industrial R & D. These are the over-all industry survey conducted by the McGraw-Hill Publishing Company and the Survey of the Ethical Drug Industry by the Pharmaceutical Manufacturers Association.

McGraw-Hill's industrial R & D survey has been conducted as part of a larger annual Spring survey of business plans for plant and equipment expenditures. The most recent survey reported R & D current expenditures by industry for 1961 as well as planned expenditures for 1962 and 1965.

The sample of companies used by McGraw-Hill in compiling data on industrial R & D expenditures is smaller than that employed by the National Science Foundation. Primarily, McGraw-Hill surveys the larger manufacturing companies that account for the major portion of industrial R & D performance. As a result, over-all estimates of total industrial R & D published by McGraw-Hill differ by 10 percent from National Science Foundation figures; individual industries show a greater difference. In 1960 for example, the National Science Foundation reported total industrial R & D expenditures of $10.5 billion, as compared to $9.8 billion published by McGraw-Hill. For the chemical industry alone, the Foundation R & D total was $1,047,000,000; the McGraw-Hill estimate was $741,000,000 for the same year.

Another major difference between the McGraw-Hill and National Science Foundation surveys of industrial R & D lies in the scope and detail of reporting. The McGraw-Hill inquiry concentrates on total expenditures for R & D and research facilities for the principal industries and industry as a whole. The Foundation survey extends beyond this to include the following items: Sources of R & D financing (Federal Government, reporting company and other); character of R & D performed (basic research, applied research, and development); amount of basic research financed by the Federal Government; amount of research performed by industrially operated Federal contract research centers; product fields of research, such as guided missiles and atomic energy devices; and the volume of research performed for the firm by outside organizations, such as university and commercial laboratories.

Although limited in scope, the McGraw-Hill survey performs a useful service. In particular, the smaller sample and the limited number of questions asked result in a quicker dissemination of the data. However, the National Science Foundation has recently speeded up the release of its over-all data through a preliminary report in the bulletin, *Reviews of Data on Research & Development*, issued within 1½ months after receipt of tabulations of the current year's survey.

The Pharmaceutical Manufacturers Association conducts an annual survey covering "human ethical drug research and development." This inquiry asks the firms for the amount spent on R & D within the firm and for outlays for work conducted under contracts or grants to medical schools, hospitals, commercial laboratories, etc. The data collected differ to some extent from those reported in the National Science Foundation survey of the "drug and medicine industry," as defined by the Standard Industrial Classification, principally because the Association's data are collected on an establishment basis whereas the Foundation study follows the company approach. The most recent pharmaceutical inquiry covered 1960 and included an estimate for 1961.

There appear to be no other systematic surveys covering R & D in any of the other sectors of the economy, nor are there any other regular efforts to develop estimates on a national basis.

SCIENTIFIC INFORMATION DATA

The National Science Foundation, by Congressional Act and Executive Order,[28] was given responsibility in 1959 for coordinating scientific and technical information activities throughout the country. In a more limited way, this was already a function of the Foundation. In recognition of the need for more data on the volume of funds expended on scientific information, the Foundation had earlier surveyed Federal obligations for this activity, in fiscal years 1953 and 1954, as part of the bench mark survey of Federal scientific activities described above. Although limited in scope, this effort afforded some notion of the dimension of Federal scientific information activities at that time.

A systematic attempt to measure the total national outlay of funds for dissemination of scientific information is now under way at the Foundation. As a first step in this direction, an annual survey of obligations for scientific and technical information was recently introduced in the Federal sector.

The hazy demarcation between R & D and scientific information activities necessitated wide exploration of concepts and definitions in this area during the initial years of the Federal survey. The discussion enabled the Foundation to make considerable progress in identifying scientific and technical information activities in such a way that their full scope and cost could be adequately measured and analysed. Scientific and technical information is now defined by the Foundation as:

. . . knowledge or data resulting from the conduct of research and development, and required for organizing, administering, or performing research and development. It encompasses any information, existing in recorded or other communicable form, which describes the status, progress or results of research and development in any area of science or technology, and which has some potential use in furthering the advancement of current and future research and development. *Excluded* from this definition of scientific and technical information are: (1) raw scientific and technical data that have not been analyzed, processed or organized for use by scientific personnel engaged in research and development, (2) statistical and general-purpose data that are collected and organized for reasons other than their specific use in

[28] National Defense Education Act of 1958, Public Law 85-864, Title IX, Section 901, Executive Order 10521, as amended March 13, 1959.

research and development, and (3) information prepared primarily for the purpose of informing or instructing the general public or individuals engaged in subprofessional or undergraduate levels of scientific and technical endeavor.

Because of the intertwining of scientific information and R & D, some overlap must be expected in the statistical reporting of these two activities. R & D on the communication of scientific information is obviously part of R & D as a whole, as are scientific information operations and services which are carried on in direct support of R & D activity. The Foundation is exerting great efforts to obtain separate identification of these component activities in order to avoid double-counting when expenditures for various scientific activities are added together.

In the survey of Federal scientific information activities for the fiscal years 1960, 1961, and 1962, which was reported in *Federal Funds for Science, X,* data were collected from the agencies on obligations for intramural scientific information and on contracts and grants predominantly concerned with such information. Excluded was the portion of scientific information activity which was incidental to the main project covered by a grant or contract for R & D or any other noninformation activity.

Reported Federal obligations for scientific information amounted to about $76,000,000 in the fiscal year 1960, $86,000,000 in the fiscal year 1961, and $99,000,000 in the fiscal year 1962. These obligations were equal to approximately 1 percent of total Federal obligations for R & D for the same years.

Industry's part in the scientific information picture is now being explored for inclusion in the forthcoming survey for that sector. In due time, this may be followed by similar surveys in the other sectors so that over-all scientific information totals will eventually be available on a national basis.

EVALUATION OF R & D DATA

The complexity of R & D activities and their relationship to many policy decisions has stimulated considerable interest in the evaluation of the National Science Foundation R & D data. The various types of conceptual and methodological difficulties that place limitations on the accuracy of the data need not be catalogued here because these matters have been discussed in detail in the regular reports on Foundation surveys. It does appear appropriate, however, in the light of experience in the survey program, to acknowledge that conceptual and other related problems can never be eliminated; and, as some are solved, new ones will arise. Realism suggests that users of the data should recognize and learn to live with the factors that cause problems rather than allow such matters to becloud their judgment.

Some Sources of Statistical Problems

It should be clear that the nature of R & D and the associated scientific activities are, in themselves, a major source of many of the statistical problems. Any R & D survey program is, in a sense, an effort to impose a socio-economic system of categorization and quantification on a complex of activities which is constantly changing and greatly involved with abstract hypotheses and processes. Such a universe resists summarization in dollar and manpower terms.

This resistance is reflected in the perennial differences in respondent viewpoint in interpreting survey concepts and definitions and in the continual need for arbitrary decisions. Persons in different fields or at different organizational levels will tend to view a survey concept somewhat differently. What appears to be basic research to the physicist may be classified as applied research by the mathematician; what is basic research to the chemist may be applied research to the physicist, and so on along the continuum. Similarly, an official in an organization supporting research may classify a given project differently from the scientist who is carrying out the work in a university laboratory.

Arbitrary decisions are often necessary in the definition, classification, and measurement of socio-economic phenomena such as R & D expenditures and employment. Survey definitions, for example, must convey clearly and concisely, in language which is meaningful to a wide range of respondents, the content of a particular category of phenomena. Stress must be placed on salient characteristics and key features which distinguish this one category from all others. Since only the most important criteria for identifying a complex activity can be brought within the brief compass of a definition, other criteria must be omitted and taken for granted. This sometimes leads to criticism of survey definitions by persons who assign critical importance to one of the omitted criteria, but it should be borne in mind that only encyclopedic definitions can include all relevant criteria.

Respondents, for their part, must make arbitrary decisions when they use the definitions in classifying their various activities, particularly when the latter are very closely interrelated. Research shades into education, basic research merges with applied research, development may phase into production, and so forth. When the respondent must decide, for survey purposes, where one of these cuts off and the other begins, he may have to classify under different categories expenditures for activities which are not too different. Here again, occasional criticism has been voiced by persons who conclude from the published data that respondents have placed the cutoff at the wrong point with respect to some pair of activities. The Foundation feels, however, that, given carefully and clearly worded definitions, the respondents themselves are in the best position to classify R & D activities correctly. As it happens, most of the activities covered in the surveys are not at the borderlines between categories. Although the problem is interesting intellectually, it does not appear to involve significant amounts of funds.

In addition to the conceptual problems stemming from the nature of R & D itself, there are certain conditions external to scientific activities which tend to influence the interpretation of survey definitions and affect the level of reported figures. First, there are political or psychological considerations. The relatively recent growth in the popularity of support for basic research is a well-known example. As certain fields—such as solid state physics or oceanography—have received increasing public attention, they too have taken on something of an aura. It cannot be claimed that the waxing and waning of such statistically irrelevant factors as the "stylishness" of a particular category are without effect on the accuracy of the survey data. Here, however, it appears that the gradual education of respondents, through the disciplining effect of their own survey experience and the reading of Foundation reports, is leading them to report as objectively as possible.

Secondly, the environment in which the reported R & D takes place may also influence the interpretation of definitions or limit the respondent's awareness of the full range of possible interpretations. If an organization is engaged primarily in engineering, there will be a tendency to classify as engineering certain activities which another organization might regard as chemistry or physics. Furthermore, the reported data may be influenced by the differing accounting records and other sources from which the survey estimates are drawn. For instance, errors are less likely to occur in data drawn from detailed laboratory records of R & D projects than in estimates of R & D expenditures derived from accounts organized around finished "end products" categories. In the latter case, it may be difficult to identify R & D costs intermingled with non-R & D items.

A further environmental factor influencing the reporting of R & D data—as well as some other socio-economic measures—is the circular process by which the careful reading and analysis of survey data and reports may stimulate respondents to re-examine and revise their own reporting and R & D planning. This situation emphasizes the obligation of those surveying R & D activities to produce the most accurate data possible.

Procedures for Ensuring Accuracy

The Foundation stresses survey procedures designed to ensure the accuracy of data, recognizing, at the same time, the limitations which have just been described. Survey procedures are designed to take account of the number and nature of the subsectors within each sector. In the Federal Government, the entire population—about 25 agencies—is covered by direct-mail questionnaire, with 100 percent response. In the industry survey, covering about 12,000 firms, the sampling procedures are revised, when necessary, in the light of changes in the industry classification and size of firms. Here, the response rate has been more than 95 percent; almost all firms employing 1,000 or more have responded.

The colleges and universities are usually covered on a full population basis by direct-mail survey. Sampling techniques are occasionally employed with respect to the smaller colleges. Certain types of schools not likely to be performing R & D—such as junior colleges and schools of theology—are also included on a sampling basis when warranted by the nature of a particular survey. The response rate has been high among those schools known to be performing R & D.

In surveys of the other nonprofit institutions sector, two approaches are necessary. Sampling techniques are employed in querying the 4,000 philanthropic foundations in the United States. The 100-percent sample group here includes all foundations identified in earlier studies as having supported research plus all others with total assets of $5,000,000 or more, or total annual expenditures of $250,000 or more. Sampling ratios are employed for the remaining size groups. For all other subsectors, a mail questionnaire is sent to all institutions previously identified as having supported or conducted scientific research or development and to others for which there has been some evidence of such activity. The response rate for all the "other nonprofit" groups combined was 91 percent in the last full sector survey for 1957.

A number of features of the survey program facilitate accurate reporting by respondents. One is the availability of the staff of the Foundation and of its contracting organizations for personal visits to respondents to discuss difficulties which may arise in relating existing accounting or personnel records to survey categories. Furthermore, special conferences are sometimes held earlier with sector representatives to discuss the design of a forthcoming questionnaire. In the case of the industry survey, an additional feature is the "shuttle" form. This is a system of pre-entering the data for the previous year already reported by the firm before distribution of the survey form for a given year. The shuttle system alerts respondents to their earlier estimate and thereby tends to increase comparability in reporting from one year to the next.

Accumulated survey experience on the part of thousands of reporting organizations has also brought better and more widespread understanding of the scope and purposes of the surveys as well as a higher rate of response. In some cases, respondents have adopted bookkeeping procedures which employ survey concepts.

Another safeguard of accuracy is the analytical editing of all responses by survey staff. This editing draws on insight gained from consulting the files of previous surveys and on familiarity with the distinctive characteristics of the various subsector groups.

A further check on accuracy, at the sector and national level of aggregation, is the intersectoral transfer table which has been described in the foregoing. The combining of dollar data from all surveys, in this matrix, brings to light gaps or inconsistencies in the reports of expenditures for sector performance of R & D or in the reported sources of these funds.

Some Omissions in Data

It should be borne in mind that the present national and sector totals for R & D funds and personnel do not cover certain items. In terms of subsectors, state and local governments as a whole are the most significant omission. However, state and local institutions of higher education are included. Another omission is the small but important group of independent inventors and consultants. The difficulty of reaching these persons through a conventional statistical survey has prevented their inclusion; nevertheless, the Foundation is fully aware of the valuable service they perform. Some "independent" R & D also takes place in industrial laboratories in the spare time of industrial scientists and engineers; this, too, is difficult to cover by the usual survey procedure. The dollar volume of R & D attributable to all these omitted groups, however, is believed to be quite small in comparison to the reported total.

Capital expenditures for R & D are not included in the national totals, as has been noted, because the conceptual and reporting difficulties in this area have not yet been surmounted for all sectors in a comparable manner. The foremost reporting difficulty here is that of identifying, in total outlays for multipurpose facilities, the portion going for R & D facilities. Such multipurpose facilities include industrial laboratories designed to perform routine quality control and also R & D and graduate school laboratories where instruction and research proceed side by side. A further conceptual problem is the fact that organizations differ in their accounting approaches to capital goods on the basis of money value and expected life. Lastly, it has recently become more difficult to reach a general consensus among R & D organizations as to the difference between "materials," which are included in operating expenditures, and "equipment," which is a capital item. Some R & D now requires very expensive new apparatus and equipment, which, like some conventional materials, may be consumed in one or several uses. This blurring of traditional distinctions between capital and noncapital items complicates the solution of conceptual problems. Further exploration of this subject is, however, expected to lead to definitions which will permit across-the-board coverage.

Proper Use of R & D Statistics

Statistical data are always more valuable to the user when their scope and limitations are known and taken into account. Over the years, the staff of the National Science Foundation and of agencies with Foundation survey contracts have had an opportunity to probe these limitations, in their evaluations of the annual survey responses. Published Foundation reports have communicated technical information concerning survey procedure and problems to an ever wider audience. This has led, both within the Foundation and throughout the research community, to a broader understanding of the proper interpretation and use of the data.

It is now commonly realized that data on R & D funds or personnel cannot be equated with the input of "creative energy" or the output of new knowledge, products, and processes. Furthermore, the dollar data do not represent what *should* be spent or what *can* be spent but simply what *is* currently expended, in dollars, in the conduct of R & D. Because of the difficulties in making fine distinctions among component activities, data on the larger aggregates, such as total R & D, are recognized as being stronger, i.e., more accurate, than those for smaller breaks such as basic research. In turn, the total for basic research as a whole is more accurate than the estimates for the field and discipline subcategories of basic research.

The fact that the gradual expansion of statistical materials on inputs into R & D, scientific information, and other scientific activities is making it possible to relate these activities statistically to other socio-economic inputs strongly argues for enlightened and judicious use of the data.   There is great interest in comparing R & D expenditures with relevant trends and ratios in other economic indicators for the United States and in R & D data for other countries.   It is obvious that comparing United States R & D expenditures with other series drawn from a diversity of domestic and foreign sources involves relating sets of data developed along very different conceptual and methodological lines.   In such cases, great care must be taken to ascertain whether apparent differences or similarities between sets of trends or ratios are due to statistical variations or to actual differences in the phenomena which are being compared.

HISTORICAL DATA

For the economic analyst, policy planner, or student of science and technology, the trend data on R & D are one of the most important products of the National Science Foundation R & D surveys.   Such information facilitates the exploration of various hypotheses concerning the relationship between research, national economic growth, and other socioeconomic indicators.   There is also considerable public interest in the general trend of dollar and manpower inputs into R & D for the years preceding the Foundation base year of 1953–1954, but the necessary materials on which to build a series for those years are exceedingly scant and poor.   All the difficulties of a current survey are compounded in any effort to recapture historical magnitudes years later.   For this reason, the Foundation has not undertaken to develop a time series for the 1940's.   However, as a contribution to general knowledge of estimates performed by other groups for years prior to 1953, the Foundation has contributed to a review of the sources of earlier R & D statistics.[29]

The most notable of the past efforts to develop R & D time series in terms of national totals, with component sector detail, were those of Vannevar Bush[30] and the Department of Defense.[31]   Dr. Bush's staff

[29] U. S. Department of Commerce, Bureau of the Census, "Research and Development, 1940 to 1957," *Historical Statistics of the United States, Colonial Times to 1957*, Chapter W, Washington, D. C., Supt. of Documents, U. S. Government Printing Office, 1960, pp. 609–614.

[30] *Science, The Endless Frontier*, Report to the President on a Program for Postwar Scientific Research, Washington, D. C., Supt. of Documents, U. S. Government Printing Office, 1945, p. 80, Table 1.

[31] U. S. Department of Commerce, Bureau of the Census, *Statistical Abstract of the United States, 1960* (Eighty-first edition), Washington, D. C., Supt. of Documents, U. S. Government Printing Office, 1960, p. 538, Table 706.

worked during 1944–1945, under pressure of time and with very in-adequate materials, to develop five expenditures series, covering vary-ing portions of the 1920–1944 period, for industry, nonprofit industrial research institutes, Federal and state government, colleges and uni-versities, and the endowed independent research institutes. The span of years covered by each of the series differed somewhat, with the two longest series—industry and government—covering 1920–1940 and 1923–1944 respectively. National totals were presented for each of the even years of the 1930–1940 decade, since estimates for these years were included in all five series. No common statistical pro-cedure or surveys were employed for the various series. They were developed on the basis of existing estimates made by public and pri-vate organizations with the additional use of several special inquiries. Extrapolations and other adjustments were made when necessary. Despite the limitations of data produced in this manner, the Bush estimates have enjoyed wide and productive usage.

The Department of Defense series, which began with the year 1941, covered Federal Government, industry, and colleges and universities, and other nonprofit institutions combined into one sector, with na-tional totals. These expenditures data were constructed on a differ-ent basis from the Bush materials and included separate estimates for each sector as a source of R & D funds and as a performer of R & D. The Research and Development Board of the Department of Defense, which first worked up the series in 1951–1952, sponsored a special in-dustry R & D survey for 1951 and was also able to draw on better in-formation on Federal funds for R & D than had been available to Dr. Bush. However, no recurring survey program was employed in this effort. Following the first publication of the series, for the years 1941–1953, it was updated annually on a "best judgment" basis for some time after the National Science Foundation surveys were initiated. This was done largely in order to provide current figures relatable to the estimated 1941–1953 trend. The series was discon-tinued with the year 1958 because it was felt that the Foundation data were a more accurate indicator of both level and trend for the post-1953 years.

The obvious statistical and conceptual shortcomings of both the Bush and Department of Defense series are less important than the notable fact that these were the first widely circulated expressions of interest in trend data on R & D input. Broader public interest in this type of data was stimulated by the awareness, on the part of Dr. Bush and the Department of Defense, of the importance of national R & D totals as background to policy discussions. This awareness pointed the way to the establishment in 1953 of the more soundly based statistical and analytical program of the National Science Foundation.

FUTURE TRENDS

The current interest in projections of data on scientific R & D and other related activities stems from a recognition of the critical role which these activities play in the development of national strength—economic, military, and cultural. Those responsible for science policy decisions in both the public and private sectors understandably look to the National Science Foundation for clues to the R & D input in the decade ahead. For its part, the Foundation is interested in participating in the growing effort to analyze the past experience and to plan for the future in the light of available statistical guides.

Yet, useful as they are, aggregate historical data such as the National Science Foundation time series and annual transfer tables are simply broadly descriptive of the past and can serve only as general background in predicting the future. This is true of all economic time series, particularly new ones. It is further obvious that any national science resource planning effort which attempts to take into account the required proportioning of human and material resources to meet the future needs of science and technology can receive only very general guidance from aggregate data relating to either the past or the future. Planning needs to draw on much specific knowledge with respect to resources employed in many components of R & D and related activities. But past data on the deployment of resources in science and technology are not specific enough for planning purposes, and it is very difficult to predict the future in this area with any specificity because of the dynamic nature of R & D.

Obviously, it is well recognized that the rapidly evolving scientific effort will require new types of trained manpower, equipment, and facilities over the years to come. But *what* new types will be needed cannot be foreseen in any useful detail, now. Similarly, we know that new approaches to research will radically alter the relationship between research personnel and research facilities and equipment in many areas, but we cannot foretell specifically *how* the "mix" will change.

Within the complex of science and technology, there is therefore a great variety of matters to be taken into account in any effort to anticipate future requirements of manpower and material resources. In addition, the picture is complicated by the fact that the forward movement of science and technology is shaped by a host of individual institutional decisions. For it must be recognized that, despite the undeniable weight of the Federal sector in the programming and financing of R & D, many significant decisions in this area are made by academic, industrial, nonprofit, and state and local government units. This bespeaks a healthy democratic diversity, but it further increases the number and types of variables that must be borne in mind in looking ahead.

However, the basic planning dilemma in the situation just described does not reside so much in the large number of variables involved but rather in the dynamic nature of science and technology. Techniques for managing numerous variables are available, but the techniques are useless without adequate data being available. Since appropriate data on the future cannot be derived from the relatively limited past information on trends and interrelationships, it is necessary to turn to other sources.

The most important source of clues to the future is the thinking of the research community itself. Future R & D trends will be shaped by the cumulative impact of the changing plans of organizations—public and private—throughout this community. Good information on the future plans of research organization is therefore the first essential for any program of R & D projections.

A second essential in such a program is continuing access to the thoughtful judgment of scientists on the likely evolution of the quest for knowledge, applications, and developments in various fields. From this can come an estimate of changing resource requirements which must complement information on organizational plans.

Another essential in a sound projections program is a clear articulation of underlying assumptions concerning the future political and economic environment of R & D. These assumptions relate to the rate of national economic growth and to the international situation, as well as to more immediate matters such as the availability of funds and manpower. In dealing with such factors, it is obviously more realistic to work with alternative assumptions concerning the future than with one set of ground rules. Survey respondents have limited patience with complex inquiries, however, and it is a challenge to find means of incorporating such alternatives in statistical schedules.

The distinction between the probable and the preferred is another factor which must be recognized in estimating the dimensions of future R & D inputs. The probable represents what is likely to happen under given circumstances, on the basis of past experience and present plans. The preferred represents what those involved in planning think *should* or *must* happen if certain identified national goals are to be achieved. Contemporary science policy discussion requires the exploration of the future from both these viewpoints in order to derive some estimates of the gap between the two types of estimates which emerge. But these two approaches must be clearly separated in any program of statistical projections.

Guided by these beliefs, the National Science Foundation has been developing, sector by sector, surveys designed to obtain information on future planning by R & D organizations. In the Federal area, the Foundation began several years ago, on an exploratory basis, to make projections of Federal Government R & D obligations. In the first of these efforts, agencies were asked to estimate their anticipated research and research plant obligations for the fiscal years 1958 through 1962, a period which went two years beyond the then current budget cycle. The second Federal projections survey covered obligations for development as well as research and included a larger span of years—fiscal years 1959 through 1964. Benefitting by the experience gained in the earlier study, this inquiry requested manpower information in addition to estimated obligations for R & D and R & D plant.

The third survey of Federal agency plans for R & D and R & D plant is being planned at the present time.[32] This inquiry covers a longer period of time—fiscal years 1961 through 1970—and requests much more detail for certain aspects of R & D. In this survey, as in the earlier ones, the respondents are provided with a statement of certain underlying assumptions concerning such matters as the future course of political and economic events. As before, the agencies are requested to furnish their estimates on two distinct levels: first, in terms of an extension of current levels of support, taking into account an agency's understanding of the usual fiscal, facility, and manpower constraints on expansion; and second, in terms of augmented or accelerated projections, reflecting the level of funds which the agency believes will be needed to fulfill its mission, limited only by scientific and technical considerations, i.e., the nature of the "state of the art."

In the industry sector surveys, the Foundation is now asking respondents to estimate the dollar level of R & D which they expect to reach in the year immediately ahead of the principal survey year. Survey experience thus far indicates that company projections are more accurate with respect to company-financed R & D than with respect to federally financed work. There is a tendency to underestimate the future level of Federal R & D financing, probably in an

---

[32] Estimates in all three Federal projections surveys are for internal government use and are not available for public distribution.

effort to avoid giving weight to Federal contracts which have not yet been signed.

Concurrently, in the university sector, a study is being made of the projected scientific and engineering physical facility and apparatus needs for teaching and R & D at 700 institutions of higher education, including associated scientific units. Several other Federal agencies, including the Atomic Energy Commission, the National Aeronautics and Space Administration, and the National Institutes of Health, collaborated with the Foundation in the development of the questionnaire.

In this inquiry, detailed data are being requested on anticipated needs for physical facilities, such as science buildings, laboratories, etc., and for the movable scientific apparatus necessary to make each facility operational. Information is also being asked on major separate and special facilities and apparatus for teaching and R & D where the building has been set up primarily to house the scientific apparatus. Anticipated sources of financial support are also covered. Other summary questions concern future student enrollment, land requirements, and the availability of major utilities.

In addition to the projections, a current inventory is also being made of scientific and engineering physical facilities, including apparatus, which were in existence on July 1, 1962, or for which funds had been firmly obligated as of that date.

Obviously, estimates enter into surveys of projections, particularly for years well beyond the current planning or budget cycle of the respondents. To be useful over a period of time, moreover, forward estimates have to be periodically revised. However, comparisons between Federal agency projections in the first two surveys and actual obligations later made for the fiscal years covered indicate that even these exploratory inquiries were fairly accurate from an over-all point of view. At the agency level, as would be expected, there were certain variations caused by later events which could not have been anticipated when the projections were made. Nevertheless, the information emerging from these exploratory studies was useful from both a statistical and administrative point of view.

As a general contribution to thinking and planning in the area of science resources, the National Science Foundation, in 1961, published the report, *Investing in Scientific Progress*.[33] This was a special effort to explore, in quantitative terms, the nation's future need for resources to be allocated to highest education in science and engi-

---

[33] See footnote 3.

neering and to basic research—taken together as the "keystone of scientific progress." This report has stimulated much valuable constructive discussion and interest in science resource planning.

While these statistical efforts have been in progress at the Foundation, scientific groups associated with the Federal Government or with other organizations throughout the country have been taking a hard look at the probable nature of substantive scientific development in various fields. Hopefully, both these studies and the statistical surveys of the Foundation will provide the material for good judgments on the *likely* course of dollar and manpower inputs into various R & D over the next few years. From this can come the necessary comparison with what *should* be done in the light of the nation's larger goals. The decisions which emerge from such a comparison will have to take account of what is feasible in terms of the country's capacity to produce scientific manpower and to allocate to R & D development the necessary resources.

SPECIAL STUDIES

Index of Research and Development Costs

The upward trend in dollar expenditures clearly indicates a greatly increased national effort devoted to R & D. However, the figures also obviously reflect changes produced by inflation in the unit costs of scientific personnel, materials, equipment, and other elements of R & D costs. To eliminate this inflationary factor in the R & D data as expressed in current dollars and to measure only the trend in "real" effort, the current dollar series must be deflated by means of an R & D cost index.

The Foundation at present supports the construction of such an index on an exploratory basis. A number of other public and private agencies concerned with rising costs and the adequacy of R & D budgets have requested this necessary complement to the current R & D expenditures series. As a first step, the National Science Foundation, in cooperation with the Department of the Army, is constructing an index applicable to the Army's R & D budget. The Bureau of Labor Statistics, U. S. Department of Labor, is serving as the contractor and is making available its facilities and long experience with price indexes. In later phases of the project, the areas of applicability may be extended to include other defense and nondefense R & D and ultimately all sectors of the economy.

To serve as a deflator of R & D expenditures, a cost index should possess certain characteristics. First, the index should register periodic changes in prices of the particular goods and services which enter into the R & D budget. More generalized indexes which are sometimes used as deflators, either in part or as a whole, lack representativeness with respect to R & D budgets. This is true of the wholesale price index, the consumer price index, and the GNP deflator, which are all suitable for the deflation of expenditures in broader areas of commodities and services than R & D.

Furthermore, a fixed R & D "market basket of goods and services" must be utilized for pricing, over time, in order to incorporate in the index of R & D costs only those price changes resulting from inflation or deflation. However, account must also be taken of other causes of price change, such as the availability of new products, new processes, and substitutions.

Next, since it is not practical to include all items entering into a budget, a sampling procedure must be adopted which will identify representative items for pricing, taking into account the various elements affecting prices, such as differences in geographic location and in type-of-performing institution. Finally, in order to combine the prices of these representative items into an index, they must be assigned weights which reflect their relative importance in the total R & D budget.

The information and analysis required in the construction of an R & D cost index also reveal, almost by definition, certain aspects of the financial structure and interrelationships underlying the R & D. Thus, research on the index will yield insight into the relationships between personnel costs and materials and equipment costs; supporting personnel costs and scientific personnel costs; direct and indirect costs; current and capital expenditures, etc.

This new information may also provide useful background for the projection of research budget requirements by public and private organizations. By using data on the structure of a research budget, as revealed by the expenditure patterns of the index, past trends in cost elements can be assessed, and evaluations can be made of possible future cost changes in goods and services required by similar research organizations.

Output Measures of R & D

The National Science Foundation time series on expenditures and manpower allocated to R & D have revealed a heavy commitment of natural resources to science and technology. If present trends continue, even heavier demands on national resources will be made in the future, making it most appropriate to consider means of constructing measures of scientific output.

The development of measures of scientific output will permit an "input-output" framework of analysis for relating the product of scientific effort to the data on scientific expenditures and manpower. Such a framework will be useful to decision makers concerned with the allocation of limited resources to science, and it will provide considerable insight into past and future evaluation of the nation's scientific commitment.

Formidable problems, however, are encountered in the construction of measures of scientific output. Several methods which have already been suggested or explored reflect the difficulty of obtaining adequate measures. These approaches fall into three main categories, as follows:

1. Use of publications, citations, or other items relating to printed materials.
2. Use of data on patents.
3. Use of data covering potential economic value of innovations.

Attempts to provide measures of scientific output must consider at least three types of issues:

1. The nature and content of scientific output. This is a problem of identification of what should be used as a measure of scientific output.
2. The quantification of scientific output. Subsequent to identification, an appropriate unit of scientific output needs to be defined.
3. The weighting of scientific output. An optimum measure should give adequate weighting to such factors as the varying quality or relative importance of units of scientific output. For example, if publications are used as an output measure, some means must be found of taking account of the number of different articles, by the same investigator, describing the same findings. The difficult problem of varying quality can be reduced to the extent that it can be demonstrated that quality variation over time is small.

One critical decision in designing a measure of scientific output is the selection of the scale or level at which output should be measured. Measuring the scientific output of individuals or small groups such as industrial laboratories may involve different types of criteria than measuring the R & D product of a major sector of the economy as a whole. Frequently, the microanalytical approach to the firm or similar organization offers considerably more usable data on research output than can be obtained on the macroanalytical scale for a sector. On the other hand, when separate findings for many small units are aggregated at the next level, such as that of the subsector or sector, questions arise with respect to the homogeneity of "outputs" of various research laboratories.

With such problems well in mind, the Foundation is preparing to review the present situation with respect to alternative approaches to research output measurement. A symposium on this broad subject is being planned as a first step. Following that, particular attention may be given to the use of publications as a measure of scientific output.

Other Analytical Studies

The statistical framework described in the foregoing sections has been constructed and elaborated over the years to furnish a means of identifying and measuring the significant magnitudes and interrelationships in the nation's R & D activities. Surveys which regularly supply the relevant data for this framework are obviously the most appropriate means of furnishing data on sectoral and national expenditures and employment in R & D and on trends in these items over the years. Surveys also provide a wealth of descriptive detail to aid in interpretation of the data.

Within the wide scope of scientific R & D activities, however, there are areas where better understanding is to be gained, not by the mass collection of data but through selective studies in depth. In such instances, it is more appropriate to employ the methodology of the case study. This permits a sharp focus on the salient qualitative and quantitative features of one or several situations which are illustrative of a particular problem.

In employing the case method approach to R & D activities, the Foundation has begun with the industry sector and is supporting inquiries into the area of management decisions dealing with R & D and innovation. This is a subject of considerable general interest and of great relevance to an understanding of the relationship between R & D and innovation and technological change in a free-enterprise society. At the same time, such studies may indicate new approaches which can be taken in the regular statistical inquiries.

Case studies have recently been completed or are still in progress at the Carnegie Institute of Technology and the Case Institute of Technology. At Carnegie, for instance, a recently published study[34] investigated the major determinants of the spread of 12 important

[34] National Science Foundation, "Diffusion of Technological Change," *Reviews of Data on Research & Development*, No. 31, Washington, D. C., Supt. of Documents, U. S. Government Printing Office, 1961.

technological innovations within 4 major industries after the initial adoption of a particular innovation by one firm. Theories were constructed and tested to explain differences in the rates of diffusion among firms and industries.

At the Case Institute of Technology, a study has focused on a possible approach to a quantitative procedure for allocating R & D funds within a company. The inquiry is aimed at a better understanding of the problems of (a) allocating over-all budget funds to R & D and (b) selecting R & D projects that yield maximum returns. Data for the analysis were derived from the R & D records of cost and payoff of three major chemical companies. The mathematical approaches developed were based on these limited data and are therefore not applicable to every type of company. However, it is hoped that this effort will stimulate others of a similar nature, and that a more generally applicable theory of R & D allocation may eventually result.

In a far-sighted provision of the National Science Foundation Act of 1950, the Foundation was instructed to appraise "the impact of research upon industrial development and upon the general welfare." In addition to the industry case studies, which serve this purpose, the Foundation is now considering expanding the scope of its analytical studies to take in certain aspects of the social and economic impacts of research. For instance, the National Aeronautics and Space Administration and the Atomic Energy Commission have joined with the Foundation in mapping out a selective group of studies which will cast light on the manner in which space and atomic energy research have altered existing social and economic patterns and created new ones.

R & D knows no national boundaries, and much can be learned from studies of the R & D efforts of other countries as well as from an interchange of statistics among countries relating to these activities. For some years, the Foundation has been working with the Committee on Applied Research (CAR) of the Organization for Economic Cooperation and Development (OECD, formerly, OEEC) to encourage the member nations to undertake surveys of R & D expenditures and manpower along lines appropriate to their economies. Some countries have already made such inquiries. The United States' primary contribution to stimulating the measurement of R & D inputs in other countries has been in sharing the benefits of a longer and more detailed experience with concepts, methodology, and other aspects of survey procedure rather than in any more direct participation.

Interest in comparisons between the scientific efforts of the United States and the Soviet Union has always been great, but the data employed in many discussions have been inadequate and noncomparable. The Foundation has been supporting a study of USSR inputs into research and development, at the Center for International Studies of the Massachusetts Institute of Technology. It is hoped that, from the heterogeneous mass of official and nonofficial information concerning Soviet activities, some preliminary but reliable estimates can be drawn of that country's comparative investment of manpower and other resources in R & D.

CONCLUSION

In the preceding discussion, a statistical framework has been described for measuring scientific R & D and related activities. It has been shown that many aspects of this framework have already been explored and acted on more thoroughly than others. Operating expenditures for R & D have received primary attention because of their great absolute and relative magnitude. In order to measure inputs covering the full range of scientific activities, however, there must be further statistical investigation of scientific information, testing and standardization, and general-purpose data collection. Capital investment in plant and equipment is also a facet of input for which coverage must be improved in all sectors.

Some of the steps which are being taken to achieve fuller coverage have been described. It appears, however, that even if a complete statistical picture of the nation's expenditures for all the aforementioned scientific activities were on hand, the total would differ very little from the current, more limited, view. The very nature of scientific activities implies that R & D will receive the major portion of the outlays.

Economic and statistical research in scientific activities is a relatively new field of study. As the Federal Government, represented primarily by the National Science Foundation, has obtained and published the statistical and analytical materials which have been described, inquiry into the socio-economic aspects of scientific activities has been stimulated in both academic and business circles. Such growing interest and investigation contribute greatly to public understanding of the critical contribution of scientific R & D and its related activities to the nation's cultural, economic, and military well-being.

REFERENCES

Government

National Science Foundation, *Federal Funds for Science, I. Federal Funds for Scientific Research and Development of Nonprofit Institutions, 1950–51 and 1951–1952.* Washington, D. C., Supt. of Documents, U. S. Government Printing Office, 1953.

——, *Federal Funds for Science, X. The Federal Research and Development Budget, Fiscal Years 1960, 1961, and 1962,* Washington, D. C., Supt. of Documents, U. S. Government Printing Office, 1962.

——, *Funds for Scientific Activities in the Federal Government, Fiscal Years 1953 and 1954,* Washington, D. C., Supt. of Documents, U. S. Government Printing Office, 1958.

——, *Scientific Activities in Six State Governments,* Summary Report of a Survey, Fiscal Year 1954, Washington, D. C., Supt. of Documents, U. S. Government Printing Office, 1958.

——, *Scientific Manpower in the Federal Government, 1954* (NSF-57-32), Washington, D. C., 1957.

——, *Scientists and Engineers in the Federal Government, October 1958,* Washington, D. C., Supt. of Documents, U. S. Government Printing Office, 1961.

Industry

Maxwell Research Center, Syracuse University (prepared for the National Science Foundation), *Research and Development by Nonprofit Research Institutes and Commercial Laboratories, 1953,* Washington, D. C., Supt. of Documents, U. S. Government Printing Office, 1956.

National Science Foundation, *Funds for Research and Development in Industry, 1958,* Washington, D. C., Supt. of Documents, U. S. Government Printing Office, 1961.

——, *Publication of Basic Research Findings in Industry, 1957–59,* Washington, D. C., Supt. of Documents, U. S. Government Printing Office, 1961.

——, "Funds for Performance of Research and Development in American Industry, 1960 (A Preliminary Report)," *Reviews of Data on Research & Development,* No. 30, Washington, D. C., Supt. of Documents, U. S. Government Printing Office, September 1961.

——, "Diffusion of Technological Change," *Reviews of Data on Research & Development,* No. 31, Washington, D. C., Supt. of Documents, U. S. Government Printing Office, October 1961.

——, *Science and Engineering in American Industry. Final Report on a 1953–54 Survey,* Washington, D. C., Supt. of Documents, U. S. Government Printing Office, 1956.

——, *Science and Engineering in American Industry. Report on a 1956 Survey,* Washington, D. C., Supt. of Documents, U. S. Government Printing Office, 1959.

Colleges and Universities

National Science Foundation, "Capital Expenditures for Research and Development in Colleges and Universities, Fiscal Year 1958 (A Preliminary

Report)," *Reviews of Data on Research & Development,* No. 28, Washington, D. C., Supt. of Documents, U. S. Government Printing Office, June 1961.

———, "Indirect Costs of Research and Development in Colleges and Universities, Fiscal Year 1960," *Reviews of Data on Research & Development,* No. 32, Washington, D. C., Supt. of Documents, U. S. Government Printing Office, March 1962.

———, *Scientific Research and Development in Colleges and Universities— Expenditures and Manpower, 1953–54,* Washington, D. C., Supt. of Documents, U. S. Government Printing Office, 1959.

Other Nonprofit Institutions

Andrews, F. Emerson, Russell Sage Foundation (prepared for the National Science Foundation), *Scientific Research Expenditures by the Larger Private Foundations,* Washington, D. C., Supt. of Documents, U. S. Government Printing Office, 1956.

Battelle Memorial Institute (prepared for the National Science Foundation), *Research by Cooperative Organizations, A Survey of Scientific Research by Trade Associations, Professional and Technical Societies, and Other Cooperative Groups, 1953,* Washington, D. C., Supt. of Documents, U. S. Government Printing Office, 1956.

Maxwell Research Center, Syracuse University. *op. cit.*

National Science Foundation, *Research Expenditures of Foundations and Other Nonprofit Institutions, 1953–54* (NSF-58-2), Washington, D. C., 1958.

———, "Scientific Research and Other Programs of a Selected Group of Private Philanthropic Foundations, 1960," *Reviews of Data on Research & Development,* No. 35 Washington, D. C., Supt. of Documents, U. S. Government Printing Office, 1962.

———, *Scientific Research and Development of Nonprofit Organizations—Expenditures and Manpower, 1957,* Washington, D. C., Supt. of Documents, U. S. Government Printing Office, 1961.

National Totals and Trends

Bush, Vannevar, *Science, The Endless Frontier,* Report to the President on a Program for Postwar Scientific Research, Washington, D. C., Supt. of Documents, U. S. Government Printing Office, 1945.

National Science Foundation, *Investing in Scientific Progress, 1961–1970* (NSF-61-27), Washington, D. C., 1961.

———, "Trends in Funds and Personnel for Research and Development, 1953–61," *Reviews of Data on Research & Development,* No. 33, Washington, D. C., Supt. of Documents, U. S. Government Printing Office, March 1962.

U. S. Department of Commerce, Bureau of the Census, "Research and Development, 1940 to 1957," *Historical Statistics of the United States, Colonial Times to 1957,* Chapter W, Washington, D. C., Supt. of Documents, U. S. Government Printing Office, 1960, pp. 609–614.

———, *Statistical Abstract of the United States, 1960* (81st edition), Washington, D. C., Supt. of Documents, U. S. Government Printing Office, 1960, Table 706, p. 538.

3

.

The Measurement of Value of
Scientific Information,[1,2] *Miles W. Martin, Jr.*

One of the most difficult tasks facing the scientist or scientific administrator today is the evaluation of scientific information. In the past, so far as measuring the value of scientific documents is concerned, we have relied primarily on the subjective evaluations of experts. It is true that several attempts have been made to develop a retrospective index of the value of a scientific document by some type of citation count, but no generally acceptable index has been attained. James R. Kuppers (Ref. 1) makes the point quite well when he says that, "at present, judging the merit of a scientific publication ultimately requires a subjective evaluation." Paul Weiss' an alogical description of the life functions of a body of knowledge (Ref. 2) can be viewed as an attempt to develop a suitable index based on citation counts. John Buchley's comments on Weiss' paper (Ref. 3) to the effect that the citation count evaluation of the research impact of a paper can be measured only years after its publication is typical of the controversy which has centered about proposed indices.

There is no doubt that until a suitable measure is developed, a suitable index would be a welcome device. One can seriously question, however, the possibility of developing suitable indices until at least a conceptual foundation for adequate measures of the communicative characteristics of messages has been laid.

An index is a measure of some property which is positively correlated with the property we are primarily interested in. We often

[1] The research reported on here was sponsored by the Office of Science Information Services, National Science Foundation. A full and detailed report of the research is available from that office.
[2] The author is grateful to Professor Russell L. Ackoff for summarizing his behavioral theory of human communication for inclusion in this chapter.

measure a substitute property because it is easier to attain or less costly to measure than the desired property. We can use such an index only if the substitute property is correlated with the property we are interested in. For example, if we are interested in measuring the value of a scientific document but are having difficulty in doing this directly, we may accept citation counts as an index of value only if citation counts and value are correlated. Clearly, this correlation cannot be objectively established until an accurate and reliable measure is available, whether it be objective or subjective in origin.

In this chapter, an attempt is made to evaluate the usefulness of citation counts by comparing the ranking of journal articles using this index with the ranking of the same articles using the subjective evaluation of well-informed people in the relevant field. Serious doubt is cast on the adequacy of citation counts.

The point of view which we have adopted is that the value of a unit of information resides in its effect in terms of action or response by the scientist and, ultimately, in its effect on his scientific productivity.

There is no doubt that even an index of the amount or value of information in a scientific document that could only be used retrospectively would have considerable value in directing the increasingly difficult storage and retrieval of scientific information. An index— and particularly a measure—which could be applied *prospectively,* however, would have much greater value since it could also serve as a filter to prevent the literature from being flooded with material of little or no value.

The feasibility of developing a new and objective measure of the value of scientific documents is examined here by attempting to apply a modified version of a theory of human communication developed by Ackoff (Ref. 6) to the measurement of value of an artificially constructed message in a laboratory situation. The application of the theory to a scientific document is then tried and some of the problems involved are discussed.

THE EVALUATION OF CITATION COUNTS

An extensive literature search revealed that very little had been done in attempting to evaluate existing indices and measures. An outstanding exception was Estelle Brodman's "Choosing Physiology Journals" (Ref. 7). In this article she questioned the validity of one of the fundamental assumptions made in the usual citation count studies that "the value of a periodical to a professional worker is in direct proportion to the number of times it is cited in the professional literature." She obtained a ranking of periodicals in order of value as judged by members of the Department of Physiology, Columbia University, and another ranking in order of number of citations in four of the leading journals in the field. Such a low correlation was observed that "a grave doubt was thrown on the validity of the . . . basic assumption," and Brodman concluded that little dependence could be placed on citations as a guide to the value of a periodical.

We were unable to find any continuation of work along these lines, particularly any attempt to evaluate scientific articles by comparing different criteria where the distinction between indices and measures was recognized. We found J. H. Westbrook's article "Identifying Significant Research" (Ref. 8) to be the closest approach to this type of study in recent years, although his concern was to evaluate scientific laboratories.

In our experiment, all of the citations made in articles appearing in the *Journal of the Operations Research Society of America* (*JORSA*), 1958 through 1960, were tabulated, and those articles which had been cited most frequently (eight in all) were defined as a class of high-citation articles. A class of "normal" citation articles was then selected by choosing eight articles at random from certain years of all articles not in the high-citation class. This class matched the high-citation class with respect to total number of articles and number from any given year in any given journal. The effect of elapsed time and journal origin was the same, then, for both classes.

All citations except those of books were recorded on 3-inch-by-5-inch cards as shown in Table 1:

TABLE 1

Citation Record Form

Author: (cited article)	Date of publication	Cited article
Title: (cited article)	Where published	
Type of citation:		
Author	Date of publication	Citing article
Title	Where published	

Citations were classified according to type, i.e., *mentioned* at the end of the article, *actually mentioned* in the body of the article, or *dependent mentioned* if the citing article could not have been written without the article being cited having been written. Approximately 780 citations were recorded.

Eight high-citation articles and eight normal-citation articles were selected for comparison by specialists. The faculty of the Operations Research Group at Case were considered to be specialists and served as our panel of experts in the experiment. Each specialist was given a matched (in journal and year) pair of articles and asked to state which of the two, in his opinion, was the more valuable. They were not given any criterion of value but were asked to use their own standard of evaluation.

The two sets of journal articles used in the sample are described in Table 2:

TABLE 2

Samples of Articles

	Article	Journal	Year	Number of Citations
	A	*JORSA*	1957	7
	B	*JORSA*	1957	6
	C	*JORSA*	1958	6
High citation articles	D	*JORSA*	1958	5
	E	*JORSA*	1956	4
	F	*JORSA*	1955	4
	G	*JORSA*	1954	4
	H	*Man. Sci.*	1956	4
	A'	*JORSA*	1957	0
	B'	*JORSA*	1957	1
	C'	*JORSA*	1958	0
Normal-citation articles	D'	*JORSA*	1958	3
	E'	*JORSA*	1956	0
	F'	*JORSA*	1955	0
	G'	*JORSA*	1954	0
	H'	*Man. Sci.*	1956	0

A total of sixteen experts in Operations Research independently evaluated matched pairs of high- and normal-citation articles and in ten instances chose the high-citation articles as being more valuable.

In six instances, normal-citation articles were chosen as being more valuable than the high-citation articles.

Information collected on the citation record cards was analyzed for the effects of elapsed time and publication source on the number of citations received as shown in Table 3:

TABLE 3

Number of Citations per Year Elapsed Time Since Publication

Years Since Publication	Number of Citations
0	48
1	137
2	150
3	104
4	88
5	64
6	47
7	41
8	11
9	19
10	6
11	7
12	3
13	3
14	6
15	4
16	2
17	0
18	5
19	3
20	2
21	4
22	1
23	1
24	1
25	2
26	4
27	0
28	1
29	1
30	1
31	1
32	0
33	2
80	1

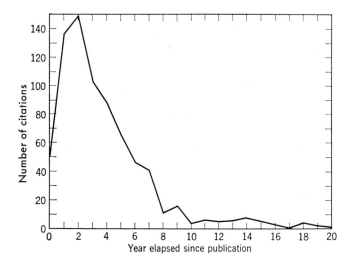

FIGURE 1. Number of citations by year elapsed time since publication for articles cited in JORSA, 1958–1960.

These results are presented in Figure 1.

The experts who had evaluated the sample articles were asked, informally and after they had completed the experiment, for the criteria which they had used in evaluating the articles. The five most frequently mentioned criteria were:

1. The amount of inspiration it gave to others working in the field.
2. The quality of the research done.
3. The number of applications that could be made from the results reported.
4. The amount of synthesis of known facts, provided it is carefully done.
5. The effect of the article on general principles of the discipline.

Conclusions

The object of the experiment was to help us decide whether or not citation counts should be used as an index of value for scientific articles. We took the opinion of experts as a measure of value and asked whether high-citation articles tended to be those which experts agreed were the more valuable ones. Our results indicate that experts choose ordinary-citation articles almost as frequently as high-citation articles as being the more valuable.

Our sample consisted of only sixteen articles, however, and we cannot say on the basis of this sample that our question has been answered unequivocally. We can say, however, that our results are consistent with the view that citation counts ought not to be used as the sole index of value of scientific articles. We conclude, on the basis of this experiment, that the usefulness of citation counts has been opened to serious doubts. This conclusion is in substantial agreement with Estelle Brodman's findings in 1944 (Ref. 7).

An experiment done along similar lines to the exploratory one performed here but with a much larger sample would, in our opinion, be sufficient to enable us to decide whether or not citation counts ought to be used as an index of value.

The effect of elapsed time since publication on the number of citations received which we determined from the citation record cards are more biased towards recent years than some studies in other fields have indicated (Refs, 2, 8). It may be that the pattern in Operations Research differs from that in most other areas because Operations Research is a relatively new field. The results bear out, however, the views expressed by some experts in several fields when they were asked to evaluate articles in their respective fields, namely, that they generally considered only recent articles in their readings.

THE FEASIBILITY OF IMPROVED MEASURES

We have concentrated our exploratory efforts on the development of an objective measure of the amount and value of information contained in an article.

We were looking for a measure of the "value of a unit of scientific information." This, of course, presupposes the ability to identify a "unit of scientific information," which, in turn, presupposes an ability to measure information, scientific or otherwise. To be sure, Claude Shannon (Ref. 4), and Hartley before him, developed a measure of information, the unit of which is called a "bit." But information, as treated by Shannon, is a physical concept which has no relationship to the meaning that is conveyed by the message, or its effect on the receiver. (It is really a measure of the amount of message rather than the amount of information conveyed by a message.) Semantic and pragmatic considerations are explicitly and consciously excluded from Shannon's work. This does not make his concepts and measures any the less useful for communications engineering, but it renders his concepts almost useless for evaluating human communication. For this reason, following the example set by Colin Cherry (Ref. 5), communication theorists distinguish between (Shannon's) communication theory and *human* communication theory.

Ackoff (Ref. 6) made an effort to provide a conceptual and metrical foundation for a theory of human communication. This work, as modified subsequent to its publication, is briefly summarized here since it is used as the springboard for subsequent discussion of the problem at hand.

TOWARDS A THEORY OF HUMAN COMMUNICATION

Purposeful State

An individual is said to be in a purposeful state if:

1. There is at least one possible outcome O_1 of his behavior which has some relative value to him in that situation; and
2. there are at least two alternative courses of action, C_1 and C_2, which have unequal and greater-than-zero efficiences for O_1.

Therefore, an individual is said to be in a purposeful state if he wants something and has unequally efficient alternative ways of obtaining it.

The state consists of:

I the individual

$C_1, C_2, \cdots, C_i, \cdots, C_m$ the alternative courses of action; $m \geq 2$

$O_1, O_2, \cdots, O_j, \cdots, O_n$ the possible outcomes of action

The state variables are:

P_i the probability that I will select C_i; $P(C_i|I)$

E_{ij} the probability that C_i will yield the outcome O_j; i.e., the efficiency of C_i for O_j; $P(O_j|I, C_i)$

V_j the relative value of the jth outcome to I

A purposeful state can be represented as shown in Table 4.

The alternative courses of action are assumed to be defined so as to be exclusive and exhaustive (i.e., only one can be selected at a time, and one must be selected). The outcomes are assumed to be similarly defined. Hence, the sum of the efficiences of any course of action over all objectives must be equal to 1.0. The sum of the efficiencies of all courses of action for any one outcome may lie between zero and m.

The value of a purposeful state to an individual, $V(S)$, may be defined simply as its expected value:

$$V(S) = \sum_i^m \sum_j^n P_i E_{ij} V_j \tag{1}$$

TABLE 4
A Purposeful State

Relative values		V_1	V_2	$\cdots$	V_j	$\cdots$	V_n	
Outcomes		O_1	O_2		O_j		O_n	Sum
P_1	C_1	E_{11}	E_{12}		E_{1j}		E_{1n}	1.0
P_2	C_2	E_{21}	E_{22}		E_{2j}		E_{2n}	1.0
$\vdots$								
P_i	C_i	E_{i1}	E_{i2}		E_{ij}		E_{in}	1.0
$\vdots$								
P_m	C_m	E_{m1}	E_{m2}		E_{mj}		E_{mn}	1.0
								m

The left-edge diagonal labels read: Relative values, Outcomes, Courses of action, Probabilities of choice.

Communication

An individual I_2 is said to communicate with I_1 if a message produced by I_2 changes the characteristics of I_1's purposeful state; i.e., it produces a change in his state variables P_i, E_{ij}, or V_j. To the extent that the message affects the probabilities of choice P_i, it is said to *inform;* to the extent that it changes the E_{ij}, it is said to *instruct;* and to the extent that it changes the V_j, it is said to *motivate.* Hence a message is conceived of as having three possible types of effect and, therefore, content; it does not exclusively involve the transmission of information. Any one message may inform, instruct, or motivate, or do any combination of these. Information refers to *what* an individual does, instruction to *how* he does it, and motivation to *why* he does it.

The properties that a message is found to have depend not only on the message and the receiver but also on the researcher who must represent the situation as a purposeful state. Different observers could represent the situation differently. This, of course, is true of all psychological measurement. What is not so commonly recognized, however, is that it is true of all measurement. However, the conceptual constructs of observers tend to converge and become alike after much experience with the measure.

This means that, by changing the representation of a purposeful state, it is possible to change what appeared to be information in one formulation into instruction or motivation in another. This explains, in part, the looseness of common usage of these terms. On the other hand, for any specific representation of a purposeful state, a message entering it can be characterized in terms of its information, instruction, and motivation.

In the following sections, measures of each of these modes of communication are developed. They are not final in any sense. They are intended to (1) show how measures can be developed within the conceptual framework developed here and to (2) represent our best preliminary judgment as to what these measures should be.

Information

The amount of information contained in a purposeful state is a point on a scale bounded at the lower end by *indeterminism* on the part of individual I (i.e., he has no basis for choice) and at the upper end by complete *determinism* (i.e., he has a complete basis for choice, whether correct or not).

In an indeterminate state, the probability of choice for each of m courses of action is equal to $1/m$. Therefore, the distance of a state from complete indeterminism is measured by the quantity

$$\sum_{i=1}^{m} \left| P_i - \frac{1}{m} \right| \tag{2}$$

For an indeterminate state this sum is equal to zero. In a determinate state, one P_i is equal to 1.0 and the remaining $(m-1)$ P_i are equal to zero. Therefore, the distance between a determinate and indeterminate state is

$$\sum_{i=1}^{m} \left| P_i - \frac{1}{m} \right| = \left(1 - \frac{1}{m}\right) + (m-1)\left| 0 - \frac{1}{m} \right| = 2 - \frac{2}{m} \tag{3}$$

The ratio of Eq. 2 to Eq. 3 is a measure of the proportion of the maximum information a state *can* contain to that which it *does* contain, i.e.

$$\frac{\sum_{i=1}^{m} |P_i - (1/m)|}{2 - (2/m)} \tag{4}$$

If we multiply this proportion by the maximum amount of information a state can contain, we have a measure of the amount of information a state does contain. The units of such information may well be called "inbits" (information bits).

The amount of information a state can contain is conceived of as the number of binary choices between alternative courses of action that must be made to select one course of action from among the set of available courses of action. Therefore, if there are m courses of action, the maximum amount of information the state can contain is $m - 1$ units. A unit of information is the amount involved in one determinate choice from two alternatives (a binary choice). The number of hubits in a state $A(S)$ is given by

$$A(S) = (m - 1) \frac{\sum\limits_{i=1}^{m} \left| P_i - \frac{1}{m} \right|}{2 - \frac{2}{m}} = \frac{m}{2} \sum\limits_{i=1}^{m} \left| P_i - \frac{1}{m} \right| \qquad (5)$$

Now the amount of information communicated may be said to be the difference between the amount of information contained in the state of the receiver immediately preceding the communication (i.e., the *initial* state) and his state immediately following the communication (i.e., the *terminal* state). Let $A(S_1)$ represent the amount of information in the initial state and $A(S_2)$ the amount in the terminal state. Then the amount of information communicated, A_c, is given by

$$A_c = A(S_2) - A(S_1) \qquad (6)$$

It should be noted that this measure contains no implication concerning the correctness or incorrectness of the information received. Correctness depends on the value of the information, which is to be discussed later. Furthermore, it should be noted that this measure is relative to a specific receiver in a specific state. The same message may convey different amounts of information to the same individual in different states, or to different individuals in the same state. Consequently, to specify the amount of information contained in a message, it is necessary to specify the individual(s) and state(s) relative to which the measure is made. If more than one individual or state is involved, it is also necessary to specify what statistic (e.g., an average) is to be used to characterize the set. Generality of information, then, may be defined in terms of the range of individuals and/or states over which it operates.

Written-in messages are not the only source of information. One may obtain information by observation. The measure of information suggested here is equally applicable to observation since, in fact, observation can be considered as a kind of message.

We do not yet have an understanding as to why a particular message may or may not change the individual's probabilities of choice; i.e., inform him. But a reasonable conjecture can be formulated which is at least capable of being tested in principle. It may be that the mechanism of information consists of changing the receiver's subjective probabilities associated with the pairs of actions and outcomes. That is, he modifies his estimates of the E_{ij} in light of the message and, hence, changes his probabilities of choice in the direction of increasing his own estimates of the measure of his performance in the situation.

It will be observed that the measures yielded by Eq. 6 may be negative. This means that a message may not only convey information; it may also withdraw it. This is not as unreasonable as it may appear at first glance. For example, imagine a person who is first told, "it is raining outside now," and almost immediately thereafter, "it is not raining outside now." If the first message conveyed any information to him the second must have withdrawn it. Moreover we recognize the loss of information through "brainwashing," a form of communication.

The transmission of negative information is the movement of a purposeful state in the direction of indeterminism. The information withdrawn may or may not be correct. The value of the information involved must be treated separately.

Suppose that in state S_1 there are two courses of action, C_1 and C_2, whose probabilities of being chosen are $P_1 = 1.0$ and $P_2 = 0$. Now suppose in a later state, S_2, a message has changed these probabilities to $P_1 = 0$ and $P_2 = 1.0$. According to the measure proposed here, there is no change in going from S_1 to S_2 in the amount of information in the states. But information has been withdrawn and replaced. The concepts and measure suggested thus yield considerable flexibility in dealing with the communication act. They are not restricted merely to adding information.

Instruction

To inform is to provide a basis for choice, i.e., a belief in the greater efficiency of one choice than another. Hence information modifies objective probabilities of choice by modifying subjective estimates of probabilities of success. Instruction is concerned with modifying the objective probabilities of success, i.e., efficiency. An individual's state of instruction can be characterized by the amount of control he can exercise over the outcomes in the state. He has maximum control over the outcome if he is capable of bringing about any of the possible outcomes. Instruction is the process of imparting such a capability to him where it is lacking.

Consider a course of action C_1 and two outcomes, O_1 and O_2. He has perfect knowledge of C_1 if he can use it to make either outcome occur with certainty, depending on his desires. If he cannot make the likelihood of an outcome change by his manipulation of C_1, then he does not control that alternative. Suppose, for example, that $E_{11} = 1.0$ no matter what the person desires, and hence $E_{12} = 0$. Then his choice is much like pushing a button that releases a course of action over which he has no further control.

The amount of control an individual has in a state can be measured as follows. Consider a case in which there are two outcomes, O_1 and O_2, and one course of action, C_1. If, when $V_1 = 1.0$ (and therefore $V_2 = 0$) $E_{11} = 1.0$, and when $V_2 = 1.0$ (and therefore $V_1 = 0$) $E_{12} = 1.0$, the individual has maximum control. Therefore the amount of control is reflected in the range of E_{ij} as a function of V_j.

Specifically, the amount of control an individual has over a particular C_i relative to a particular O_j is given by

$$B\,(C_i|O_j) = (E_{ij}|V_j = 1.0) - (E_{ij}|V_j = 0) \tag{7}$$

The amount of control over C_i for all O_j's is given by

$$B(C_i) = \sum_j B\,(C_i|O_j) - 1 \tag{8}$$

The 1 is substracted because, if there are two outcomes, O_1 and O_2, and $B(C_i|O_1) = 1.0$, it follows that $B(C_i|O_2) = 1.0$ because O_1 and O_2 are exclusively defined (therefore, $V_2 = 1 - V_1$).

The amount of control, hence instruction in a state, then, is given by

$$B(S) = \sum_i \sum_j B\,(C_i|O_j) - m$$

$$= \left[\sum_i \sum_j (E_{ij}|V_j = 1.0) - (E_{ij}|V_j = 0) \right] - m \tag{9}$$

Units of instruction may be called "hubits." The amount of instruction conveyed by a message is

$$B_c = B(S_2) - B(S_1) \qquad (10)$$

Motivation

The measure of motivation can be developed in exact parallel with that of information; i.e., the amount of motivation in a state C is given by

$$C(S) = (n - 1) \frac{\sum_{j=1}^{n} |V_j - (1/n)|}{2 - (2/n)} = \frac{n}{2} \sum_{j=1}^{n} \left| V_j - \frac{1}{n} \right| \qquad (11)$$

Hence the amount of motivation communicated is

$$C_c = C(S_2) - C(S_1) \qquad (12)$$

The units of motivation may be called "mobits."

Value of Communication

The value of a communication can be defined as the value of the terminal state minus the value of the initial state:

$$V_c = V(S_2) - V(S_1)$$

$$= \sum_{i=1}^{m} \sum_{j=1}^{n} (P_i + \Delta P_i)(E_{ij} + \Delta E_{ij})(V_j + \Delta V_j) - \sum_{i=1}^{m} \sum_{j=1}^{n} P_i E_{ij} V_j \qquad (13)$$

where ΔP_i, ΔE_{ij}, and ΔV_j represent the change in state variables between S_1 and S_2. By expansion we get

$$V_c = \Sigma\Sigma \, \Delta P_i E_{ij} V_j + \Sigma\Sigma P_i \, \Delta E_{ij} V_j + \Sigma\Sigma P_i E_{ij} \, \Delta V_j$$
$$+ \Sigma\Sigma \, \Delta P_i \, \Delta E_{ij} V_j + \Sigma\Sigma \, \Delta P_i E_{ij} \, \Delta V_j + \Sigma\Sigma P_i \, \Delta E_{ij} \, \Delta V_j$$
$$+ \Sigma\Sigma \, \Delta P_i \, \Delta E_{ij} \, \Delta V_j \qquad (14)$$

The first three terms represent the value added to the initial state by the information, instruction, and motivation communicated respectively. The value of any of these expressions may be either positive or negative. If, for example, the first term is negative, the receiver has been misinformed; if positive, he has been informed.

The last four terms of Eq. 14 represent the values of the various possible interactions. For example, the fourth term is the value of the joint contribution (not the sum of the independent contributions) to the value of the information and instruction communicated. The last term represents the joint contribution to the value of the information, instruction, and motivation in the communication.

SOME OBSERVATIONS ABOUT THESE MEASURES AND CONCEPTS

Looking at the measures and concepts presented in light of the problem at hand, it will be seen that they measure the content of a message by the effects of the message on its recipient. This, of course, is completely consistent with our observation that "the value of a unit of information . . . resides presumably in its effect in terms of action or response by the scientist. . . ." The concepts and measures are behavioristic, not in the sense of Watson's mechanistic behaviorism but in the sense of Singer's and Tolman's teleological (functional) behaviorism.

The distinction between the amounts of information, instruction, and motivation, on the one hand, and between the amounts and their value on the other seems to be particularly relevant to scientific documentation. It is easy to identify articles and books which are intended to be predominantly informational, instructional, or motivational.

The measures developed here all apply to the individual receiver. If we want to measure the value of the communication to the sender, we must determine how the receiver's response to the message affects the expected value of the sender. All the concepts necessary for doing so have been introduced here.

Now suppose we want to measure the scientific value of a message. Either we must measure the value of the message to scientists individually and combine these measures in some suitable way or we must deal with science institutionally (as a social entity) and measure the value of the message relative to it. If the first alternative is taken, the three major problems are: (1) how to select the sample of scientists on whom measurements are to be made; (2) how to distribute the observations (sample) over time; and (3) how to amalgamate these individual measurements into a composite measure. If the second alternative is taken, we must be able to define science as an institution in such a way as to permit our observing its responses to stimuli. It seems clear that however difficult the first alternative may appear, it is the less difficult relative to our present state of knowledge. Furthermore, it conforms with some important current practices such as the use of referees in the selection of papers for publication in a journal. Here, the editor, in effect, uses the evaluations of a very small number of scientists as a basis for estimating the value of the article.

In this study we have not considered either the sampling or amalgamation problems. We have concentrated on measuring the impact of a message on an individual scientist at a particular moment of time.

It is apparent from even a cursory examination of the measures proposed that considerably more effort would be required to use them than most potential consumers of such measures would feel is justified. It is important to realize, however, that even if the measures proposed here are not practically applicable to, say, evaluating articles which have been submitted for publication or which have been published, they may still have another important and practical application. Consider the following evolutionary cycle of measurement which has frequently been repeated in the history of science:

1. Subjective evaluations are used.
2. Objective indices are developed which correlate positively with subjective evaluations.
3. Objective measures are developed and "validated" initially by checking against subjective evaluations. In time, however, the balance of confidence shifts and subjective evaluations are validated by checking against objective measures.
4. If the objective measures are costly to obtain, objective indices are developed which correlate positively with objective measures. These are then frequently used in place of the measures.

The development of a measure which is not a practical substitute for subjective evaluation may still be useful in providing a basis for standardizing subjective evaluations or in developing objective indices.

The documentation area, as it exists today, relies largely on subjective evaluations. The only indices of these evaluations which have been seriously suggested—those based on citation counts—have been found to be inadequate. Very little has been done to determine the consistency of subjective evaluations, and nothing has been done to develop measures of the type proposed here.

The attempt to measure information and instruction which is reported in this chapter has several objectives:

1. To determine in a simple case whether the results obtained conform with common sense and subjective evaluations.
2. To determine whether the results reveal anything about the communication process that is not likely to be picked up by common sense.
3. To determine how complex, time-consuming, and costly the proposed process of making measurements is and how it might be simplified.

EXPERIMENTAL APPLICATION OF THE THEORY

It was decided to test, and hopefully to illustrate, the feasibility of the foregoing theory in measuring the amounts of information and instruction communicated in a simple case. Techniques for measuring the amount of value placed on outcomes have been developed in modern utility theory and can be used to determine the number of mobits communicated. It therefore seemed advisable to concentrate on measuring inbits and hubits in this exploratory experiment. In order to do this, in general, the following steps would have to be taken:

1. Identify the courses of action (C_i) with respect to which the message is relevant.
2. Identify the outcomes (O_j) with respect to which the message is relevant.
3. Construct a purposeful state characterized by the C_i and O_j identified in steps 1 and 2.
4. Place the individual I in the purposeful state and motivate him relative to O_1 so that V_1 is equal to 1.0. Then observe P_i and E_{i1} for each C_i
5. Motivate him so that $V_1 = 0$ and make similar observations.
6. Repeat steps 4 and 5 for all O_j. The amount of information and instruction in the initial state relative to each outcome can now be measured.
7. Expose I to the message.
8. Repeat steps 4 through 6. The amount of information and instruction in the final state relative to each outcome can now be measured. The change in the amount of information and instruction contained in the states before and after the message is a measure of the amount of information and instruction transmitted by the message.

The following experiment was set up along these lines.

Experimental Design

Subjects were asked to calculate square roots of three- and four-digit numbers selected from a table of random numbers.

The courses of action C_i by which the square roots of the numbers could be obtained were restricted to the use of a slide rule and a desk calculator. The outcomes from these courses of action were two—the right answer or the wrong answer. To be right, the answer had to be correct to three significant figures. This degree of accuracy was chosen because it is difficult to obtain the third significant figure with a slide rule. The calculator is accurate to five significant figures if a method for obtaining square roots is known, but it is of little value if a method is not known.

Throughout the experiment the individual was motivated towards the correct score, i.e., the value relative to the correct score outcome was equal to one. No test was made with this value equal to zero as it was assumed that the individual could always obtain the wrong score if he wished.

The experiment was set up such that the individual was in a room alone except for the person administering the experiment. There were no interruptions. The individual subjects were graduate students in Operations Research and Physics at Case Institute of Technology. The individual was given a slide rule, a desk calculator, a table of square-root figures appropriate for use with the calculator, pencils, and a form for the answers.

Each three- or four-digit number for which the square root was to be calculated was written on the blackboard within easy sight of the individual. At the end of a 40-second interval, the number was erased by the person administering the experiment and the next number written in its place. This procedure was used in lieu of the more usual one of flashing a picture on a screen for a given period of time. The 40-second interval was chosen because it was the average time it took a calculator operator to obtain a square root in pretests, and because it is also a sufficient amount of time for a slide rule user to complete his calculations.

The experiment was divided into four stages. Each stage consisted of a set of 20 random three- or four-digit numbers. The stages were arranged as follows:

Stage I. The individual was given the choice of using the slide rule or the calculator for each of the 20 numbers. He could change the instrument used between numbers but could only use one or the other on any given number, not both.

The percentage of times the subject chose to use the calculator was considered his probability of choosing the calculator in the initial state. The percentage of times he chose to use the slide rule was considered his probability of choosing the slide rule in the initial state. These probabilities are represented by the symbols P_{c1} and P_{s1} respectively.

The percentage of correct scores obtained with the use of the slide rule was considered the efficiency of using the slide rule in the initial state, E_{s1}, and the percentage of correct scores obtained by using the calculator (if the calculator was used on at least half of the numbers) was considered the efficiency of the calculator in the initial state, E_{c1}. If the calculator was not used for at least one-half of the numbers, the subject proceeded to stage II.

Stage II. This stage was only conducted if $P_{c1} < 0.5$ and was conducted solely with the aim of obtaining E_{c1}. In this stage only the calculator was allowed to be used, and E_{c1} was given by the percentage of correct scores attained.

Thus from stage I and/or stage II, the amount of information and instruction in the initial state could be calculated. The subject was then given a message.

The message was a set of instructions for using the calculator to get square roots. The message included two worked examples, and the individual was allowed sufficient time to understand the procedure involved. The time period was usually about ten minutes.

Stage III. The procedure in this stage was the same as in stage II. From the results, the efficiency of the calculator in the final state for obtaining the correct answer, represented by E_{c2}, was obtained.

Stage IV. The procedure in this stage was the same as in stage I. The probability of choosing the calculator and the probability of choosing the slide rule (P_{c2} and P_{s2}) were obtained by using the method outlined in stage I. In the first instance, the individuals were told at the end of each stage the number of correct answers they obtained for the stage.

Six individuals were run through the complete procedure outlined in the foregoing, and the results were collected. It was noticed that in some cases there was an increase in E_{c2} from the third stage to the fourth stage. This indicated that learning took place, apart from the message. Since this was the case, there might also be a learning effect between stage II and stage III which was not caused solely by the message. In this case, the difference between E_{c1} and E_{c2} caused by the message might be overestimated. We decided to repeat the experiment as outlined in the foregoing but not to give the individuals concerned a message. Six individuals were run through the process in this manner and their efficiencies before and after becoming familiar with the operation of the calculator were measured. It was also possible that probabilities of choice in stage IV were affected by giving the individual scores at the end of each stage. Accordingly, six more individuals were run through the experiment with the message but without any scores, and the results were obtained as before.

It should be pointed out here that reversing the order of stages III and IV and only running the present stage III if $P_{c2} < 0.5$ would have saved some time. It is also true that there is no guarantee in the experiment, as it was run, that obtaining the correct answer was the only goal of the individual subject.

In the results given in the next two sections the following symbols are used:

P_{c1} = probability of choosing the calculator before the message
P_{s1} = probability of choosing the slide rule before the message
P_{c2} = probability of choosing the calculator after the message
P_{s2} = probability of choosing the slide rule after the message
E_{c1} = efficiency of the calculator for obtaining the right answer before the message
E_{c2} = efficiency of the calculator for obtaining the right answer after the message
E_{s1} = efficiency of the slide rule for obtaining the right answer before the message
E_{s2} = efficiency of the slide rule for obtaining the right answer after the message
A_{s1} = the amount of information the subject has before the message
A_{s2} = the amount of information the subject has after the message
A_c = the amount of information (inbits) transmitted by the message
B_{s1} = the amount of instruction the subject has before the message
B_{s2} = the amount of instruction the subject has after the message
B_c = the amount of instruction (hubits) transmitted by the message
V_1 = value of correct answer outcome
V_2 = value of incorrect answer outcome

The Amount of Information (Inbits)

As outlined in the theory, the amount of information in a state is given by

$$A_s = \frac{m}{2} \sum_{i=1}^{m} \left| P_i - \frac{1}{m} \right|$$

where m is the number of choices of action.

In this case $m = 2$, and, hence,

$$A_s = \sum_{1}^{2} \left| P_i - \tfrac{1}{2} \right|$$

More specifically

$$A_{s2} = \left| P_{c2} - \tfrac{1}{2} \right| + \left| P_{s2} - \tfrac{1}{2} \right|$$

and

$$A_{s1} = \left| P_{c1} - \tfrac{1}{2} \right| + \left| P_{s1} - \tfrac{1}{2} \right|$$

Now from the foregoing,

$$A_c = A_{s2} - A_{s1}$$

In this case

$$A_c = \left|P_{c2} - \tfrac{1}{2}\right| + \left|P_{s2} - \tfrac{1}{2}\right| - \left|P_{c1} - \tfrac{1}{2}\right| - \left|P_{s1} - \tfrac{1}{2}\right|$$

The Amount of Instruction (hubits)

It is seen that the amount of instruction, and hence control, in a state in the general case is given by:

$$B(S) = \left[\sum_i \sum_j B\left(C_i|O_j\right)\right] - m$$

where $B(C_i|O_j)$ is the amount of control individual I has over a particular C_i relative to outcome O_j.

$$B(C_i|O_j) = (E_{ij}|V_j = 1.0) - (E_{ij}|V_j = 0)$$

where V_j = value of outcome j.

Thus, for the general two-choice two-outcome case,

$$\begin{aligned}
B(S) = \ & (E_{11}|V_1 = 1) - (E_{11}|V_1 = 0) + \\
& (E_{21}|V_1 = 1) - (E_{21}|V_1 = 0) + \\
& (E_{12}|V_2 = 1) - (E_{12}|V_2 = 0) + \\
& (E_{22}|V_2 = 1) - E_{22}|V_2 = 0) - 2
\end{aligned}$$

For the specific case,

$$\begin{aligned}
B(S_2) &= E_{c2} - 0 + E_{s2} - 0 + 1 - (1 - E_{c2}) + 1 - (1 - E_{s2}) - 2 \\
&= 2(E_{c2} + E_{s2} - 1)
\end{aligned}$$

Similarly,

$$B(S_1) = 2(E_{c1} + E_{s1} - 1)$$

Now,

$$B_c = B(S_2) - B(S_1)$$

Therefore,

$$\begin{aligned}
B_c &= 2(E_{c2} + E_{s2} - 1 - E_{c1} - E_{s1} + 1) \\
&= 2(E_{c2} - E_{c1})
\end{aligned}$$

since $E_{s2} = E_{s1}$ by assumption.

In this experiment not all the terms involved were tested for, and at least two assumptions were made. First, it was assumed that the subject could always obtain the wrong answer if required so that all E_{ij} equaled 1 when $V_1 = 0$ or when $V_2 = 1$. Second, since many of the subjects had a small or zero P_{s2}, the measure for E_{s2} was not reliable or could not be measured without further testing. The efficiency of the slide rule was assumed to be constant throughout. This assumption seemed reasonable as the message contained nothing relevant to the slide rule.

Eighteen subjects in all participated in the experiments. Six were given messages and told their test scores at the end of each stage. Six were given messages but not told their test scores, and six were given neither messages nor test scores.

The inbits and hubits communicated to each individual were calculated in the manner just indicated and are given in Table 5.

TABLE 5

The Number of Hubits and Inbits Communicated

	Subject	Hubits	Inbits
Message and scores	1	−0.1	1.1
	2	0	1.6
	3	0	−0.2
	4	0.56	0.24
	5	0	1.2
	6	−0.3	0.6
No message and no scores	7	0	0.5
	8	0	−0.1
	9	0	−0.3
	10	−0.9	0.9
	11	−0.9	0.7
	12	0	0
Message and no scores	13	0.1	0
	14	0.8	0.2
	15	0	0.2
	16	−0.2	1.9
	17	−0.1	1.1
	18	0	1.2

From these results, the average amounts of information and instruction transmitted in each stage were computed as follows:

$$\bar{A}_c = \bar{A}_{s2} - \bar{A}_{s1} = \overline{|P_{c2} - \tfrac{1}{2}|} + \overline{|P_{s2} - \tfrac{1}{2}|} - \overline{|P_{c1} - \tfrac{1}{2}|} - \overline{|P_{s1} - \tfrac{1}{2}|}$$
$$\bar{B}_c = \bar{B}_{s2} - \bar{B}_{s1} = 2(\bar{E}_{c2} - \bar{E}_{c1})$$

Message and scores

$$\bar{A}_c = 0.467 + 0.467 - 0.453 - 0.453 = 0.027 \text{ inbit}$$
$$\bar{B}_c = 2(0.741 - 0.363) = 0.746 \text{ hubit}$$

No message and no scores

$$\bar{A}_c = 0.35 + 0.35 - 0.5 - 0.5 = -0.3 \text{ inbit}$$
$$\bar{B}_c = 2(0.517 - 0.375) = 0.282 \text{ hubit}$$

Message and no scores

$$\bar{A}_c = 0.467 + 0.467 - 0.417 - 0.417 = 0.1 \text{ inbit}$$
$$\bar{B}_c = 2(0.925 - 0.542) = 0.766 \text{ hubit}$$

It is not at all surprising to note that in each stage of the experiment more instruction than information was communicated. The message was intended to be primarily instructive. The results also agree with common-sense expectations in that more hubits were communicated in the two groups in which the subjects were given the message.

The most information and instruction was communicated when the subjects were given the message but not scores. When both the message and scores were given to the subjects, the amount of instruction communicated was slightly less than when scores were not given, and the amount of information communicated was only about one-fifth as much as when scores were not given. It was apparent from conversations with the subjects who participated in the experiment that they believed that they had done better with the calculator than was actually the case. Thus, when they were not told their scores during the course of the experiment, their tendency was to use the calculator more often during the last stage. They were less inclined to use the calculator in the last stage when they found out how they had actually performed in the earlier stages. Slightly surprising is the fact that those subjects who were not given scores, and who generally believed that they had done better in the first two stages than was actually the case did, in fact, do better when using the calculator in the third stage. It seems as though their increased confidence, though falsely grounded, increased the efficiency with which they could use the calculator. Giving scores had what may be described as a negative learning effect.

When no message was given, the subjects nevertheless received some instruction from the practice gained in using the calculator, although they became less determined in choosing between the slide rule and calculator in the last stage. It appears, then, that practice has a positive learning effect where instruction is concerned, whereas the giving of test scores has a negative learning effect. On the other hand, both practice and the giving of test scores seem to have had a negative effect where the communication of information is concerned.

In conclusion, it appears that the behavioral theory of human communication which we tested can be used to measure the amounts of information and instruction communicated in an artificially simple case. We feel certain that there would be even less difficulty in measuring the amounts of motivation communicated in a similar case, although we did not do so in this exploratory study.

OBSERVATIONS USING AN ACTUAL SCIENTIFIC DOCUMENT

It is to be expected that there would be a considerable difference between applying the theory in artificially constructed simple cases, as discussed in the foregoing, and using it to measure the amounts of information, instruction, and motivation communicated by scientific documents. To get some idea of how far we had to go before the approach used in the experiment could be made to work in the real world, we briefly examined Chapter 11 of *Progress in Operations Research* (Ref. 9). Our major purpose was to see whether it was possible, with the use of the experience just gained, to describe a purposeful state which was meaningful and relevant to a given, real-life scientific message.

From the Introduction to Chapter 11, Ref. 9, we tried to determine the major objectives of the chapter. It is intended to be "a review of past developments [in Operations Research] and their causes . . . [in order to] indicate the lines of growth that exist, and [to] clarify some of the conditions and problems which we must face." It seemed to us that some of its purposes are (1) to influence individuals not presently committed to Operations Research to undertake it as a profession (by indicating its growth potential and the nature of its major problems yet to be solved) and (2) to motivate Operations Researchers to devote more energy in certain areas (those which are likely to be productive in the future) and to certain types of problems (those which must be faced if work of greater significance is to be achieved).

From the Introduction alone, it appears that Chapter 11, Ref. 9, is intended to be mainly motivational and partly informative, with little or no instruction given.   Values are to be changed with respect to choosing Operations Research as a profession, working in certain areas in Operations Research, and working on certain types of problems.   It also seemed likely at this point that information would be given as to specific courses of action which might be taken to achieve these goals, i.e., available techniques, skills, and approaches which make up the "conditions" under which desirable growth can be achieved.

In similar fashion the other sections of the chapter were examined and an attempt was made to describe the purposeful state.

The Purposeful State

Chapter 11, Ref. 9, seems to be aimed at: (1) Middle and top level management of industrial and military organizations; (2) professional Operations Researchers; and (3) prospective Operations Researchers.

The outcomes which seem to be relevant to this chapter are: (1) The introduction of new and capable scientists into Operations Research; (2) managerial recognition of the usefulness of Operations Research; (3) increased effort on the part of Operations Researchers in the areas of (a) handling of risk, (b) the analysis of organizations, (c) competition, and (d) planning for civil government.   For each of these possible outcomes there is a complementary, or negative, outcome.

The courses of action which seem to be relevant to these outcomes are:

1. The decision of scientists to move into the field of Operations Research.
2. The decision of management to provide Operations Researchers with challenging problems of broad scope.
3. The development of optimization methods in the simulation of complex operating systems.
4. The use of statistical surface exploration procedures in the study of complex systems.
5. The development of quantitative models of human behavior.
6. The reading of books and articles contained in the bibliography.
7. Working on long-range procurement problems.
8. The development of theories of functional interdependencies within organizations.
9. Developing measures of the operational performance of primary detection systems.
10. Developing adequate measures of effectiveness for inventory problems.
11. Developing adequate measures of information content and significance.

A further characterization of the purposeful state would require the measurement of the values of the possible outcomes to management and present and future Operations Researchers, as well as measures of the probabilities of selecting the courses of action outlined and the efficiencies with which the courses of action lead to the desired outcomes. This has not been done, but we now have a more precise idea of what would be required to measure the amounts of information, instruction, and motivation communicated by Chapter 11, Ref. 9. The amounts of time and effort required at this stage of the development of the theory to analyze an actual scientific article are great, but the prospect is by no means discouraging, for our conceptual framework dictates the stages in which the problem is to be solved, and there is every reason to suppose that it is feasible to solve the problem by using this approach. That is not to say, of course, that the problem is solved or even nearly solved.

FUTURE DIRECTIONS

It seems to us that this initial exploration into the area of developing and evaluating measures of the value of scientific information clearly indicates two lines which ought to be further developed. (1) The usefulness of citation counts as an index of the value of scientific information can be realistically determined by comparing the rankings of articles by experts' opinions with the rankings using citation counts. This ought to be done on a larger scale than was possible in this study, and, we believe, along the lines developed in this study. (2) The behavioral theory of human communication which was used in this study appears to be a fruitful one with respect to providing a conceptual framework from which useful measures of scientific information can be developed. More basic research in the theory itself is needed to enrich its store of concepts. For example, we suspect that subjective estimates of the efficiencies of available courses of action play a large role in determining the probabilities of selecting courses of action, but have not formally taken account of this in the theory. We have also seen, during the course of the experiments, that there appears to be positive learning with the repetition of performance of a course of action, but negative learning when the subject is told the results of his performance and his scores are lower than his expectations. This phenomenon and its role in human communication ought to be accounted for by the theory. On the empirical side, more work ought to be done in trying to apply the theory to the measurement of both artificially constructed messages and actual scientific documents. Such experiments would, hopefully, suggest new and useful modifications of the theory while helping to develop the practical skills which will be necessary should the time come to apply the theory on a large scale.

REFERENCES

1. Kuppers, James R., "Literature Citation Counting," *Science,* Vol. 133, No. 3459, April 14, 1961, p. 1138.
2. Weiss, Paul, *Science,* Vol. 731, 1960, p. 1716.
3. Buckley, John, "The Life of Scientific Publications," *Science,* Vol. 132, No. 3427, Sept. 7, 1960, pp. 625–626.
4. Shannon, Claude E., and Warren Weaver, *The Mathematical Theory of Communication,* University of Illinois Press, Urbana, 1940.
5. Cherry, Colin, *On Human Communications,* Technology Press and John Wiley and Sons, New York, 1957.
6. Ackoff, Russell L., "Towards a Behavioral Theory of Communication," *Management Science,* Vol. 4, No. 3, April 1958, pp. 218–234.
7. Brodman, Estelle, "Choosing Physiology Journals," *Med. Lib. Ass'n. Bull.,* Vol. 32, 1944, pp. 479–483.
8. Westbrook, J. H., "Identifying Significant Research," *Science,* Vol. 132, October 28, 1960, pp. 1229–1234.
9. Magee, John F., and Ernst, Martin L., "The Challenge of the Future," in *Progress in Operations Research,* Vol. 1, Russell L. Ackoff, Ed., John Wiley and Sons, New York, 1961, Chapter 11, pp. 467–491.

4

.

Integrated Research and Development
Management Systems, Donald G. Malcolm

The PERT (Program Evaluation and Review Technique) information system, designed to provide progress information to the management team of the Navy Polaris program is a significant example of what modern industrial engineering, working in conjunction with operations research and computer specialists, can achieve. PERT was created by a "system design" approach quite similar in its scope and orderly development to that taken in the development of hardware items. It is the purpose of this chapter to describe the basic PERT system, its current extensions into the cost and reliability areas, and to touch briefly on some industrial applications being made.

PERT was designed to deal with the measurement and control of *time*, i.e., compliance to plans, scheduling, planning, and prediction of progress. Other management research in this area, by the Navy, the Air Force, and industry, is extending the PERT concept into measurement and prediction of *cost* and *performance*—where performance refers to the performance of the item under development. Thus, PERT and its extensions represent a long-range research program directed to the objective of an integrated R & D management system wherein the time, cost and technical performance factors are effectively portrayed for planning, as well as for management control and communications purposes.

Admiral Raborn, Director of Special Projects Office, which has managed the Polaris program, often tells his people that "If you can think out a plan, you can also write it down." This message supports the planners to encourage their technical staffs to reduce to writing the ideas they have in their minds. This is a necessary first step in

124

"creating on schedule." General Schriever, Commander of the Air Force Systems Command which develops the many weapons systems of the Air Force, has stated that one of their most serious problems in space and missile development concerns the development of management methods. These two men, entrusted with a large portion of our creative R & D, have thus laid down a challenge to all of those who are working in the management systems area to develop management systems which can keep up with the rapidly advancing technology in the development of missiles and space vehicles. Both men endorse PERT, the subject at hand, as a tool necessary in the reduction of both time and cost in our defense effort.

It has been the concept of "concurrency," i.e., concurrent design and development in order to reduce development time, that has created the need for a new technique, predictive in nature and able to cope with concurrent, interrelated activities thus created. The increased coordination and attendant information required are graphically shown in Figure 1, which illustrates the added number of interactions required to operate in a concurrent fashion in the development of weapon systems. It is the increased number as well as compressed time for these interactions and communications that requires accurate, quick-responding information systems.

Military management has recognized the need for a significant development effort with time-phased goals to develop management tools that can keep up with the dynamics of the creative technical work involved. Recognition of this problem and investment of research time and effort to help to solve it are unique contributions in and of themselves, for it generally is quite difficult to establish research projects in the operational research management area.

Since initial application in Polaris, the concept has spread through many Air Force, Navy, and Army programs, and it is being used in private industry for the management of the new product activity where savings on the order of 20 percent have been claimed.

The Navy's program in PERT was part of a time-phased program, much the same as we see in the development of a missile. We speak of generations of missiles, each one having greater range and other operational capabilities than the preceding generation. Likewise, in establishing management systems, the concept of going at it in a series of generations was conceived, and PERT represents the first such generation of a management information system. It tackles primarily the problem of *time* compliance in a development program. Second and third generations of this management system are currently under development in the Navy: one in terms of *cost*, dedicated

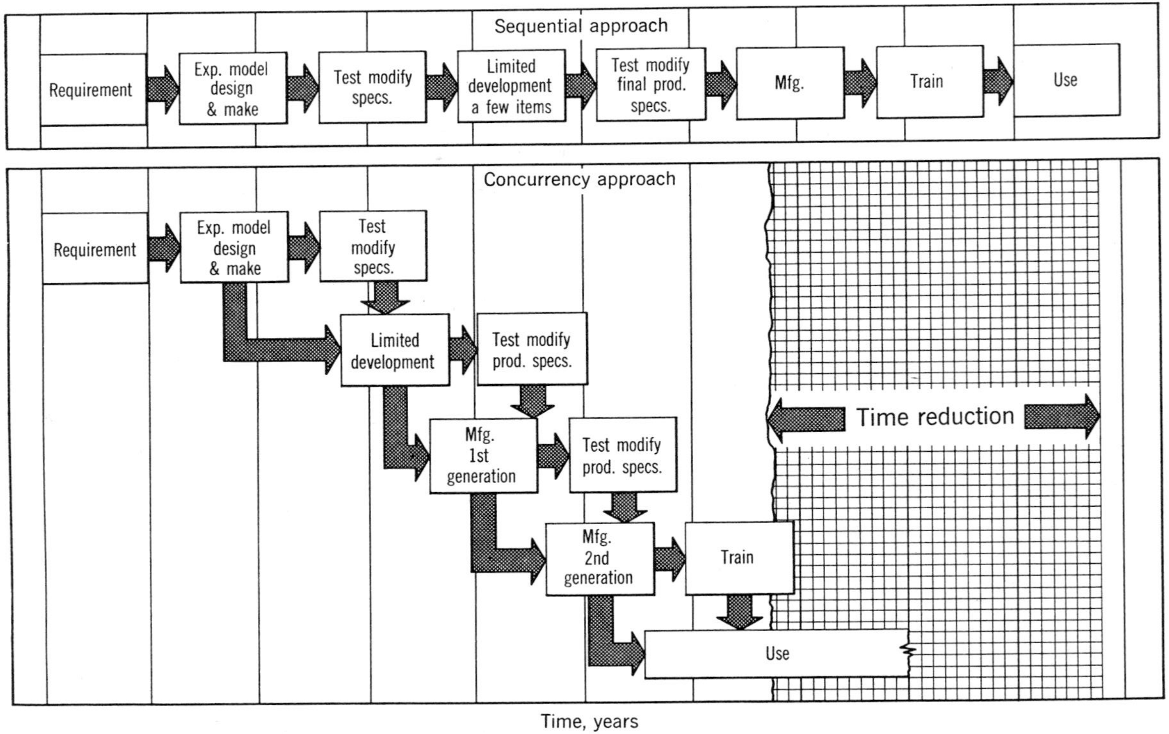

FIGURE 1. Reducing the time for weapon system development.

126

to integrating cost or resource information with the time information; and another which is tackling the *performance*—or reliability—measurement and control. In the latter area, it is hoped to provide a foreward look at the nature of the reliability problems early enough to make the most useful trade-offs and reallocation of resources.

A DESCRIPTION OF THE PERT APPROACH

In the PERT approach, the development program is first portrayed graphically as a network of interrelated activities necessary to achieve prescribed milestones, or events. Figure 2 shows a typical network or flow plan for a small portion of the Polaris program. *Events* are shown as squares in the diagram and *activities* as the connecting arrows. The "critical path" is the longest path through the given program. It is this part of the program that management is most vitally interested in determining, shortening, and monitoring. The computer has been programmed to sort out from the many concurrent paths as to which is the longest and next longest, etc. Figure 3 sums up some of the major definitions used in PERT.

The relationship of the network approach developed and used in PERT and traditional Gantt charting is worth commenting on. Figure 4 illustrates this difference. In Gantt charting there is no dependency or interconnection between activities shown. Coordination functions and precedent relationships are not shown in Gantt charting; these are of major significance in large R & D programs where many activities must be performed concurrently and be properly coordinated. Planning for these points and utilizing this plan in monitoring make it more possible to "create on schedule"—a requirement in our current weapons system program. The use of the "network" is thus a significant innovation to the body of industrial engineering techniques.

The next step in the PERT process is to obtain elapsed time estimates for each activity in the network from engineers responsible for their completion. Three estimates are obtained for each activity, representing the range of time which can be expected. These estimates—optimistic, most likely, and pessimistic—are transformed into a probability statement indicating the chances of the activity taking different lengths of time to be achieved. The flow plan and time estimates are then fed into a computer which computes and sorts out the longest path from all the possible paths to any event. All other paths to an event thus have "slack" in them and represent areas where resources may be reallocated. The path having zero slack allocated

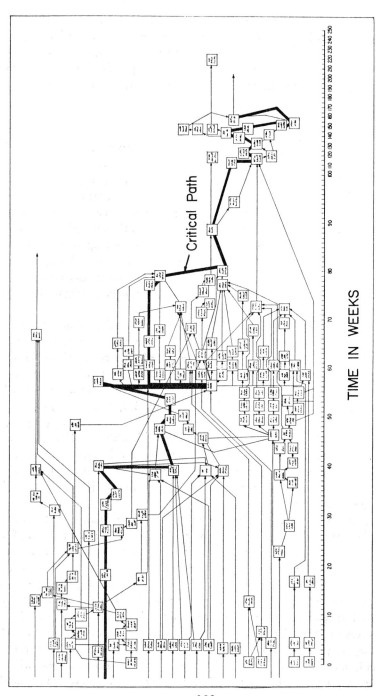

FIGURE 2. PERT system flow plan of "network."

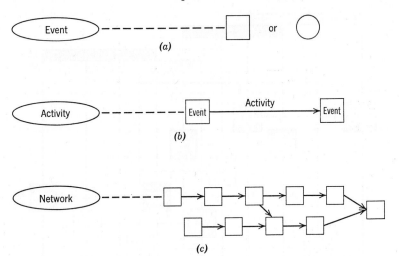

FIGURE 3. Some major definitions used in PERT. (a) An instantaneous occurrence, the accomplishment of which must be known at an unambiguous point in time. (b) The time-consuming effort or work necessary to proceed from one event to another. (c) A flow chart made up of one or more series of events joined by activity lines to depict their interdependencies and interrelationships.

with it has been termed the "critical path" (see Figure 2). Thus PERT is a "management-by-exception" tool providing the manager with information where slips are likely to occur and what their magnitude may be. It also indicates where slack exists in the program and is a guide for reallocating some of the resources to reduce total program time. This identification of slack areas also forewarns the manager of where *not* to buy attractive time reduction opportunities that may be proffered.

In Figure 5 typical data available to a manager are shown. Use of the three estimates makes it possible to develop a probability measure for meeting the schedule. The magnitude of this number may be used as a guide for determining the relative seriousness of the potential schedule slip or for rescheduling.

In operation, PERT is maintained and updated according to a regular plan. Figure 6 is such an operating description of PERT. Another feature of PERT is the possibility for "simulating" a change. The manager may introduce a synthetic time reduction and find out what would happen to the total program as a result. Often time-reducing changes do not buy equivalent time reduction in the program

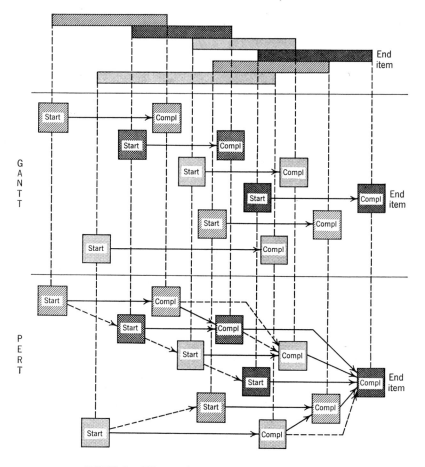

FIGURE 4. Difference between PERT and Gantt methods.

and may better be rejected. Many displays are possible from the data available in the PERT computer files. Figure 7 is illustrative of how critical paths at higher management levels in the program can be developed by aggregating the data. A variety of such reports are available.

Figure 8 assesses the role of the computer in PERT. It is highly important for management to specify what it wants out of the computer, and not have the computer lab tell management what it wants. It has happened often in the use of the PERT technique that the computer lab can see many possibilities of analyses and outputs of interest to them, which end up complicating the situation and making it difficult for management to see the real simplicity of the technique. The "management system design function" is one which is being established in many organizations and serves as a buffer between management and the computer lab. The specialists in this organization know the needs of management and are also able to communicate effectively with the computer specialists. The role of the system designer is becoming better recognized as the requirement for improved management controls is being more formally stated in companies.

EXTENSIONS OF PERT

Up to this point, we have discussed PERT. Let us now discuss some of the problems involved in extending management systems into second and third generations. In the PERT approach, only time estimates are obtained. It is possible to obtain for each one of the time estimates a cost estimate. Generally speaking, it is recognized that at any given level of performance, if a reduction in the time of an activity is desired, it will take a disproportionate amount of resources applied to the task to get it done quicker. Furthermore, if greater performance is desired at a given cost, it will take longer to achieve, or for any given level of time, it will cost more. Figure 9 illustrates this relationship.

Event Number	Expected Times		Latest Times $(T_{OL} = T_{OE})$		Slacks $t' = T_L - T_E$	Original Schedule $T_s{}^*$	Prob. of Meet'g Schedule
	$T_E{}^*$ Expected	Variance	$T_L{}^*$ Expected	Variance			
50	92	38	92	0	0	82	.05
51	85	35	85	3	0	77	.09
54	74	29	82	4	8	73	.42
52	47	25	74	7	27	70	1.00−
53	70	31	70	7	0	60	.04
55	35	18	62	14	27	55	1.00−
56	60	26	60	12	0	50	.02
57	56	23	64	10	8	55	.42
•	•	•	•	•	•	•	•
•	•	•	•	•	•	•	•
•	•	•	•	•	•	•	•
X·Now	0	0	•	•	•	•	•

*Time is shown in weeks from X or time "now."

FIGURE 5.   Outputs from analysis.

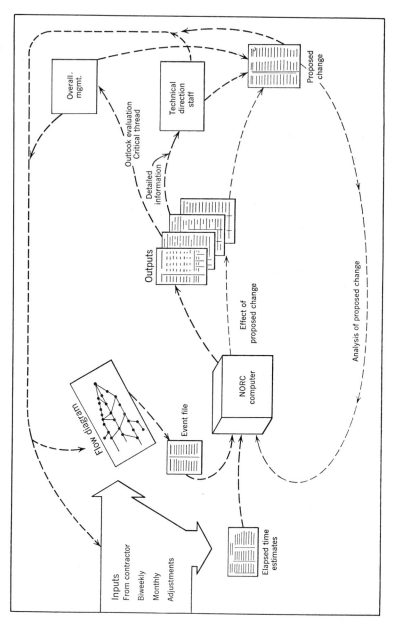

FIGURE 6. PERT system in operation.

132

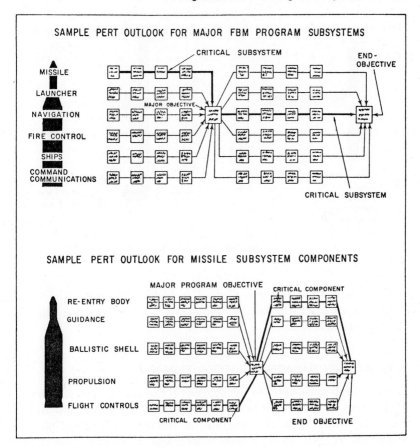

FIGURE 7.   Integrated outlook.

Early in the original PERT research, it was deemed impractical on two counts to cope with all three variables (time, cost, and performance) simultaneously in a computer model. First, related cost and time data on activities not experienced before are almost impossible to obtain with any degree of accuracy. It was almost impossible to get anyone to think significantly about such data. Further data on different degrees of the item's performance are even more difficult to obtain. Secondly, even if the data were obtainable, it would require a data-processing load of about 20 times the data that the basic PERT system requires. Therefore, it was reasoned that, if the total integrated time, cost, and performance approach were taken at the outset, the cost and data problem would defeat acceptance by the potential

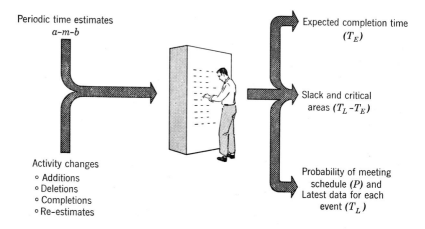

Periodic time estimates
a–m–b

Activity changes
- Additions
- Deletions
- Completions
- Re-estimates

Expected completion time
(T_E)

Slack and critical
areas $(T_L - T_E)$

Probability of meeting
schedule (P) and
Latest data for each
event (T_L)

FIGURE 8.   Computer role.

user of the system. It was decided to tackle the time variable first and then go after the cost variable after the information channels had been established.

A PRINCIPLE IN MANAGEMENT SYSTEM DESIGN

One major principle in management system design followed in PERT and its extensions bears stating. This is the principle of taking a vertical slice of the program for the study effort and pilot installation. Figure 10 represents a technical or hardware breakdown

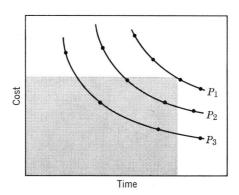

P_1

P_2

P_3

Cost

Time

FIGURE 9.   Time-cost-performance relationship for an activity.

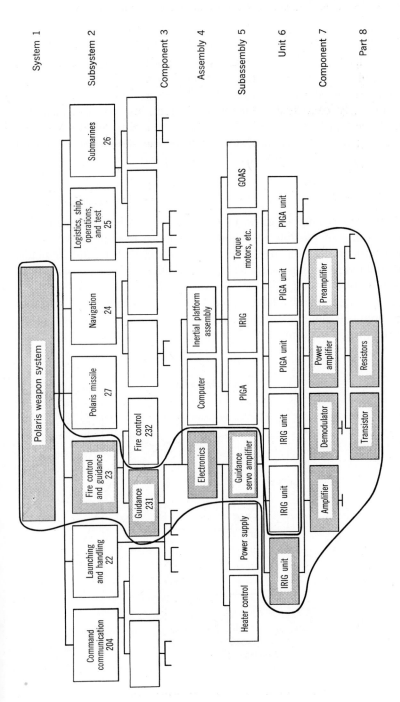

System 1

Subsystem 2

Component 3

Assembly 4

Subassembly 5

Unit 6

Component 7

Part 8

FIGURE 10. Breakdown of the Polaris system.

135

of the Polaris system. The various subsystems are shown across the top and are divided into components, etc. It was decided in PERT that one had to go right down to where the work was done, i.e., taking a vertical cut rather than the traditional horizontal cut, in order to get immediate total program results. In this way the ultimate system is completely consistent from top to bottom, and one can have the confidence that data will be properly obtained and transmitted. After debugging this vertical slice, or pilot area, the system can be spread horizontally to other subsystems in a routine way.

COST EXTENSION

There are a number of ways costs can be assigned to activities. One, a range of possible costs could be applied to each activity; or a single cost for each one of the time estimates in PERT could be made. Furthermore, there is a choice as to whether to use a single cost, direct costs, or total cost. As shown in Figure 11, PERT applications to date generally have applied direct man-hour costs, either in man-hours or dollars, to the activity showing the department, code for the man, and in many cases identifying the individual man where

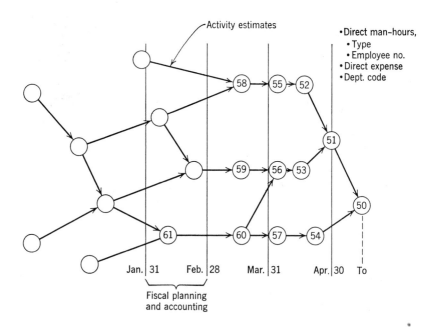

FIGURE 11.   PERT systems extension to cost.

highly skilled individuals are a scarce commodity in great demand. Quite often in R & D, one particular designer is the only person who can do a certain kind of design job. It is desirable that he not be given too many tasks to perform concurrently.

The vertical lines in Figure 11 illustrate the problem of making PERT cost data compatible with regular fiscal practices already in effect. It is seen that planned activities cut across the orderly monthly accounting periods shown. It is possible to convert from PERT activities to financial planning and accounting by knowing the rate of expenditure, but it is *not* possible to work in the other direction in the absence of a PERT diagram. This then is suggestive of the proper order of application. In short, PERT costs should be considered an input to current accounting systems.

With data obtained as indicated, the following output reports are then possible in a company using the basic PERT cost approach:

1. Expected manpower requirements, by skill, month and department.
2. Individual man loading by month.
3. Expected project direct costs, by skill, month, and department.
4. Regular PERT time outputs: (*a*) slack areas; (*b*) critical paths; (*c*) expected calendar time, impact prediction.

Figures 12 and 13 show some of the types of data available from the cost system. It is noted that PERT costs and budgeted costs may not always agree. Generally, PERT costs will be lower and displaced in time due to the fact that all direct work may not be easily identified with networked activities.

In summary, PERT costs are being used to determine manpower requirements by skill, time period or month, and the department. In several applications, technical directors have found they have overlooked certain technical skills, and this has set up the need for looking for additional people in that skill category. Individual man-loading by month, expected project direct costs by skill, month, and department are available outputs.

Cost outputs are being used in company planning for the following purposes:

1. Determining and improving utilization.
2. Balancing the work load.
3. Evaluating cost-time trade-offs: When the first PERT cost outputs are available and management has used them in improving utilization and balancing the work load, there will be other opportunities to reallocate resources to activities or to apply new resources. The effect of these in regard to the over-all schedule, or time objective, may be easily evaluated

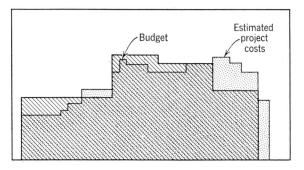

FIGURE 12.   Comparison of estimated costs.

by a simulated change, with the incremental costs known. The effectiveness can be measured in terms of the time reduction to be achieved.

4. Determination of percent of directed work: In the course of planning any project, there will be peaks and valleys in the requirements for the services of individual skills and individuals in particular. Where knowledge of this can be ascertained in advance, the time may be scheduled for other productive work that the company has available or desires to do such as a directed research effort. Furthermore, this procedure is a good project control device for management.

5. Scheduling of manpower buildup.

6. Identification and assignment of technical work.

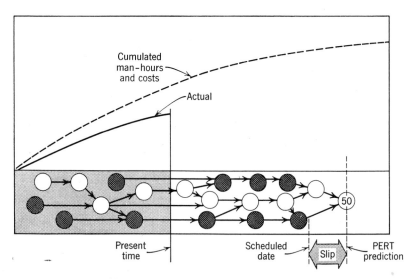

FIGURE 13.   PERT man-hour and cost report.

From the above, it can be seen that the PERT network is capable of supplying basic information useful in planning, that this information is consistent with the definition of the planned and scheduled activities, and that it is possible to utilize this information in normal fiscal channels. It appears that this approach, which may be called "operational accounting" in the R & D field, provides the necessary bridge or "common language" between planning and scheduling activities and fiscal accounting requirements.

PERFORMANCE

Turning to the third component of the management problem, the Polaris management system research activity has engaged in a project entitled PRISM (Program Reliability Information System for Management). The objectives of the project are twofold:

1. To develop a capability to provide performance trade-off information concerning the program approximately two years in the future.
2. To develop a capability to depict quantitatively the expected reliability at the subsystem level.

Two basic approaches in developing program reliability information are under consideration at this time by the project:

1. *Monitoring development plan compliance, or the RMI method* (Reliability Maturity Index). Under this method the development cycle as shown in Figure 14 is monitored to see that test specs, test procedures, acceptance procedures, etc., are written in accordance with the schedule setup. Each item of an assembly is rated in accordance with the factors shown in Figure 15. Check lists are built up for each of the rating factors shown, permitting a rating from zero to 1 to be assigned. The composite rating for each item represents an index of the reliability maturity. Management use of this information is directed toward low indices and zero compliance areas by appropriate sorting routines and report displays. The RMI is now being installed throughout the Polaris program.
2. *System reliability prediction.* The RMI method provides a measure of compliance and does *not* develop a numerical forecast of the eventual operational reliability of the end item. Since one of our most needed capabilities is the prediction of the eventual logistic requirement and operational up-time to be realized in practice, it is desirable to obtain a forecast number that can be used as a planning factor. The research program is developing a method involving the following steps:
   a. *Development of an operational model of the Polaris System.* This model is used to estimate the percent of successful launchings and utilizes data available from analyses of performance at each phase of the development cycle.

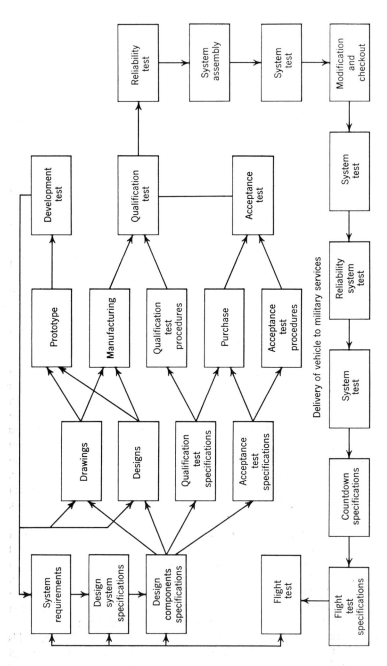

FIGURE 14. Planned missile development cycle.

140

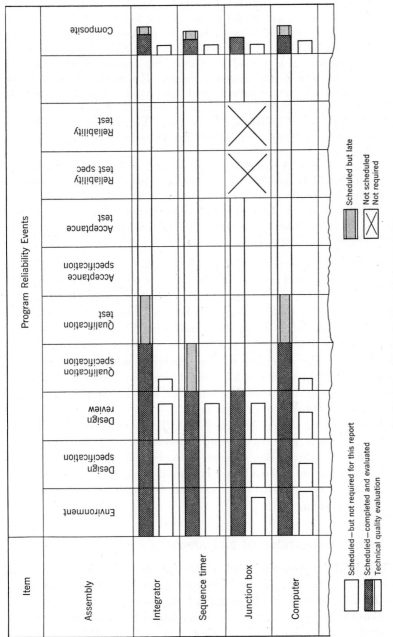

FIGURE 15. Reliability maturity index (RMI).

b. *Development of methods of analysis.* Analytic methods are being developed which will predict reject rate and fleet failure rate. Different methods are required for preliminary design, design development, manufacturing logistics, and operational phases of the development program.

c. *Development of a method for synthesizing component and subsystem estimates into a total system estimate.* The reliability estimates are made for various components, and subsystems are combined to make a total system reliability estimate (percent of successful launchings).

d. *Development of an information system.* A rapid means of collecting, analyzing, and reporting information to technical managers is being developed.

e. *Comparison with reliability requirements.* Using the predictions of (*d*), it will be possible to compare the predicted reliability with the reliability requirements, or goals, set up in the original technical plan. Furthermore, use of the computer model will permit the effect of changes in the failure rates of components and subsystems upon the total system reliability to be appraised.

As these concepts are developed and tested, it will be possible to provide management with a set of tools that will aid in enforcing the development plan; also a quantitative number predicting the reliability of the item under design will be available at all stages in the development project. From this number it will be possible to detect weak spots in the program and to initiate specific remedies. Figure 16 illustrates the objective of the reliability information system to focus on the ultimate use at all times during development. Currently, the development of predictive tools for use during the design and development phases is of greatest need.

Here again, it should be noted that the management information system purports only to develop information and does not make decisions. In short, the concept is conceived to aid the decision maker and not to replace him. It should be further noted here that there are many pitfalls and problems in devising an appropriate reliability system.

INDUSTRIAL APPLICATIONS OF PERT APPROACH

The PERT approach is being experimented with in a number of industrial areas. One of our large companies is attempting to utilize the PERT approach in the new product process. American industry is allocating greater amounts to research and has a major problem in determining whether it is getting a payoff on this investment. Further techniques for planning and controlling R & D functions are still embryonic in nature. A way to predict and plan for the timely

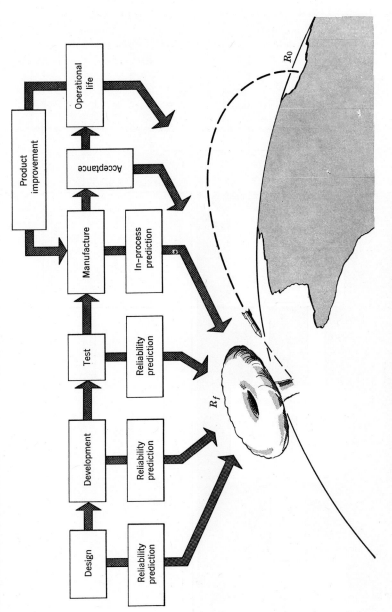

FIGURE 16. System reliability prediction throughout development cycle.

143

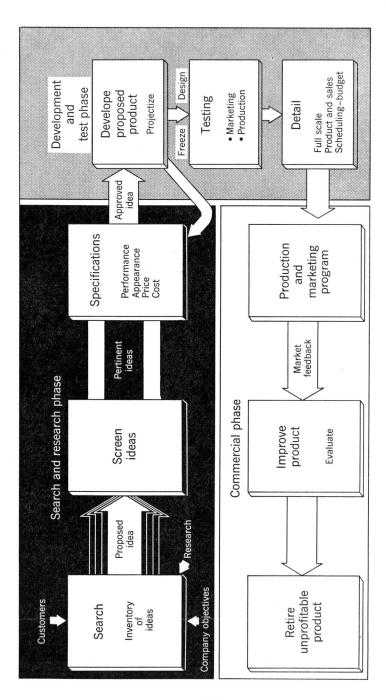

FIGURE 17. The new product process.

and efficient exploitation of company research results is most needed. Figure 17 depicts the steps in developing a new product—a process that takes about 5 to 10 years for a typical new product.

First, there is the task of searching out ideas and doing fundamental research. There are three areas shown in the search-and-research phase. The next phase is the broad area of development and test, or the development test phase, where selected ideas are brought up through reality of a pilot product. Coordination with the various other functional areas in the company is most important at this stage. The marketing, engineering, and manufacturing areas all get involved because each has an eventual responsibility. Finally, if the test product is deemed feasible, it is moved into the commercial phase where it becomes a part of the product line. Out of 400 or 500 ideas, only one or two ever reach the commercial phase.

The objective, therefore, in R & D is to attempt to get the new product process performed efficiently and in a minimum time. Yet, in many companies the mode of organization works against getting new products out in a reasonable time.

Figure 18 represents such a typical industrial concern which is

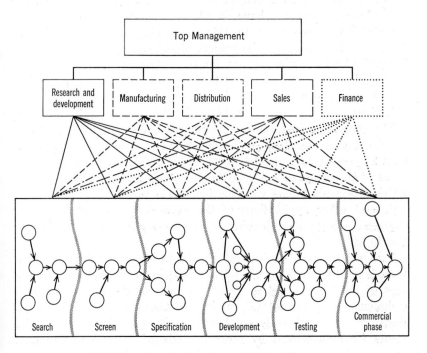

FIGURE 18.   Organization of a typical industrial concern.

functionally organized: top management with sales, research engineering, distribution and production shown, each having a say about everything that goes on in current operations; research generally responsible for coming up with the new ideas and hopefully having them well enough brought out so they will move on into production and sales quickly.

Across the bottom of Figure 18 this new product process is shown— the search, screen, specification development, testing, and commercial phases. Superimposed over these phases is a network diagram in the aggregate that shows the searching for ideas, the selection of promising ones for further refining, the specifying of what is to go into development, and the performing of development tests. Moving across to the right represents the passage of time, with the lines coming down from the top in spider-web fashion, indicating that almost all of the functional areas get involved in each of the various phases. Generally, the various functions are not involved in a coordinated way. The idea of creating a project management concept for the product early in the game and using PERT as the management tool to cut across the functional lines appears promising and follows logically after a project network is set up. This use of the networking concept will have an effect on the traditional functional organization. Some refer to this as turning the organization 90 degrees and focusing on the project objectives. A project manager is required who can reach out for the necessary staff and systems analysis he needs all throughout the program. In this way the whole organization can be coordinated and brought to bear on new product objectives.

The companies involved in this approach were confident that they could cut cost and time of the development of new products by at least 20 percent, because of better coordination between the functional areas of the company early in the process as a result of planning by which everybody knows what his function is to be.

Several other applications of the networking concept have been suggested—long-range planning, maintenance and construction activities, to name a few.

Two other areas of interest should be discussed briefly. First, there is need for training of system operators to enhance the effectiveness of the system and to reduce its installation time. Simulation techniques have proved helpful in structuring these training situations. Secondly, there is great opportunity to reduce data requirements for management by properly designed systems and to semiautomate many of the analyses made routinely by clerical personnel.

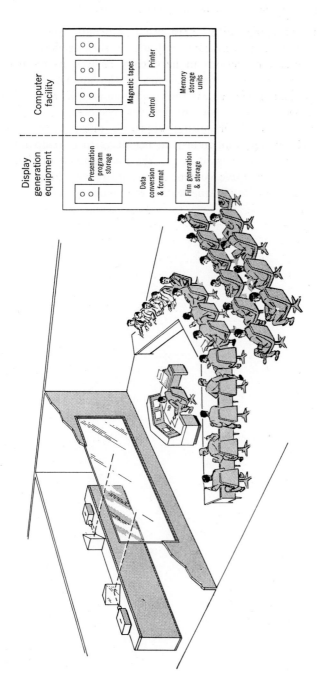

FIGURE 19. Automated management control center.

147

Cost reduction opportunities here are significant. Development of new display devices and management centers such as shown in Figure 19 offer potential reductions in hard copy as well as more ease of access to the data bank on the part of the managers. This will enhance use and utility of systems and promises a very important change in the management tools of the next few years.

In conclusion, the networking approach offers opportunity for operations researchers and industrial engineers to develop integrated planning and control tools to aid in the management of the R & D process. Such "predictive controls" are vitally needed to unharness and realize the benefits of American R & D more efficiently as well as quickly.

5.

Resource Usage and Network Planning Techniques,[1] *Peter V. Norden*

Perhaps the most fashionable subject among Operations Research groups interested in the management of research and development (R & D) today is the addition of resource-planning capability to PERT-type networks (see Chapter 4).

Various agencies of the military establishment, individual industrial companies, and professional consulting organizations have given indications of concern regarding this problem. The reasons are not difficult to ascertain: The introduction of PERT made it practical, perhaps for the first time, to record complex, involved human affairs in a systematic and comprehensible way. It is, therefore, not surprising that managers of R & D projects are developing a taste for exploring whether this capability cannot be extended to other variables of interest.

It is intriguing to speculate whether the rate at which PERT is spreading does not represent some new extreme in the rate of diffusion of innovation through the economy. Here, indeed, is a method which filled a great need, and the rapidity of its propagation is also a tribute to the effectiveness of communication among members of the Operations Research, R & D management, and Management Science Communities. This chapter discusses some experimental work done in this area at the IBM Development Laboratory for potential use by R & D managers (Ref. 1).

---

[1] Portions of this material are based on work being pursued in connection with the author's doctoral program in the Department of Industrial and Management Engineering, Columbia University, New York.

SETTING OF THE INQUIRY

The IBM Development Laboratory employs upward of 4,000 engineers and support personnel who are engaged in engineering development activities. In this environment, the responsibilities fall into four categories:

Concepts

This category comprises the assembling of a body of Operations Research and other scientific techniques relevant to the conduct of the management of the laboratory, drawing on work done inside and outside our Company, modifying this as needed, and developing original models of our own if we are able. In this context, the PERT network notion itself, and the life-cycle model (to be discussed shortly), are classed as "concepts."

Methods and Procedures

The existence of an algorithm, or a model of the structure or behavior of a system, does not in and of itself suffice for practical exploitation of the potential utility of concepts. They must be "impedance matched" to the level of verbal understanding and substantive comprehension of management and the engineers whom we service. The concepts must be translated and embedded in a shell of methods and procedures, specifying where information shall be gathered, how it shall be processed, where the summarized information shall next be channeled, and what decision sequences must be carried out. This involves the well-known field of methods and procedures work, information flow, organizational analyses, report format development, and such computer programming as is necessary.

Education and Motivation

The use of the services our group makes available to the laboratory is voluntary; that is, each project manager can utilize PERT, life-cycle, linear programming, simulation analyses, or other techniques which we might offer, or he may choose not to do so. The project managers must satisfy themselves, therefore, that the time and effort which they and their men devote to utilizing the newer techniques is worth while, compared to alternative means by which they could achieve their own objectives.

Control

This subject is familiar to managers in many contexts and is also a vast field for research. In brief, it means the development and presentation of measures of effectiveness and other indicators to provide a continuous picture of performance relative to previously approved plans and schedules. It should ultimately encompass decision aids simulating the probable outcomes of alternative admissible actions.

This chapter is concerned primarily with the first category—with *concepts*. In particular, we will present certain resource-utilization patterns on engineering projects and their relation to network schedules.

However, the study of resource consumption and network schedules involves the conduct of engineering work, internal organization, and bookkeeping, so that a number of companies have understandably decided that publication is against their best proprietary interest, even though they may be actively working in this area. Therefore, we may not be aware of comparable work as well as work that has gone beyond that being discussed herein.

Finally, we will presume the following:

1. We will assume that the reader is familiar with the Navy's PERT system (Chapter 4) in its broad forms (Refs. 2, 3). Therefore, no attempt will be made to give a description of network or critical-path-type scheduling and planning techniques.
2. We will deal only with our experiences with applied R & D projects. This will eliminate fundamental or basic research and quantity manufacturing activities from our discussion.
3. We will confine our attention to homogeneous projects. Primarily, we wish to avoid confusion with what has been variously termed "multi-project overlay," multicontract, "total program," or facility-wide models. These depict the universe in accordance with a somewhat different scheme of classification.

THE PROJECT AS A CONCEPTUAL ENTITY

Division or classification is a major conceptual problem in its own right, which has been the subject of serious inquiry. Unfortunately, these problems are beyond the scope of this chapter.

Sir Stafford Beer (Ref. 4), states, among other points, that a project is a natural base for cohesive activity and suggests that a manager who bears the title of "Sales Manager" might be more appropriately titled "Manager of Project Number Six" in the sense that this encompasses a more meaningful set of activities, over which he exercises judgment, choice, or control.

In an earlier article (Ref. 5), a tentative definition of a project, which will be used in this chapter, was proposed:

A development project is a finite sequence of purposeful, temporally ordered activities, operating on a homogeneous set of problem elements, to meet a specified set of objectives representing an increment of technological advance.

In the same article, homogeneity was defined thus:

We will call a task homogeneous if it is composed of elements, each of which has at least one technological interdependence point in common with another element during their life cycles.

When we formulated this definition, we had not had experience with PERT, but in retrospect, the compatibility of concept becomes apparent. The primary characteristic is that of connectedness, and this serves to distinguish a development project from the environment in which that project is embedded.

By this definition, a set of activities will comprise a project if the activities are all connected by a set of technological interdependencies, and the boundary of the project will be wherever further interdependence lines cannot be drawn logically. In terms of PERT practice, a project ceases with the terminal points which knowledgeable people have elected to define in the network diagram. Experience indicates that this is not a rigorous relationship, but one that is usefully approximated in practice. In a similar sense, the meterologists' "air parcel" cannot be demonstrably carved out of the gaseous envelope of the earth with finite boundaries, but has the property that certain variables of interest, such as temperature, pressure, or closure of wind patterns are more cohesive within than outside. The project, therefore, is a convenient conceptualization for study, although we know that every project has interactions and connections with suppliers, contractors, and contract administrators, generally outside a limited geographic perimeter, but these become increasingly tenuous beyond the "entity" of the project. We will, therefore, follow the operational approach of saying that the project boundaries exist where knowledgeable people have determined to cease drawing further PERT-type activity lines.

NETWORKS AND RESOURCES

Let us now consider the network schedule of some homogeneous project. This is a partially ordered set of events and activities and constitutes a topological system in the time domain.

This is an important point. The *network* representation of a development project or comparable enterprise is meaningful only in the dimension of time. That is, the sequences of activities are well-identified time precedence relationships. When experience with the time aspect of critical-path-type schedules had become familiar, it became logical to investigate the addition of resources to such a time network by using the PERT concept.

Initially, this implied associating three estimates for money, manpower, or other variable of interest with each line of the network, in the "optimistic, realistic, and pessimistic" fashion of PERT (see Chapter 4). Presumably, this would yield the capability of computing probabilities of spending no more or no less than a certain total number of dollars, with the same confidence now possible for elapsed time. Since resource usage and the time to do an activity are not independent, this scheme is equivalent to asking for nine points on a microeconomic response surface by specifying time and money *pairs*. A comparable relationship, but one which also has some intrinsic differences, is utilized in the Mauchly Associates' (Refs. 6, 7) critical-path algorithm and in Fulkerson's algorithm for network optimization (Ref. 8), which is used by General Motors in the SHARE 1188 computer program for the IBM 704 and has also been programmed for a number of other machines by several computer manufacturers.

In R & D work, however, this poses a number of practical problems. We can use a type of linear approximation between a crash execution time and a normal execution time, or a piecewise linear approximation, whenever we know more points in the interval, provided that we are dealing with activities which are well-enough defined to constitute jobs with "standard content." Lacking these, it can become very difficult to accumulate the necessary historical cost records which would give us confidence that the stipulated pairings of cost and time for the crash, normal, or intermediate situations are indeed true, or permit us to assign some equivalent "trade-off" function. Furthermore, it has been asserted that piecewise linear or linear interpolation may be totally meaningless in many situations since these functional pairings may be realizable only at certain discrete points.

Another practical objection is based on our experience with PERT networks. It is not always simple to obtain even three time estimates for a given activity from the engineer who supplies the source information. To request money or manpower data as well, or nine-point estimates, may not be feasible at the present state of the art. If the man will agree to supply these estimates at all, their accuracy is, in our opinion, somewhat suspect. A reasonable compromise might be to ask for a single manpower or dollar estimate, which can then be functionally associated with one three-point time spread. In other words, we say that a given manpower allocation will imply optimistically so many weeks, realistically more weeks, and pessimistically still more weeks to accomplish the job under discussion.

Another major question in intertwinning resource information and PERT networks is the problem of identifying or defining the work content of a given line of activity. To be sure, this may simply be a matter of the mechanics of executing the PERT or the PERT-cost concept in an actual situation. However, it seems that much of the preoccupation with the PERT-cost question is one of "how can we fit PERT schedule data, and information derived from PERT networks, into our present accounting structure?"

To the extent that we have encountered this problem, it led to a realization of the inappropriateness of many existing accounting definitions; i.e., what work is to be charged to a work order, shop order, project number, job number, etc. Rarely have mercantile charts of accounts provided sensible groups which would enable us to achieve rational acts of classification. Happily, in our laboratory we have made definite strides in reconciling a rational, operationally manageable basis of engineering work activities with the reporting requirements for corporate profit-and-loss and Internal Revenue Service accounting needs.

This, by the way, is an interesting development from the Operations Research point of view. The PERT network, drawn for a homogeneous project as discussed in the foregoing, *does* represent a cohesive entity of work. Management agencies now wish to associate resource-consumption variables with this network but want to fit them into categories which have no meaningful relation to the intrinsic work content of the project and the net. We are, in a sense, asked to map a set of variables from one domain into others without being able to define a workable transformation function. We think that this is an important methods and procedures problem, and since management has many obligations in the conventional accounting and finance realms, ways must be found to find these mapping functions, procedures, and computer programs to bring the two requirements into harmony. We only hope that we can meet somewhere in the middle. A promising compromise is to associate bundles or subsets of activities with the job orders at the ledger level (Chapter 4).

However, we should not deceive ourselves into thinking that, if we make PERT network information compatible with total management operating systems or existing accounting and reporting structures in the sense of integrated data processing, we are dealing *structurally* with an extension of the network scheduling concept.

The former is a procedural problem. The distinction seems to lie in this area: the network, as we have seen, is a topological construct. Resource consumption, in our estimation, simply does not have an intrinsic mathematical structure, which is in the class of directed graphs or networks. Rather, we are dealing with a set of resource-consumption vectors associated with each line of activity or sets of such lines. Only the event-sequencing is a partial ordering in the time domain. This point of view can free us from what might be a mental strait jacket, namely, to try to form money networks, manpower networks, facility networks, reliability networks, etc.

There are, of course, very valid approaches (sometimes facilitated by suitable computer programs) which try to compare resource-consumption forecasts associated with PERT nets with available resource levels, and identify critical shortages or bottlenecks (Ref. 9). We would suspect that in due course, such programs could automatically suggest alternative schedules eliminating such bottlenecks according to certain management decision rules preprogrammed into the system. Here again, however, we are dealing with resource consumption "bills of goods" associated with a time-domain network or networks.

This may have sounded negative; however, we gain a great deal when we think of mathematical models of resource consumption *associated with* time networks. What we gain is access to the vast and rich field of mathematical models. For the first time, PERT-type networks can give us an insight into the real internal anatomy of engineering development that underlies the expenditure patterns.

In the next section this point will be illustrated with one model which we have reduced to practice in the last year and a half. We have called it the life-cycle method of project planning and control. It is a mathematical model relating manpower usage on engineering development and similar projects to calendar time.

THE LIFE-CYCLE MANPOWER MODEL

Life-cycle is concerned with manpower curves encountered on applied research and engineering development programs. These curves depict manpower utilization on R & D projects between the start and completion of all work necessary to comply with specified and agreed-upon program objectives as a function of calendar time.

Let us recall that a project can be (and generally is) broken down into smaller parts or elements. What these elements are and how they are to be scheduled relative to each other in time, as for example in the network sense of the PERT programs, is determined by the technological content and structure of the project. The series-parallel mix of topological relationships in such a schedule implies that some *portion* of the needed work on some elements cannot be begun unless some other *portion* of work on some other element has previously been completed. This is what we designate as "technological interdependence among elements." If no such interdependence relationships existed in a given project, all elements could be started and worked through in parallel, without regard for any other elements. If there were m such elements, we would view these as m independent projects.

Conventional usage of the term "project" could lead to confusion in this context. People use the words "project" and "program" interchangeably to designate a grouping of tasks by some scheme of classification, such as common subject matter, under a common manager, supported by a common appropriation, etc. Although such groupings exhibit logical consistency, they do not necessarily require *connectedness*. In the foregoing, we have equated connectedness with homogeneity, and the latter with the notion of "project." Thus, to talk about a "homogeneous project" is admittedly redundant but is here used for emphasis. We wish to address ourselves to homogeneous projects. A project is homogeneous if it is composed of a set of elements such that each has at least one technological interdependence tie to at least one other element at some time during the life of the project. Attention is now called to the following aspects of the homogeneous project:

1. Finite problem sets.
2. Operations: activities; work; what people *do*.
3. Operands: elements; problems; what they *do it to*.
4. Purposes: objectives; *why* they do what they do.

The last point is important in the life-cycle model. The purposes change throughout the life of a project, and these changes characterize the effort cycles which will be discussed later.

Research studies have indicated (Ref. 10) that there are regular patterns of manpower buildup and phase-out in complex projects. These patterns have been described by a number of mathematical functions, generally in the family of exponential, gamma, beta, or logistic curves, by several investigators (Ref. 11). In the life-cycle model, curves are fitted to a small number of successive "cycles" of work which occur during the life of a project. The cycles do not depend on the nature or work content of the project but seem to be a function of the way groups of engineers and scientists tackle complex technological development problems. Each cycle can be described by a comparatively simple equation:

$$y' = 2Kate^{-at^2}$$

where y' = manpower utilized each time period

K = total cumulative manpower ultized by the end of the project

a = shape parameter (governing time to peak manpower)

t = elapsed time from start of *cycle* (Figure 1)

Thus the cycles can be represented by a series of curves from the same family, relating manpower used each month to elapsed calendar time, and differing only in relative size and proportions. The single parameter governing the shape of the curves can be thought of as a measure of the "importance" of the project (Figure 2). Sharply peaked manpower buildups correspond to crash projects, while shallower curves are associated with stretched-out projects.

Now, how do these cycles occur, and what do they mean? A plausible explanation is that engineering groups seem to work in definite *surges* of effort, and that each surge is associated with a particular purpose for doing the job.

In the IBM Development Laboratory in Poughkeepsie, New York, the succession of purposes with which we work on projects generally is: planning, designing, building and testing a prototype, engineering activities associated with release of the product to plant, occasional redesigning, and a small number of cycles for product support and cost reduction (Figure 3). Sometimes this sequence is preceded by an exploratory cycle. The whole sequence corresponds to one often encountered in human endeavor:

Explore	Establish feasibility.
Plan	What shall the product be like?
Decide	How shall it be designed in detail?
Do	Build it according to the plan.
Refine	Correct things which turned out differently from what was expected.
Improve	Incorporate knowledge gained in the foregoing.

These cycle designations are part of the laboratory's account-code structure in the form of a one-digit "activity code."

The mathematical model of project manpower consists of the equation for each cycle plus a linking function which specifies the

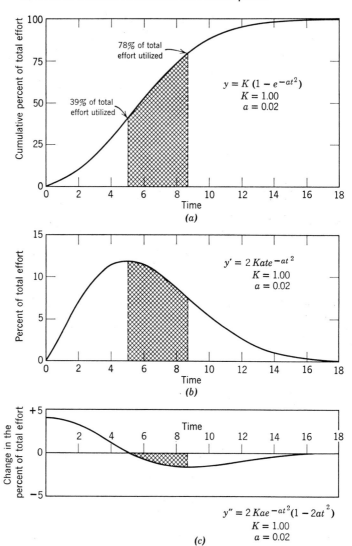

FIGURE 1.   Manpower utilization curve: (a) Cumulative manpower utilization, (b) current manpower utilization, and (c) the change in monthly manpower utilized.

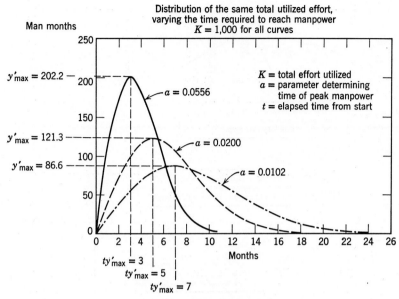

Distribution of the same total utilized effort, varying the time required to reach manpower $K = 1,000$ for all curves

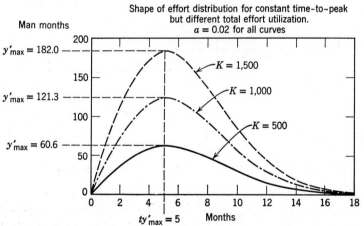

Shape of effort distribution for constant time-to-peak but different total effort utilization. $a = 0.02$ for all curves

FIGURE 2.   Manpower utilization curve, $y' = 2Kate^{-at^2}$.

relative sizes and durations of the cycles and their lags or spacing in calendar time. The linking relationships have been encouragingly stable over a wide range of projects and a number of years. This fact makes it possible to develop projections of manpower and time requirements for comparable projects, given a few actual points on the early cycles. In addition, early warning of significant departures

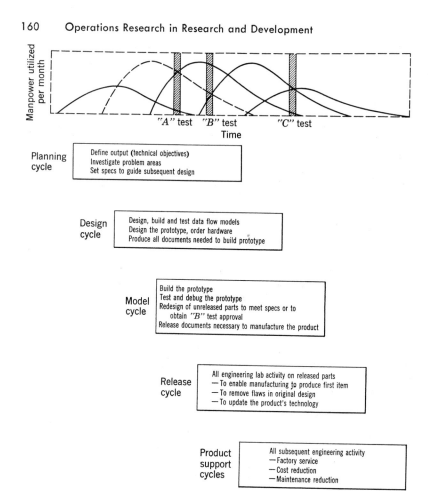

FIGURE 3.   Typical manpower pattern of an engineering project.

from current schedules can be obtained by monitoring the actual progress of a project against a prior projection is, of course, a classical control function of management. This is sufficiently important to warrant slightly more elaboration here.

Let us recall the curve of a single work cycle. This curve has many features which make it ideal to work with computationally. These features form the basis for the simplest method of estimating the coefficients of the manpower utilization curve. They enable one to arrive at quick results of considerable accuracy. Four of them are of practical value for rapid analysis, and many may be derived by the use of differential calculus:

1. The coefficient a determines the month in which manpower utilization is greatest. One can calculate this month by the formula

$$t_0 = \left(\frac{1}{2a}\right)^{\frac{1}{2}}$$

2. Conversely, if one knows the month in which manpower utilization was or will be the greatest, he can calculate the coefficient a:

$$a = 2(t_0)^2$$

3. If one knows the month in which manpower utilization has reached or will reach a peak, and if one knows or can estimate the manpower level in that month, one can calculate the value of K, the total manpower required in the cycle, by substituting for a as determined above, and solving:

$$K = e^{\frac{1}{2}}t_0 y_0$$

4. The manpower utilization curve has a point of inflection at a point at which the decrease in monthly utilized manpower slows down in the descending portion of the curve,

$$t_1 = \left(\frac{3}{2a}\right)^{\frac{1}{2}}$$

This point is useful in setting milestones for a project. When the cycle has passed this point, the work should be in the "cleanup" stages.

We compute the manpower cycle curves either by using the foregoing relationships or (particularly in projects which are already under way at the time at which the first life-cycle analysis is prepared) by statistical curve-fitting techniques which we will not discuss in detail here. Then we establish control limits at ± 10 percent of the predicted monthly manpower. This control interval was selected arbitrarily, and will be modified if it turns out to be too wide (failure to detect serious manpower overruns) or too narrow (too many "nuisance calls" to the project manager), after we have more experience. So far, the interval appears to be a reasonable start. If the actual manpower usage of a project goes outside the control interval (Figure 4, top), a new projection is made (Figure 4, bottom).

This is discussed with the project manager and, if he concurs, his manpower forecast is revised. Since an overrun in an early cycle cascades through all the subsequent cycles, this "early warning" potential of life-cycle is applicable.

One note of caution must be sounded. The linking functions (ratios

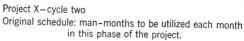

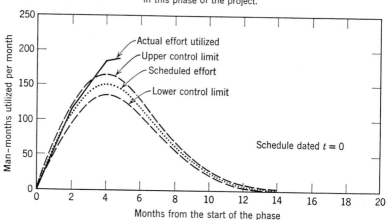

Anticipated total effort: 1,000 man-months
Maximum monthly effort expected: 152 man-months in the 4th month
Control limits: ± 10% of anticipated total effort

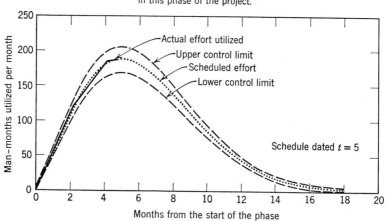

Anticipated total effort: 1,550 man-months
Maximum monthly effort expected: 188 man-months in the 5th month
Control limits: ± 10% of anticipated total effort

FIGURE 4.   Life-cycle method of project control—an illustration of the early warning technique.

of manpower and duration relating adjacent cycles) exert considerable leverage on the total project manpower forecast. We make a point of emphasizing to our management that our project engineers are not irretrievably "locked in" on the laboratory's historical performance. Quite to the contrary, as improved ways are found of conducting the technical work, our most fruitful experience to date will become the new reference patterns for future planning.

It is in this exercise of continuing improvement that the simultaneous use of life-cycle and PERT-type planning complement each other well. The curves are statistical aggregates. The network gives anatomic detail. Prior to the advent of PERT, we could only point out to a program manager that "in the third quarter two years hence, your estimated manpower is only about one half of what history indicates you will probably need."

We could not tell him *what activities* he would be working on at that time except in the broadest sense. PERT, of course, can almost pinpoint the particular jobs on which he anticipates to be working during the time period in question. This enables him to confirm or modify his manpower estimates well in advance.

In the light of the foregoing, the point made in the section entitled "Network and Resources" can be clarified. In most schemes currently called the PERT-cost concept, we are merely labeling each line of a PERT network with the manpower or other resources which we estimate it will consume. Even at the level of algorithmic abstraction presented in other approaches (Ref. 12), it is assumed that the trade-off of resources and time is *known* and can be supplied at the time at which the inputs for a computer run are prepared.

Even if we ignore for the moment that, at the level of detail of one PERT activity line, it is often very difficult to estimate two points for a linear trade-off, we would still be populating the network with guesses. Life-cycle, by supplying stable patterns of larger work aggregates, provides a measure comparable to the behavior of a gas in a closed container: mankind has found the notions of temperature and pressure of considerable practical value without the need for knowing the precise Brownian motions of each molecule.

This leads us back to the fact that project planning is best done at the detail PERT level with an activity orientation, whereas evaluation and control are profitable exercised at a more aggregate level with a functional orientation. We have found that the life-cycle model provides an orderly summary, crystallized out of past experience, at a functional level. It gives us the capability of conveniently using historical experience to shed light on the future.

THEORY OF PROJECT MANPOWER PATTERNS

Up to the present time, we have applied the method outlined above to about twenty projects with encouraging success. The inherent problems of labor-claiming and accounting practices limit the accuracy of the "actual" data reported to us through conventional administrative channels. In addition, the inevitable time lags associated with phasing personnel into and out of projects may distort the canonical shape of the curves slightly. This prevents us, for example, from questioning an actual manpower charge of 75 men in a given month, when the life-cycle projection would have indicated 70. Nonetheless, the basic pattern has been observed in a number of development engineering situations, both inside and outside of our laboratory.

We have developed the following theoretical model to explain the observations. We assert that an engineering development project can be viewed usefully as a set of unsolved problems. This unsolved problem space is exhausted in the presence of human effort and creativity in a deliberate, purposeful group-problem-solving setting. The operation of exhausting the problem space involves many activities which need not be explicitly ordered in time. However, there is a partitioning of sets of these activities. This divides unsolved problem space into a group of subspaces, which correspond to the purposes with which the problem-solving operation is concerned at various stages in the life of a project. In practice, the exhaustion operation is the design decision-making operation. In this context, the several problem subsets, each labeled by its *raison d'etre*, represents a stagewise conversion of problems into solutions.

If we make the following assumptions concerning *each* such subset, the effort-utilization patterns actually observed can be constructed:

1. The number of problems in the subset is finite, albeit unknown.
2. Human problem-solving effort constitutes an environment for the unsolved problem set and makes an impact on the problems in the set.
3. Information gathering, gestation, identification of alternatives open for choice, and deliberation consume varying amounts of time. Any planning or design decision, made as a result of such deliberations, represents an event which causes one unsolved problem to convert into a solved problem, thereby removing it from the unsolved problem space. If we assume the occurrence of these events to be independent and random, then, by the Poisson model (to be discussed later), an exponential distribution of interevent times is a reasonable assertion. It is further possible to postulate a conditional probability function for the event that a problem will be *permanently* removed from the unsolved problem space, given that an

identification event has occurred. Stated in another way, we postulate a conditional solution, given a certain distribution of insightful situations.

4. The parameter of the decision-event distribution is a compound, implicit function of skill levels of problem solvers, level of exertion, administrative actions, and other random manifestations of the problem-solving situation, and interaction with the environment.

5. The number of people working in the group at any given time is approximately proportional to the number of problems "ripe" for solution at that time. This leads to an interesting interpretation: The problem solvers act in a dichotomous manner as *catalysts* or products of the problem-solving process as much as *agents* who cause problems to be solved.

The observed patterns can be shown to follow from the above assumptions. The model leads to a succession of surges of effort or cycles throughout the life of the project. The plausibility of the above process was underscored by an excellent study by D. L. Marples at Cambridge (Ref. 13). He postulates that engineering design decisions have a treelike structure in which technical choices are made at each mode. Subject to some technical criterion, one of a number of admissible alternatives is selected, symbolically representing a branch which leads to the next (problem) node (see Chapter 11).

Consider now a reliability model due to Epstein (Ref. 14). He discusses a set of independent devices under test, subject to some environment E, which is a random process. Suppose this environment generates shocks, or some "peaks" which are destructive to the devices in question. It is then reasonable to assert that such peaks (thermal shock, extreme vibrations, etc.) are distributed in a Poisson manner with some (rate) parameter.

Let T be a random variable associated with the time interval between successive peaks. Then

$$\Pr (T > t) = \Pr[\text{no event occurs in the interval } (0, t)] \qquad (1)$$

where $t = 0$ is the time when the most recent event occurred.

Then, from the Poisson assumption

$$\Pr (T > t) = e^{-\lambda t} \qquad (2)$$

and

$$\Pr (T \leq t) = 1 - e^{-\lambda t} \qquad (3)$$

The probability density function associated with Eq. 3 is

$$f(t) = \lambda e^{-\lambda t} \qquad (4)$$

This would describe the failure distribution in an all-or-none situation: Given that a destructive peak has occurred, one device will fail with certainty. The number of items remaining and the (average) number failing per time period will also follow exponential functions.

Now suppose that the above situations were governed by a *conditional* probability of failure rule: Given that a peak has occurred at t, the probability of failure is some constant p $(0 \leq p \leq 1)$. Then it can be shown that

$$\Pr (T \leq t) = 1 - e^{-p\lambda t} \tag{5}$$

and

$$f(t) = p\lambda e^{-p\lambda t} \tag{6}$$

This would result in a time-invariant conditional failure probability. Whenever a shock occurs, a device will fail with fixed probability. The number of items remaining and number of items failing per time interval are again exponential functions.

Now consider the conditional probability of failure to be time dependent. Then it can be demonstrated that if the conditional probability of failure is some function $p(t)$:

$$\Pr (T > t) = e^{-\lambda \int_0^t p(\tau)d\tau} \tag{7}$$

whence

$$\Pr (T \leq t) = 1 - e^{-\lambda \int_0^t p(\tau)d\tau} \tag{8}$$

and

$$f(t) = \lambda p(t) e^{-\lambda \int_0^t p(\tau)d\tau} \tag{9}$$

This results in the class of Weibull distributions, well known in reliability work. The physical interpretation here would be that the probability of devices succumbing to destructive shocks is changing with time. In our case, most of the data we have observed (the life-cycle curves)

$$p(t) = at \tag{10}$$

This could imply that our engineers are learning to solve problems with an effectiveness which is increasing linearly during each cycle. When one considers that familiarity with the problems at hand can lead to greater understanding and sureness, this result is not implausible. We are experimenting with other learning curves:

$$p(t) = at^{-b} \tag{11}$$

of which our present model is a special case. Suitable choice of parameters appears to explain a number of other manpower-utilization patterns found in the literature.

CONCLUSION

We have indicated that by suitable analogy to Epstein's work, problem solving of engineering development groups may be dependent on:

1. A group idea-generation rate or the rate at which sets of potential solutions are formulated by the group for each previously identified problem.
2. A conditional probability function governing, once a set of potential problem solutions has been identified as being (by application of suitable criteria) a feasible and acceptable solution which removes the problem permanently for the unsolved problem space.

An increase in the time rate of change of (2) is a type of group learning—a time-dependent process which increases the probability that, with time, Marples' "branch bundle of alternatives," once identified, will contain an ultimately acceptable solution.

One last word on the idea-generation rate. Lorge and Solomon (Ref. 15) suggested that problem-solving effectiveness of a group is a function of the capabilities of its most competent members. Suppose that in an R & D project, this is the project engineer or some key man. He is the man who sets the pace for the program, or at least has the insight to attract a highly competent key member who in turn sets the pace. In either case, then, there is one or a small number of upper limit persons whose insight-producing rate determines the rate parameter (λ) or the exploitation-effectiveness parameter (a) of our formula. We would, therefore, assume that these people have the capabilities either to make their insights faster and/or to produce potential solutions which are closer to being right and can, therefore, be finalized more quickly. Or, in the final analysis, they may simply produce so many more insights that there is greater possibility that one good avenue of potential among them is a good one or a fruitful one. Or, again, it may be possible to regard the project group as being composed of two types of people—idea identifiers and idea evaluators. The latter could be thought of as applying feasibility and optimality criteria to the potential solutions developed by the former. It is not necessary for these two functions to be executed by separate (specialized) individuals, but the same individuals could be both creating and applying value judgments at different times or even in rapid "cycling" alternation. In the last analysis, the life-cycle model suggests that we are dealing with two processes—generation and exploitation. Both may become limiting in their effect on project progress. Both are, as suggested in Eq. 11 at least for the exploitation factor, subject to improvement by human learning.

Finally, the staffing of engineering projects is not inherently a matter of wide trade-offs of time and manpower. Rather, they seem to embody a two-stage process in which the limiting condition is the problem-identification rate or "insight environment" of the unsolved problem space. This implies that one cannot indefinitely add people and get the job done faster. Intuitively, we know that this is so, but the current model leads us to the conclusion that the limiting factor is the rate at which ideas or insights can be generated, and that the rate is not widely affected, if at all, by the number of men on the job, but rather by some capability level of the group (see Chapter 1).

Therefore, within one cycle, for all practical purposes, the parameter of the (exponential) "insight distribution" remains constant over considerable periods of time. The fact that we can add people periodically as more work pieces are identified in a derived effect.

As a matter of fact, to decide where to "saw off" a given development program and to say that "this is what we will produce rather than to continue development towards higher performance" is an implicit understanding that problems which are unearthed after a certain point in the incremental advance of technology would result in a parameter of a different value. In other words, we stop a given program when a significant advance in the direction of higher performance requirements becomes or is recognized to be much harder or more difficult. This is an intriguing speculation because it implies that, in some sense, the parameter of the "Eureka" distribution is an indirect measure of the difficulty level of the problems at hand.

Considerable further study is evidently needed, but the combined tools of network analysis and mathematical models are opening promising avenues of attack.

REFERENCES

1. Voress, H. E., Houser, E. A. and Marsh, F. E. "Critical Path Scheduling," (A Preliminary Literature Search), Bulletin TID-3568, U. S. Atomic Energy Commission, October, 1961, lists 255 items.
2. Malcolm, D. G., Roseboom, J. H., Clark, C. E., and Frazar, W., "Application of a Technique for Research and Development Program Evaluation," *Operations Research*, vol. 7, 1959, pp. 646–669.
3. PERT, Program Evaluation Research Task, Phase I, Summary Report, Special Projects Office, Bureau of Ordnance, Dept. of the Navy, Washington, D. C.

4. Eckman, Donald P. (Ed.), *Systems: Research and Design.* John Wiley and Sons, New York, 1961.

5. Norden, Peter V., "On the Anatomy of Development Projects," *IRE Transactions,* PGEM, vol. EM-7, No. 1, March, 1960, p. 41.

6. Kelley, J. E., Jr., and Walker, M. E., "Critical-Path Planning and Scheduling," Proceedings of the Eastern Joint Computer Conference, 1959.

7. Kelley, J. E., and Walker, M. E., *Critical-Path Planning and Scheduling; An Introduction,* Mauchly Associates, Inc., Ambler, Pa., 1959.

8. Fulkerson, D. R., "A Network Flow Computation for Project Cost Curves," *Management Science,* vol. 7, January 1961, pp. 167–179.

9. McGee, A. A., and Markarian, M. D., "Optimum Allocation of Research/ Engineering Manpower Within a Multi-Project Organizational Structure," *IBM FSD Report, No. 61-907-171,* Federal Systems Division, Owego, New York.

10. Norden, Peter V., "The Study Committee for Research, Development, and Engineering (SCARDE): A Progress Report," *IRE Transactions,* PGEM, vol. EM-8, No. 1, March, 1961, pp. 3–10.

11. Norden, P. V. and Bakshi, A. V., "Internal Dynamics of Research and Development Projects," *Management Sciences Models and Techniques,* The Pergamon Press, New York 1960, pp. 187–205.

12. Freeman, Raoul, "A Generalized Network Approach to Project Activity Sequencing," *IRE Transactions, PGEM,* vol. EM-7, No. 3, September, 1960, p. 104.

13. Marples, David L., "The Ducts and Valves Problem of the Advanced Gas-Cooled Reactor (AGR)[2] of the Atomic Energy Authority," *IRE Transactions,* PGEM, vol. EM-8, No. 2, June, 1961, pp. 55–70.

14. Epstein, Benjamin, "The Exponential Distribution and its Role in Life-Testing," *Industrial Quality Control,* vol. XV, No. 6, December, 1958, pp. 2–7.

15. Lorge, Irving, and Solomon, Herbert, "Two Models of Group Behavior in the Solution of Eureka-type Problems," *Psychometrika,* vol. 20, No. 2, June, 1955, pp. 139–149.

6

.

Selection, Evaluation, and
Control of Research and Development
Projects, *David B. Hertz and Phillip G. Carlson*

In order to survive in a free economy, a company must obtain and sustain a profitable competitive position. To do this requires increasing effort and considerable ingenuity on the part of top executives facing today's uncertainties, complexities, and conflicts.

Ingenuity in decision making is particularly needed in R & D. In the past a company may have devoted its research effort to finding new products and processes and improving or eliminating old ones. Today it must still do this, but it must also seek out—through planning and research on research decision problems—improved information and methods for administering and controlling a research program. Only by continually improving decision procedures will management be able to meet the competition from companies that have improved their management decision procedures through Operations Research.

The crucial research decision problems lie in the selection, evaluation, and control of R & D projects. The success of the research program, and perhaps of the company, may turn on the way these decision problems are solved—and particularly on the way the solutions match the program to the present and future talents of the research staff.

COMPANY PLANNING

In seeking criteria on which to base decisions in the selection-evaluation-control process, where do we begin? Inevitably, we must be-

170

gin with company objectives and the plans that support them, for company plans and research must reflect one another.

Long-range plans and objectives provide the basis for any program of basic research. Conversely, the findings of the program of basic research can and should be used to improve and clarify long-range objectives. Shorter-range plans and objectives provide the basis for a program of product- and process-oriented research. The continuing output of this program of research must in turn be used to improve and crystallize short-range objectives. As long-range plans develop and come closer to fruition, of course, they become short-term plans. Similarly, basic research projects, as results materialize, hopefully lead to marketed products or usable processes whose development should be supported by the program of R & D.

Long-Range Planning: Basic Research Projects

Businessmen expect to conduct their operations in the future as well as in the past. Future operations may be planned with reasonable chances of success; on the other hand, a business may bungle its way into the future with considerably smaller probabilities of succeeding.

Planning deals with uncertainty; the longer the range, the greater the uncertainty. Before making plans, management must study and evaluate the uncertainties. In R & D the outcomes of decisions with large dollar consequences will often hinge on the ability to assess large risks. The long-range plan must consider likely alternatives, the chance of each's occurring, and the profit consequences that may result.

The long-range plan can be the key to the future, posing such questions as "What product line?" "What volume?" "What profitability?" over, say, a five-to-ten-year period.

It further poses the questions, and must outline at least tentative answers to "What research?" "What facilities?" "What personnel?" "What budget?" "When?"

The questions, "What product line?" and "What research?" coupled with "What personnel?" and "When?" updated periodically, become the *objectives* and *guides* for a continuing program of basic R & D. As this basic program progresses, the clues that it uncovers concerning desirable new products, processes, and the necessary technology and materials to produce them in turn shape future answers to "What product line?"

At their inception many facets of basic research projects are rather vague and are difficult to formalize and evaluate on an objective basis. It is not easy to define such output measures and progress markers as interim objectives, payoffs, and project costs in advance. Even when the measures are defined, the actual outputs are difficult to estimate. Frequently the variance between estimate and achievement is very large; if it were not, the project would hardly need to be considered basic research. This is not simply a matter of forecasting error. Often the estimator cannot even know what methods will be used to reach the research goal. Information about the approach to the goal must be quite subjective—as compared, for example, with information about an engineering project.

Hence, selection, evaluation, and control of basic research programs must be subjective. It is the systematic organization of subjective information for research decisions that we propose for improving control of basic research programs. This will be discussed in greater detail in a later section.

Short-Range Planning: Product- and Process-Oriented Projects

Short-range plans are the basis of day-to-day decisions, for example, decisions on production, purchases, prices, inventory, and products. These too must be made in the light of uncertainty, but results can be estimated with considerable accuracy.

The objective of a program of product and process R & D is to support the short-term plans for the existing product line or products to be marketed in the near future. This program is designed to produce, relatively quickly, variations in the product to meet competitors' innovations, novel line extensions, product and process improvements, cost reductions, etc. Projects in such a program are carried out primarily by adapting known technology and materials.

Such projects for the most part may be fairly well defined, often can have firm objectives and schedules, and can be completed within reasonably short time limits. Furthermore, their individual project costs and the expected payoffs may be estimated with satisfactory accuracy. Thus it is often possible to develop quantitative, objective measures for the administration of this part of a research program. These measures and procedures for using them also will be discussed in a later section.

Although the two types of programs, basic and product- or process-supporting, are complementary, they should be separated. Admittedly, some companies appear to conduct them successfully with the same personnel and facilities. But in our experience a separation has been necessary, sometimes even a geographical separation. Otherwise, the basic research effort, presumed to be directed toward obtaining technology and products for the future, is likely to be dissipated in favor of supporting the day-to-day problems of improving processes or extending and maintaining present product lines.

A SYSTEM OF PROCEDURES

In order to carry on an effective R & D activity, a company must build a system of project selection, evaluation, and control procedures that is based on:

1. Well-defined corporate objectives.
2. An organization that smooths the way for effective relationships between R & D and the key functional areas of the company; i.e., an organization that provides for proper foci of decision making related to R & D and complementary activities.

We shall not concern ourselves here with corporate objectives; but we shall consider organization before outlining procedures related to the systematic selection, evaluation, and control of both basic and product- and process-oriented research projects.

The Organization

It is important that the organization for research be well defined and that the decision-making authority and responsibility at each phase of the program be specified. To use a simple concrete example, a generalized organization chart is shown in Figure 1. To focus our discussion, we shall consider only basic research and product-oriented R & D, but what we say can be directly extended to include process-oriented R & D.

In the organization shown in Figure 1, the two executives most directly concerned with the implementation of the R & D product program are the vice president of research and the vice president of marketing, both of whom report to the company chief executive.

Reporting to the vice president of research are the directors of basic research and product R & D, and the research administrator. At the next lower echelon are the project managers, having responsibility for carrying out groups of individual projects.

Reporting to the vice president of marketing are the directors of marketing for various product lines, and a research coordinator. At the next lower echelon are product managers who have the responsibility for marketing individual products.

The responsibility and authority for planning and conducting the program of basic research rest with the vice president of research, who develops the plans and exercises the authority through a committee

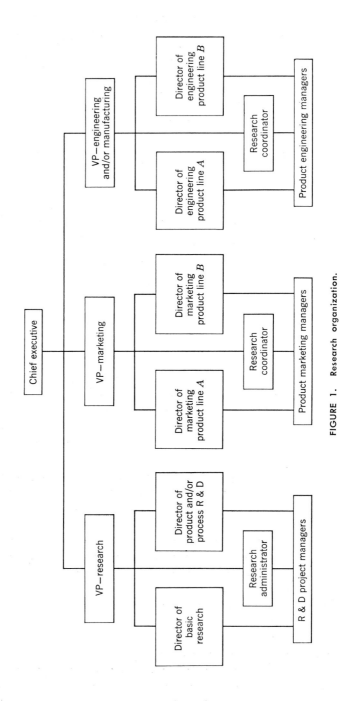

FIGURE 1. Research organization.

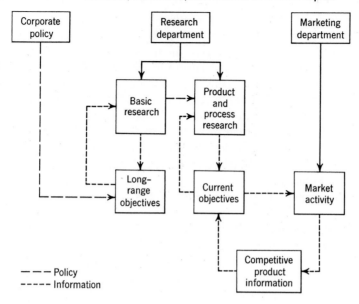

FIGURE 2.   Policy and information flow.

comprised of himself, the two research directors, and the research administrator.

The vice president of research is also responsible for performance of the product R & D program.   But it is the vice president of marketing who indicates the nature of desired product improvements and extensions.   The latter exercises his authority in this activity through a committee including himself, the affected marketing director, product manager, and research director, plus the R & D administrator and the research coordinator.   These relationships are shown in the diagram of Figure 2.

The basic research function is conducted within the research department, with guidance provided by corporate long-range objectives. The project and process research function is also conducted within the research department but receives guidance as to objectives and a measure of control from the marketing department.

Description of System

Any system for the administration of R & D must provide in some way for project initiation, selection, evaluation, and periodic review. If the system is effective, it should result in a smooth flow through R & D of well-chosen projects, whose statuses are updated and reviewed periodically. In other words, of all projects considered, those that have the best expected payoff to the company within budget and manpower limitations will receive the necessary R & D effort.

There are very difficult problems to be solved in achieving this ideal. Since competent R & D personnel are limited in number, it is important to ensure that the best projects will, in fact, receive R & D attention and that the worst (from some point of view) will be identified rapidly and eliminated.

The process for accomplishing this objective is essentially the same for both basic and product research. A diagram of the key steps is shown in Figure 3.

The first step in the procedure is the development of a proper project *proposal*. This comprises a definition of the project and relevant marketing, technical, and schedule information. It may be initiated by anyone in the organization. In our experience, most proposals are originated by members of the R & D staff, although it is reasonable to assume that they were suggested in many cases by marketing personnel.

The second step is project *selection*. It is at this point that management's role begins. This step leads to accepting, deferring, or rejecting a proposal. Accepting a proposal means that the company has interest in this kind of idea currently; deferral means the company may have a future interest; rejection means no interest. This selection is made for basic research projects by the research committee; it is made for product research projects by the marketing committee.

The third step is *evaluation*—determining the current relative importance (priority) of a selected project plus a proposed schedule for its accomplishment and fitting it into the schedule. The information necessary for evaluation is collected by the research administrator and the research coordinator and the affected project and project managers. For basic projects, priority is assigned by a scoring system based on specific subjective judgments; for product projects, priority is assigned using a payoff measure based on estimated costs and results. The major operational difference between basic research and product-oriented R & D administration is the way priorities are determined. In either case, management can, of course, use its prerogative and assign priorities as it feels appropriate. New projects having adequate priority are intended to be put into work shortly after priority assignment, with some perhaps replacing lower priority in-work projects. The remaining new projects are deferred.

The fourth step, once a project is in work, is *control*, which is exer-

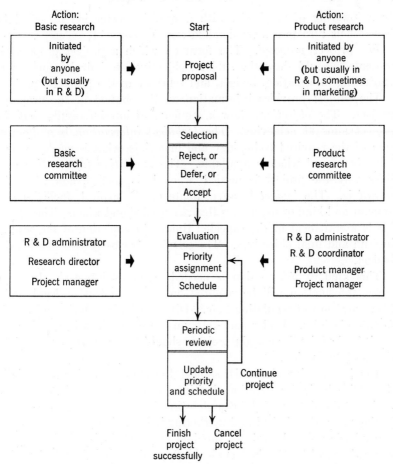

FIGURE 3.   R & D administration system.

cised by periodic review. Basic research projects are reviewed quarterly, and product projects monthly. At this point, accomplishment is measured against schedule and expenditure, and the conditions of continuation or cancellation are stated after priorities are re-evaluated. As a result of re-evaluation, management might decide to add manpower or capital to the project, extend the schedule, cancel, etc. (see Chapter 5).

Throughout this process, each project must be considered in relation to all others. For, with a given capacity of manpower and facilities, it is evident that adding a new project must be coupled with removing some other project (owing to successful completion or cancellation) or a lowering of emphasis, with a resulting extension of schedule. Now let us turn to a more detailed examination of these steps.

The project proposal. The form on which a project proposal is presented should show the subject, objectives, technical information, marketing information, budget, and schedule of the proposed project.

The *subject* provides information on the content of the proposed project. The *objectives* show a sequence of interim results that the project aims at achieving. The *technical information* is a description of the required technology and materials, what is needed to obtain them, and what is available. The *marketing information* outlines why the project is needed, when it is needed, and what the payoff is. The *budget* is an estimate of the capital, facilities and amount and kind of manpower that are needed and when. The *schedule* is a statement of the expected times of completion of the several interim and final objectives. The schedule is closely tied in with the budget.

This kind of information is needed on every proposal. In some cases, information will be required on patent and other legal problems, government regulations, etc. Different budgets may lead to different schedules. Under some circumstances, crash schedules or extended schedules for certain projects should be prepared for examination and evaluation.

The information shown is, subject to company policy, essentially the entire basis for selection decisions. For many product research projects, the data may be complete in almost all areas, particularly in the areas of technical and marketing information. Conversely, for many basic research projects, the data may well be incomplete almost everywhere, with only the technical information, an estimate of market potential for the area considered, and a near-term budget available. In both cases it will probably be necessary to update the budgets and schedules frequently.

Selection of projects. On the basis of the information in the project proposal, the appropriate management committee can select the desired projects for basic and product research. A typical score sheet for a project, incorporating the factors considered most relevant in the company's environment, is shown in Figure 4. Three sets of factors are shown: economic, technical, and timing. Subjectively, each of these is equally important in looking ahead to the ultimate payoff of a research project. At this state, the selection of both basic and product research projects is still subjective, notations for a specific project being simply that a factor is favorable, unfavorable, or that the evaluator has no opinion. Weighted scores then provide assistance in the decision on whether to accept or reject a proposal.

Proposal number B-1		Title Water Softening Agents	
Name of Evaluator John Jones-Director of Basic Research			
Technical Factors:	Favorable	No Opinion	Unfavorable
Long term objectives (s)	✓		
Interim objective (s)	✓		
Technical approach	✓		
Availability of technology within Company			✓
Availability of technology outside Company	✓		
Availability of scientific skills			✓
Adequacy of facilities			✓
Adequacy of support manpower			✓
Tie-in with existing projects			✓
Anticipated output of current approach	✓		
Innovation or novelty of output	✓		
Estimated chance of technical success	✓		
Patent situation	✓		
Production capabilities	✓		
Totals	9	0	5
Economic Factors:			
Competitive environment	✓		
Market potential	✓		
Market stability	✓		
Marketing advantages of project output		✓	
Promotional requirements		✓	
Capitol expenditure requirements	✓		
Research investment payout time	✓		
Totals	5	2	0
Timing Factors:			
Time to accomplish interim objective (s)	✓		
Time relative to supporting marketing objectives	✓		
Totals	2	0	0

FIGURE 4.   R & D project proposal evaluation worksheet.

The form shown must be tailored to the product line and the company's particular technological problems, and should then be developed through careful analysis and modified with experience.

In any application, the best possible score will comprise checks of "favorable" for all items, and for each of the three sets of factors a score of 10 might be assigned. The scores for the three factors would be multiplied, since they each contribute equally and independently to the subjective judgment of the project, yielding in this case a total

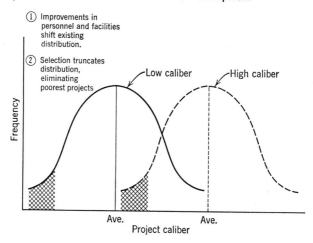

FIGURE 5.   Distribution of caliber of projects.

score of 1,000. The worst possible score will comprise checks of "un-favorable" for all items and each factor might be assigned a score of 1, thus giving a total score of 1 for the project. A method can be devised for scoring all combinations of the three choices, in order to provide a ranking, in which the intervals do not necessarily have metrical consistency; i.e., the difference between 990 and 1,000 is not necessarily the same (in quality, or priority) as the difference between 50 and 60. However, the scoring is intended to be ordinal: the higher the score, the better the project.

Actual *selection* among projects proposed must depend on (a) which kinds of project output the company wants to market or use, and (b) whether the company thinks that the ultimate payoff will justify embarking on the project. There are, of course, other considerations but they are secondary to the above.

A limitation, not always recognized, is that selection cannot be made from among all possible proposals but only *from those proposals submitted*. If the only projects from which a selection can be made have low commercial or technological possibilities, then the whole program will be similarly of low quality from an expected-profit point of view. There are two ways that the average caliber of projects can be improved; both are illustrated in Figure 5, which gives several cases of the distribution of the caliber of proposals submitted.

First, the average caliber of proposals submitted can be increased by an improvement in the creative abilities of the research and marketing organizations i.e., by increasing the quality of ideas. This improvement, by itself, could result in a shift of the average of the (untruncated) distribution in the direction of improved caliber. Note that adding more personnel of the same creative ability will increase the number of ideas but not the average caliber of those submitted.

The second method that the average caliber of projects proposed can be improved is by truncation of the distribution, i.e., by removal of the lower portion (the poorest projects), as shown in Figure 5. It is a method for achieving the latter (which, of course, can be done whether the average is high or low) through the use of effective selection, evaluation, and review procedures which is to be discussed here.

The measures of the quality of an R & D and marketing organization and its abilities in creating "good" proposals are perhaps intangible, but they can be developed into more useful measures. One such measure might be a comparison, between "identical" companies, of the cost of advertising per dollar of sales. An example is shown in Figure 6. Company A shows sales of about 20 dollars per advertising dollar; company B shows sales of about 10 dollars per advertising dollar. Both companies have about the same annual sales, have directly competitive lines—product by product—and use prime television time as the principal advertising medium, to which sales are very sensitive at the current advertising levels. The cost-of-advertising ratio of 2:1 has prevailed for several years. One might conclude—other factors being equal—that the public prefers A's products to B's, and requires *less inducement* to buy them. If this can be interpreted to

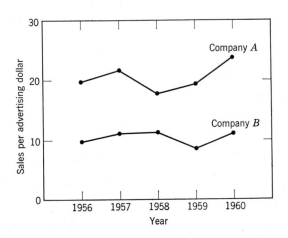

FIGURE 6.   Research-marketing effectiveness.

mean that A's products are actually *better* than B's products, then there is a good chance that company B can improve its sales per advertising dollar by raising the caliber of its R & D and hence the quality of its products.

Evaluation. Once a project has been selected, it is then further evaluated and scheduled. The evaluation consists of the following operations:

1. *Determining* the status of the project.
2. *Deciding* how to continue.
3. *Assigning* a suitable priority.

The status of a new project is based on the data in the selected proposal form. The status of a project in work is based on the original information and the amount accomplished and learned since the previous review. The difference between expected performance and actual performance often may be the basis for action.

Figure 7 shows a form for recording both original and re-evaluated information. For basic projects, priorities are reset using the subjective scoring method as in Figure 4.

Perhaps the two most significant estimates in a project budget are (*a*) the expected *residual* project cost, C_i and (*b*) the expected change in gross profit, Δp (on a discounted-cash-flow basis) which can result from the successful completion of the project. The priority of a project should be related to the over-all cost and the expected payoff. A priority number, $\pi_i = \Delta p/C_i$, i.e., the ratio of expected change in gross profit, as a result of this project, to *residual* project cost, can be useful in decision making. This states that the higher the expected gross profit or the lower the initial project cost, the greater the priority. Also as the project progresses the priority changes as the budgeted funds are lowered (or increased) or there is a change in the expected payoff. For this calculation C_i is not allowed to go below $C_o/2$. Note that a project having its payoff the same as, and on schedule with, the original budget increases priority at every review until the budget is half gone. It then remains at that maximum value until it is finished.

This kind of procedure (based on expected changes in gross profit, expected avoidance of losses, in-pocket return, or other payoff measures) has gained acceptance in several instances. Admittedly it is an incomplete priority measure as it does not consider the risk of project failure; nor does it consider such other substantial costs as advertis-

PROJECT STATUS REPORT

PROJECT TITLE   A B C MAINTENANCE

R. P. A. NUMBER   30120

START DATE *   MAY, 1963   ESTIMATED COMPLETION DATE* DEC., 1963   INITIAL PRIORITY   125

TOTAL ESTIMATED PROJECT COST $ 21,025   BUDGET   19 63 $ 21,025

                                                                      19 ___ $ _____

*
AS COVERED BY PROJECT PROPOSAL   TO COMPLETE $ 21,025

                          BUDGET   MAN-HOURS 137.7 $ 1430

REVIEW DATE _____JUNE 15, 1963_____   ACTUAL   MAN-HOURS 223.5 $ 2438   FOR   MAY, 1963

ACCOMPLISHED TO DATE   X Y Z SOLVENT / HYDROCARBON COMPOSITION DEVELOPED.

NEW FORMULATION DECREASES USAGE 25 PER CENT DUE TO INCREASE IN SPRAY RATE, COMPENSATED

BY COARSER PARTICLES. MEETS FLAMMABILITY REQUIREMENTS.

CURRENT PRIORITY _____500_____   ACTION TAKEN ____ACCELERATE UNDER NEW APPROACH

COMMENTS 25% DECREASE IN USAGE WOULD INCREASE TOTAL UNITS SOLD BY ESTIMATED 600,000 CASES

($ 2,800,000 SALES). NEW APPROACH UNDERTAKEN TO DEVELOP WATER-BASED FORMULATION TO RETAIN

PRESENT USAGE RATE. ESTIMATED COST SAVINGS $1,000,000 PER YEAR. (FOUR FOLD)

REVIEW DATE _____

ACCOMPLISHED SINCE LAST REVIEW _____

FIGURE 7.   Typical project status report.

ing, sales, and testing, associated with the marketing of a product in addition to the R & D cost.

Figure 7 is an evaluation (project status) sheet for recording the current status of a project—accomplishment of interim objectives, amount spent as compared with objectives, and the estimate of time and money required to complete the project.   It further shows a summary of action for previous reviews and the action to be taken as a result of this review.   As mentioned above, some of the possible actions are to accelerate or decelerate the project or to cancel it.   A selected alternative could be accompanied by a change in the payoff or cost estimates and result in the assignment of a new priority.

Projects performed in support of existing products are generally planned to run for about six months but may run as long as a year. As stated above, they are reviewed *monthly*. The review interval should be chosen to meet the company's marketing and technological characteristics.

Control. Basic research projects can run for two to three years and, as stated earlier, are either reviewed *quarterly*, unless current events call for interim review, or on the basis of interim objective target dates. Certainly, the needs and nature of the research effort vary considerably from industry to industry. But in our experience, the duration of projects and the needs for review as stated for the case described are typical.

The evaluation and review procedures lead to the issuance of two reports concerning project status. First is a manpower schedule (Figure 8) showing, by R & D project manager, the allocation of manpower to the various projects under that manager. Manpower is identified by project, and a summary of the status of each product support project is obtained, month by month. Of the pairs of numbers given for each project for each month (Figure 8, line 8), the first is the scheduled assignment of scientists and the second is the scheduled assignment of supporting technicians.

The stars (*) indicate when certain interim project objectives are scheduled. This gives each R & D manager a running account of manpower assignments by project for the next several months. Thus,

			5/63	6/63	7/63	8/63	9/63	10/63	11/63	12/63	TOTAL	
1	O		MANPOWER SCHEDULE									O
2	O		SUMMARY REPORT AS OF: END OF APRIL, 1963									O
3	O		FOR: P. JONES									O
4	O											O
5	O		MAN-MONTHS									O
6	O		5/63	6/63	7/63	8/63	9/63	10/63	11/63	12/63	TOTAL	O
7	O 30120			★		★			★			O
8	O A B C	MAINTENANCE	0.5 0.4	0.5 0.3	1.0 0.8	1.0 1.2	1.0 0.8	1.0 1.4	0.5 —	0.5 1.1	6.0 6.0	O
9	O											O
10	O											O
11	O											O
12	O											O
13	O											O

FIGURE 8. Manpower schedule.

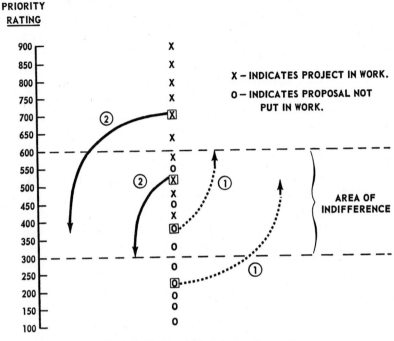

FIGURE 9.   How the priority system works.

he has a means for direct control of manpower, knowing what must be added to get new jobs performed, what will be available if a project is canceled, etc. (see Chapter 5).

The second report (Figure 9) lists projects by order of priority. Figure 9 is designed to assist in making decisions on putting projects in work or taking them out of work.   It shows a ranking of priorities of all projects that have been selected.   There are three ranges of priority values: a high range, which encompasses all projects that are in work; a low range, encompassing all projects that are not in work; and an intermediate, or indifference, range of projects that may or may not be in process.

If a new project is assigned a priority higher than the upper bound of the indifference region, and if the timing is right, the project will be started. If the timing is not right, the R & D administration may choose to defer the project.

There are often considerations other than the systematically determined priority for initiating a project. If it is vital that work on the project be started immediately, then some provision for manpower and facilities must be made. If manpower and facilities are to be maintained at the same level, then some other project may be displaced. With good fortune and effective planning, some successful project will be on the verge of completion (or some unsuccessful project ready for abandonment) and the new project can be fitted in. If not, then a low-priority project (indifference range or below) competing for the manpower and facilities needed will have to be at least temporarily deferred. If there is no project using the needed type of manpower and facilities with low enough priority to be deferred, then the new project must itself be deferred or other means found for putting it in work.

The objective (Figure 9) is to present a priority ranking of projects with a region of indifference, as shown, to avoid instability, that is, putting the same project in and out of work frequently. Projects with priorities greater than the upper bound value should be started and low-priority projects in work, in theory the lowest priority project deferred as necessary. Similarly, any project with a priority below the lower bound should be terminated, and the highest priority project awaiting implementation started. Also, any project with priority in the indifference range may be either in process or deferred, with no action called for until a priority change moves the project out of the indifference region.

The setting of the indifference region is of course, a management decision. If management finds that all the projects in the indifference region are in process deferred, it may want to decrease (expand) the R & D activity or lower (raise) the average score of the indifference region. If it happens that projects are continuously displaced with better ones, this probably indicates that upon receipt of information from research, old projects are "downgraded" and the information is used to develop better ones. If this happens, it does not mean that research facilities are being wasted, but simply that the quality of project input is (initially) too poor to make it worth-while to finish a project. Should this continue, it might indicate that no worth-while research is really possible in the particular technology-market combination.

The basic research projects and product projects are evaluated separately on their own individual scales. No attempt has been made to try to compare them directly.

With the ranked status of all selected projects—both in and out of work (Figure 9)—plus the allocation of manpower among projects, by project, for the next six months (Figure 8), management has a basis for concluding that the best possible projects are in process subject to the limitations of manpower and facilities. Again, this also provides a basis for decision: if only those projects above the upper limit are being worked on and all manpower is assigned, management may want to increase manpower or facilities to permit including a greater number of projects in the program. Similarly, if only the projects below the lower limit are not in the research program, management may want to cut back on manpower facilities.

SUMMARY

The foregoing system for administering industrial R & D embraces two facets of R & D: basic research, which is tied in with long-range plans to develop new technology and products; and product and process research, which is tied in with short-range plans to achieve the company's current objectives. The research projects that make up the program must be selected from among those suggested; then they must be evaluated, scheduled, engineered, and reviewed. This is a continuing process, with old projects being completed or canceled and new ones being added frequently. Much of the evaluation is on a subjective basis. The type of procedure suggested can lead to better selection, evaluation, and control of the R & D process.

The systematic control of a procedure so highly individualistic as R & D is naturally subject to many limitations. The R & D process is not sufficiently repetitive in detail to be controlled as manufacturing can be; nor is each step sufficiently independent to allow for controls of the type used in sales. The procedures described attempt to integrate the subjective judgments of scientists, marketing, engineering, and manufacturing personnel into a framework of value measures to allow management to make decisions on the basis of consistent information. It is recognized that the information may be biased with respect to markets, costs, or technological feasibility. However, development of the historical record is the only thing that will allow management to recognize and counterbalance such biases and errors. Without a consistent system, adequate records will not be developed. It is this system that this procedure is designed to supply.

REFERENCES

1. Peter F. Drucker, "Long-Range Planning, Challenge to Management Service,' *Management Science,* vol. 5, no. 3, 1959.
2. Carl Heyel, editor *Handbook of Industrial Research Management,* New York: Reinhold, 1959.
3. G. R. Gargiulo, J. Hannoch, D. B. Hertz, and T. Zang, "Developing Systematic Procedures for Directing Research Programs," *I.R.E. Trans.,* vol. EM-8, no. 1, March 1961.
4. C. M. Mottley, and R. D. Newton, "The Selection of Projects for Industrial Research," *Operations Research,* vol. 7, no. 6, 1959.

7

.

Studies of Project Selection Behavior
in Industry, *Albert H. Rubenstein*

Industrial R & D has grown tremendously since World War II, with most of the growth occurring in the past 5 to 10 years (Ref. 16). The two major components of this growth are the great expansion of the several hundreds of R & D efforts in existence before 1945 and the entry of thousands of new organizations into the field since then.

In the early postwar years, opportunities abounded for new and improved products, new and improved processes, and whole new product lines and markets. A company with a competent, "large enough" R & D laboratory could pick a number of products and processes already in its field of interest and expect to reap the benefits of applying science to their improvement or replacement by better products and processes.

During this period, when the benefits of R & D appeared to far outweigh the costs of doing the R & D, most company managements were not overly concerned about the need for a precise method of selecting particular projects and for evaluating the returns from them. Control of expenditures in many cases was informal and very few R & D laboratories were terminated or curtailed. The major increases in total expenditures in the industry sector came from the rapid expansion of those laboratories which were either having obvious success in producing results or where the hoped-for results were expected to be hastened by increases in budgets and personnel.

The general support for and optimism about R & D still continues, despite some overt disappointments in individual industries and companies, but a subtle change has been occurring in the attitudes of management toward their R & D activities. A great many of the large companies which have traditionally supported R & D on the basis that "they have faith in its returns" are asking more pointed and more frequent questions about certain aspects of the total R & D activity. In particular, they are looking more closely at: The alternative projects available to the laboratory; the methods and criteria for selecting between these alternatives; the control of progress on projects; and the evaluation of returns, once the projects have been completed and their results applied.

We have recently undertaken an exploratory study of the subprocess of idea generation and project selection within the total R & D process. These functions are considered critical in the total process because they involve important resource allocation decisions that may be difficult or impossible to reverse at later stages of the R & D process.

Most of the research in this field up to now has concentrated on the formal aspects of the decision problem—the evaluation of alternative project proposals, based on assumptions about costs, returns, and probable outcome of proposed projects. Many of the assumptions and formulations used in these studies (and in use by industrial management) ignore the behavioral aspects of the estimating and decision-making process which may have an important bearing on project selection.

A number of studies that we have conducted have raised interesting questions and possibilities for studying the behavior of the people involved in idea generation, estimation, and project selection. We are now planning a three-year field study, designed around "real-time" observation of these functions in several industrial research laboratories.

The background of work in this field and the procedure of the current and proposed research are covered in the following sections.

THE IMPORTANCE OF PROJECT SELECTION IN THE TOTAL R & D PROCESS

The early phases in the life of an R & D program—the generation of ideas, their initial examination for feasibility, and the choice of which ones to support—are critical in the over-all effectiveness of the program. The decisions resulting from these phases involve the allocation of resources and assignment of personnel in a pattern that is costly to modify or reverse. Where large efforts are involved and choices are mutually exclusive, these decisions may, in the short run, be irreversible.

The managers of an R & D activity seek continuously to avoid two general kinds of error: (1) Failure to undertake "good" projects and (2) undertaking "bad" projects. (See Chapters 5 and 6.) The reasons for the difficulty most R & D organizations have in avoiding these two types of error are inherent in the R & D process itself:

1. The outcomes of individual projects, programs, and of the whole R & D process are highly unpredictable. That is, for other than technologically trivial projects, project selection involves decision making under (at best) risk—where probability distributions can be associated with outcomes—or (at worst) uncertainty—where such probability distributions are not available.

2. The outcomes of individual projects occur with time lags of months or years, during which period some of the factors entering into the initial project selection decision—e.g., market demand, material prices, competition, available supporting technology—may change significantly.

Particularly in those areas of R & D that entail specific objectives, time constraints, and limited funds, the point of greatest flexibility in resource allocation is during the project selection phase. In later phases, when work is actually in progress, it becomes increasingly difficult to change direction or reallocate resources economically.

Effective project selection is important to both small and large R & D organizations. Several thousand industrial companies are currently supporting R & D at what may be a minimal level or a level that may be less than the minimal effort needed for accomplishing anything more than routine product or process improvement or technical service work. When such an organization does decide to fund one or more projects aimed at a radically improved or brand new product or process, it may be stretching all of its available technical resources to do it. Under these circumstances, the choice of which project or projects to support is critical.

Even for the large company with massive R & D resources, these are critical choices. If the R & D personnel are competent and in the forefront of their fields, there may be many more promising project opportunities than can be supported at any given time. The search then ensues for an optimal "project portfolio" that will provide the highest expected returns on the R & D money invested (see Chapter 6).

Managers of all sizes of companies have become increasingly insistent in the past few years that their R & D personnel devote more time and more careful analysis to this critical problem of project selection.

In many technologies—both civilian and military—the total allow-able time from conception of an idea for a project to introduction of its results into the factory, the field, or the market place has been drastically shortened because of competitive pressures (Ref. 25). In many instances, total allowable time or "lead time" has been cut to the point where an orderly sequence of follow-on activities is not pos-sible (see Chapter 4). That is, functions such as plant and equip-ment design, plant and equipment construction or purchase, product engineering, test and evaluation, market research, initial promotion and advertising, and training of workers must be started before there is assurance that the new product or process will be successful tech-nically and economically. Consequently, additional resources are al-located without the assurance that the project will ultimately be com-pleted and be economically successful. This acceleration of a pre-viously leisurely process places additional importance on the project selection process.

BACKGROUND OF RESEARCH ON PROJECT SELECTION, ESTIMATION, AND BEHAVIOR OF INDIVIDUAL DECISION MAKERS

Until the past 3 to 4 years, most of the formulations suggested for project selection in the management literature were fairly simple, *ad hoc* expressions, including terms for anticipated costs and returns and, generally but not always, a term for risk or probability of success. For example, one of the earliest in the literature (Ref. 17) used the index of return (I.R.):

$$\text{Value of a new project} = \frac{\text{Estimated I.R.} \times \text{probability of success}}{\text{Estimated cost of research}}$$

where the I.R. is computed as:

I.R. = (the value of the process savings for 1 year
+ 3 percent of the sales value of new products each year for 5 years
+ 2 percent of the sales value of improved products each year for 2 years)

Most of the early formulations for project selection and even those currently under development evade the issue of how the estimates in these formulations are derived. Most of them ignore or do not deal directly with the uncertainties involved in the estimates of costs and returns; the potential trade-offs between costs, returns, and risk; the time patterns of costs and returns; and other aspects of the problem.

In a recent survey of the capital budgeting and engineering economy literature, Rubenstein and Horowitz (Ref. 18) found that most of the formulations used for capital investment decisions, such as purchase of plant and equipment, were not readily adaptable to project selection in R & D. The primary deficiencies included inadequate representation of the actual time patterns likely to occur with costs and returns, and omission of terms representing the risk or uncertainties associated with the anticipated flow of costs and returns.

Recently, some work has been done in attempting to develop formulations that will overcome some of these deficiencies. But none of the work in this field to date has probed deeply enough into the sources of and bases for the various estimates of costs, returns, and risks which form the heart of the project selection decision.

The Operations Research group at Case Institute of Technology (Ref. 4) recently completed a major study of project selection and the allocation of the R & D budget. Its primary results were analytical methods of budgeting and project selection based on the techniques of operations research and culminating in a "manual" for the guidance of management in such matters. It obtained data from three chemical companies during the course of the study on budgeting and project selection procedures, R & D expenditures, company performance, and the expenditure and time patterns of specific projects. A related study by Hess (Ref. 14) examined some of the sequential decision aspects of project selection and budgeting—the reappraisals and re-allocation decisions that occur during the life of a project. In both studies emphasis was on the formal aspects of the problem—the characteristics of the decision payoff matrix, rather than on the behavior of the decision-makers and the factors influencing the decision process in the firm.

Other studies (Refs. 10, 11, 15, and 23) in the field of Operations Research have attacked the project selection and related allocation problems on a formal basis, employing estimates of the variables in the project selection payoff matrix—costs, returns, and probabilities of outcomes—but not examining the sources of these estimates or the possible effects these variations in these estimates may have on the results of the project selection procedure.

Recent experimental work on "subjective probability" holds promise for a better understanding of the behavior of individual decision makers in situations similar to the project selection context. Although the precise definition of subjective probability and, indeed, its very existence have been the subject of some controversy, recent work has indicated that it is possible to measure subjective probability experimentally and develop subjective probability distributions which can be handled mathematically. In a review article on behavioral decision theory, Edwards (Ref. 7) refers to the definition of subjective probability (personal probability) presented by Savage (Ref. 22):

> Subjective probabilities have the same mathematical properties as objective probabilities, but there the resemblance ends. A subjective probability is a number that represents the extent to which an individual thinks a given event is likely. Individuals can freely choose any subjective probabilities they like, prior to the first occurrence of an event; thereafter the change in subjective probability as a result of experience is governed by Bayes's Theorem. This means that if two people observe a series of coin flips, they may start out with subjective probabilities of heads which differ widely from each other, but after a number of flips they will end up with subjective probabilities very close to each other and to the ratio of heads to total flips.

In reviewing a number of experimental studies in an earlier paper, Edwards (Ref. 8) indicated that:

> . . . on empirical grounds the Savage kind of subjective probability measure is unacceptable. . . . A Savage subjective probability measure requires that the sum of the probabilities of a mutually exclusive, exhaustive set of events be one. People do not behave that way; they may, for example, assign subjective probabilities greater than .5 to both the occurrence and the nonoccurrence of an event.

Reporting on one of his own experiments, Edwards (Ref. 9) found that:

> Subjective probability functions obtained from bets on which subjects could only win or break even indicated that subjective probability exceeded objective probability at all points between 0 and 1. But functions obtained from bets on which subjects could only lose or break even indicated that subjective probability equalled objective probability. In other words, there was a vigorous interaction between the sign of the payoff and the shape of the subjective probability function.

In a series of experiments at Carnegie Institute of Technology, Cyert, March, and Starbuck (Ref. 5) found empirical validity in the proposition that individuals can and do modify their subjective estimates of reality to accommodate their expectations about the kinds of payoffs associated with various possible errors. They further found that in the face of conflict, the group or "organizational" estimating process produces compensating estimation procedures, based on past experience with biased individual estimates. This series of studies is of particular interest in connection with our research on project selection, since the experimental procedure employed estimating tasks that included variables labeled "sales" and "costs." The results indicated significant differences in the estimates, depending on the labeling of the data as "costs" or "sales."

Additional experimental work relative to individual values in a decision-making context has been reported by Wallach and Kogan (Ref. 26) utilizing a series of situations that are likely to occur in everyday life. The fictional person involved in the situation must choose between two courses of action. The subject is given quantitative estimates of the critical probabilities associated with the choice between the alternatives and asked to indicate the lowest probability (e.g., one chance in ten, two chances in ten, etc.) which he would consider acceptable in selecting one of the alternatives.

The classical experiments of Asch (Ref. 1) on the effects of group pressures on individual judgments, the studies by Torrance (Ref. 24) of the role of expressed disagreement in small group behavior, and the many studies of deviant member behavior in small groups provide relevant notions and potential test instruments for evaluating the effects of individual, interpersonal, and organizational factors on both the idea generation and the estimation behavior of people in the project selection process.

STATEMENT OF THE PROBLEM

Our current research is aimed at a better understanding of the following aspects of the R & D process in industrial laboratories:

1. The generation of ideas for new projects.
2. The estimation of the significant aspects of each proposed project (anticipated costs, anticipated returns, time patterns of costs and returns, potential interdependencies and trade-offs, and probabilities of success).
3. The criteria used for selection between alternative proposals.
4. Review and evaluation of estimates and decisions during the life of the selected project.
5. Comparison of outcomes with estimates (e.g., actual costs and returns compared to estimates thereof).
6. Possible modification of the estimation and selection procedures, based on (4) and (5).

The approach is descriptive and explanatory rather than prescriptive. That is, an attempt will be made to describe systematically how these decisions and the supporting analyses are made and to discover the factors which influence the idea generation, estimating, and selection behaviors of the people involved. No attempt will be made in this study to develop an optimum or recommended method for making project selection decisions. It is anticipated that a better understanding of this complex process will provide the basis for improved decision-making and estimation procedures on the part of R & D management; but this will depend on proper application of the hoped-for findings of this study.

The process of idea generation and project selection is being studied within a decision-making framework. The choice between alternative project opportunities is viewed as being influenced by three major aspects of decision-making:

1. The characteristics of the decision payoff matrix—a presentation of the alternative proposals available, the probable states of nature which may exist in the future, and the estimated values of each alternative proposal for each probable future state of nature.

For example, in the simplest case of project selection, we might consider two alternatives: (1) undertake project X; (2) do not undertake project X. Two states of nature are possible (in this very oversimplified case): (1) the project would succeed if undertaken; and (2) the project would fail if undertaken. The matrix coefficient values in Table 1, indicate the *value* of the outcome for each combination of alternative and probable state of nature.

TABLE 1

Payoff Values

Alternatives	Probable States of Nature	
	1. X Would Succeed	2. X Would Fail
1. Undertake project X	High value	Low value
2. Do not undertake X	?	?

If we choose alternative 1 and undertake the project, we get a direct outcome that can be evaluated. If we choose the other alternative, we may never know what the outcome would have been. In the very competitive field of R & D, however, where we play against both nature and competing companies, we may get feedback on the outcomes from the actions of our competitors. Their decision to undertake a project which we did not undertake can affect the value of our decision.

The two other aspects of decision-making under consideration are:

2. The characteristics of the decision makers.
3. The decision process in the organization.

Most of the recent research on project selection has concentrated on the construction and analysis of the payoff matrix and the development of decision strategies for optimizing the project portfolio, based on the information contained in the payoff matrix and certain assumptions about the general character of the decision maker's risk preferences.

The search has been for: (1) combinations of projects which will yield optimal results for a given total expenditure (R & D budget) or (2) criteria for project selection that will provide a cutoff point which will separate desirable projects from undesirable ones, based on a scale such as return on investment, pay-back period, or some other measure of worth (see Chapter 6).

Among the factors which may influence the idea generation, estimation, and project selection behavior are:

Technical

These factors include the state of the particular art and related arts at the time an idea is proposed or a project is selected. Some fields are newer than others and may be more attractive or easier to exploit than others which have been under study for some time. Some fields require a high concentration of talent from various disciplines. Some are amenable to pencil and paper analysis; others require massive experimental or test apparatus.

Economic

In some lines of business, almost any major improvement can lead to high economic gains for the company. In some of the older industries, such as primary metals processing, food processing, and metal working, however, technological breakthroughs are rare and many of the basic products and processes which involve massive capital investment have resisted drastic change for decades. Some companies view this as a highly attractive situation, where first-rate R & D can bring about revolutionary changes and great economic gains, as have occurred in more science-based industries such as chemicals, pharmaceuticals, and electronics. Others view it as an absence of opportunity for great economic gains and rely on R & D primarily for modest improvements in the basic process and in the products produced by that process.

As indicated above, many of the economic computations used in project selection are highly simplified and fall far short of representing the actual economic relationships between the variables of cost and return. Recently, however, many companies have adopted or modified the discounted cash-flow technique, from capital budgeting, for use in project selection (Ref. 6). In this technique, the time patterns of costs and returns are calculated and, by using a proper discount or interest rate, the present value of the project is calculated. This has tended to focus some of the behavior of the various people involved in project selection upon a common decision model, and holds promise for improving the actual estimates that go into the computation. At least one industrial company has programmed the cash-flow model on a medium-sized digital computer and continuously simulates the cash-flow from particular projects as progress is made on the projects and as new information about the relevant economic variables becomes available.

Individual

Despite the formal terms in which the project selection procedure is often clothed, emphasizing the economic rationality which underlies it, the raw material for these decisions is heavily influenced by personal factors. These include: risk propensity, career aspirations, scientific orientation, time in the company, personal reputation, historical "batting average" (proportion of good guesses to bad), and other factors which contribute bias to the decision process.

Organizational

Some of these factors are: the distribution of power and influence in the company; relations between functional areas (e.g., marketing vs. research); organizational location of the estimators and the decision makers; criteria for evaluating R & D performance; reward and penalty system (degree of asymmetry and response time); general reputation of R & D performance in the company; analytical sophistication of the estimators and decision makers; availability and use of records on past performance.

RELATION OF THE CURRENT RESEARCH TO PREVIOUS WORK

Interest in the generation of ideas and selection of projects has been reflected in a number of studies conducted or supervised by the author over the past decade. This interest has not, until the present investigation, been the primary focus of a major study. The field study

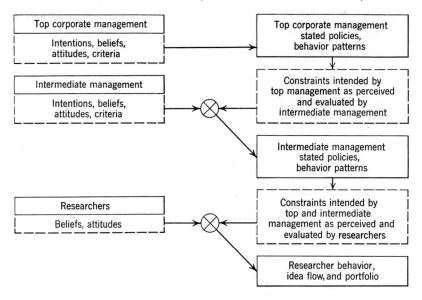

FIGURE 1.   Perceived constraints on R & D decision making.

phase of a study by Hertz and Rubenstein (Ref. 13) indicated the importance of the communication channels available to the researcher in his search for ideas and information. The composition of the research team and the distribution of research specialties in the laboratory were seen to be major constraints on the initial selection of projects and the modifications in approach or objective which occurred during the life of a project.

The current study grew out of some preliminary findings and tentative notions developed during a long-term study of the organization of R & D in decentralized companies (Ref. 19).   One phase of that study related to the chain of perceived constraints on R & D decision making (Figure 1), which helped to explain some of the decision-making behavior encountered in the research laboratories of a number of large companies.

In that study, the focus was on the gross aspects of the R & D portfolio, or distribution of effort.   For example, in some laboratories, which were parts of operating divisions of decentralized companies, major emphasis was placed on the categories of work shown toward the upper end of Table 2.   In addition, the "time-horizon" reflected in the project portfolio—the preferred time until completion of the project or economic payoff from the project—favored short-term, quick payoff projects, over longer-term projects which might have a total ultimate return far greater than that of the short-term work undertaken.

Rubenstein and Brewer (Ref. 20) found, in a study of R & D in the electronics industry in the Chicago area, that a short time-horizon was characteristic of project portfolios in a large percentage of the companies investigated. Of 51 companies studied, only 13 customarily undertook R & D projects with expected maturity greater than 2

TABLE 2

Some Categories for Describing the R & D Portfolio

Over-All Strategies Which Describe the General
Intent of the R & D Program

1. Service on current materials, processes, and applications (M, P, A)
2. Minor improvements one at a time on current M, P, A
3. Continual minor improvements on current M, P, A

. . . .

4. Major improvements on current M, P, A
5. Intentional departures from current M, P, A, one at a time

. . . .

6. Attempts to meet a future market mission

. . . .

7. Coverage of a technical field of current interest
8. Coverage of a technical field of potential interest

. . . .

9. Search for knowledge for its own sake

years. Some possible consequences of this short time-horizon (short relative to that of other segments of the electronics industry) was reflected in a survey of technical achievements in the electronics industry which was part of the over-all study. Chicago area companies were mentioned much less frequently than companies of comparable size in other regions as having made "major research and development advances or technical breakthroughs" over the period 1945–1960.

As another phase of the decentralization study, Rubenstein and Avery (Ref. 21) used a questionnaire for analyzing the flow of new ideas in several R & D laboratories. Its instructions requested the respondent to select the three best ideas for R & D work which he had originated during the preceding year, and to select the three best ideas originated by others—whether inside or outside his company—

during the same period. He was not asked to disclose the content of the ideas so he did not have to exclude those which were proprietary to his company or which were subject to security classification. The single criterion he was asked to use in choosing the six ideas was that he had believed that these ideas, more than others, should be studied and used in some way by his company.

The body of the questionnaire consists of a series of multiple-choice questions which the respondent is asked to answer separately for each idea, and a series of questions in which he is requested to designate by name who originated the three ideas from others, who transmitted these ideas to him, whom he consulted about his own ideas, and whom he tried to convince that each idea should be used.

One use to which the results of this analysis were put was to examine the areas of common interest between members of four laboratories of two large companies. Each company has a separate research laboratory and a separate development laboratory. These two laboratories in each company are organizationally designed to collaborate closely in the flow of projects through the R & D process. An analysis of the generation and flow of ideas indicated that in both companies the two departments shared strong general interests in ideas for new products and processes. There was, as expected, a difference in the time-horizon of research vs. development people, although there was substantial overlap in the frequency distributions of time-horizon on ideas. Despite this apparent overlap of interests, however, the analysis yielded few cases of specific ideas shared between research and development personnel in the early stages of idea generation.

The situation in these two companies—both highly science-oriented —contrasts sharply with the situation in many companies where there is a major gap in interests between research and development. In many of these latter cases, there is very little common ground in terms of scope and time-horizon of ideas. Consequently, transition from research to development is a difficult, expensive, and time-consuming process.

In other applications of the "idea flow" technique, Avery (Ref. 3) compared the scope and time horizons of several categories of people in ten research and development laboratories: laboratory managers, supervisors of groups or sections in the laboratory, and non-supervisory professionals. The latter group was further broken down into those who were mentioned frequently by others as "best idea" men (men from whom they heard the "three best ideas of others") and "nonbest idea" men.

Analysis indicated decreasing similarity in the patterns of perceived "best ideas" in seven out of the ten laboratories as one went down the hierarchy. That is, the patterns of best ideas mentioned by supervisors conformed more closely to that of the laboratory managers than did the patterns of nonsupervisory professionals. This led to some interesting questions about the process of supervisor selection in the laboratory and about the way in which new researchers learned what kinds of ideas were acceptable in the laboratory and what kinds of projects they should associate with in attempting to further their careers as researchers and company employees.

In a series of interviews with more than 100 researchers in the ten laboratories where the idea-flow questionnaire was administered, Avery (Ref. 2) analyzed this learning process. Respondents represented all levels in the laboratory hierarchy and a wide range of "organizational age"—the length of time the respondent had been in the laboratory. They were asked to describe what they had learned, what problems they had encountered, what surprises they found, etc., as they first adapted themselves to the milieu of the industrial laboratory. This analysis shed some hopeful light on the frequently observed conflict between the values that appear to be held by scientists and the values generally found in business organizations. He found a number of mechanisms that are used by researchers and their supervisors in attempting to achieve an accommodation of values which will permit productive activity on the part of the new researcher.

Gloskey (Ref. 12) analyzed the decision-making process in a chemical company, as it related to project selection and evaluation. One part of the study was concerned with interviews with more than a dozen executives in the company who were supposed to be involved in estimating and decision-making on project selection. Thirteen estimating or decision-making areas were examined, including estimates of potential markets, research costs, and total estimates of the whole project; calculations of return on investment; and decisions on price and termination of projects. Of these 13 areas, he found that no one admitted responsibility for three of them, including total analysis of the economics of proposed projects. In another part of the study, he performed post mortems on several unsuccessfully terminated projects and found inadequate estimating or decision-making procedures associated with most of them.

During the Winter quarter of 1961–1962, four graduate students in industrial engineering at Northwestern were undertaking a pilot study on certain aspects of our research on idea generation and project selection. This was being done in a course on field study methodology which is part of our sequence of graduate courses in organization theory.

In this pilot study, the students were carrying out investigations in several local industrial R & D laboratories. They were concentrating on the phase I—or historical phase—of the study. They were learning about the procedures used for project selection up to the present, the changes that have occurred and the reasons for change, the roles of the various people involved in the project selection procedure, and characteristics of the organization that may affect project selection.

They were examining a sample of completed projects and attempted to reconstruct the decision-making process which led to their identification as potential projects; the estimating procedures and estimates that permitted them to be compared to alternative proposals; the criteria used in the actual choice which led to their establishment as projects; the reviews and re-estimates that occurred during the lives of these projects; and the ultimate outcomes of each of them in terms of degree of technical, economic, and "organizational" success.

Three of these four students planned to work in this general area for their M.S. theses. The fourth, plus one of the three Master's candidates, were also considering doctoral dissertations in this general area. Their interests ranged from primary concern with the mathematical aspects of the payoff matrix to primary concern with individual and organizational aspects of project selection. In the latter area, one of them was working on an extension of the work of Avery in studying the generation and flow of ideas in the R & D activity.

PROCEDURE

The pilot studies were conducted in the Chicago area in industrial R & D laboratories. The sample of companies to be studied in the over-all project were selected according to industry, size, and degree of scientific sophistication so as to provide comparable pairs or triads. Since the total number of companies studied in depth during phase II was limited to about half a dozen, the sample is not representative of "all industrial research." An attempt was made, however, to select the sample companies from among those industries where the project selection process can be most advantageously studied, where the number of projects worked on, the number of new products and processes developed, and the technological and economic circumstances are such as to provide statistically interesting numbers of projects.

The study was divided into two phases for each company studied:

Phase   I: Historical reconstruction of initial estimates and re-estimates on several completed (or otherwise terminated) projects and comparison with actual outcomes.

Phase II: Real-time observation of the idea generation, estimation, selection, and review behaviors of R & D personnel and others involved in the total R & D process (marketing, production, general management, etc.) for a three-year period.

The study design included interviews and tests related to individual and organizational factors, observation of meetings and conferences, interviews during and after estimates and decisions have been made, and other attempts to get an accurate picture of the relevant behavior and the factors underlying it. The subjects included all of the important decision makers, estimators, and idea sources in the R & D activity and related company activities.

REFERENCES

1. Asch, Solomon E., "Opinions and Social Pressure," *Scientific American,* Vol. 193, No. 5, November 1955.
2. Avery, Robert W., "Enculturation in Industrial Research," *IRE Transactions on Engineering Management,* Vol. EM-7, No. 1, March 1960.
3. Avery, Robert W., "Technical Objectives and the Production of Ideas in Industrial Laboratories," January 1959 (unpublished).
4. Case Institute of Technology, Operations Research Group. *The Economic Effects of Research and Development Activities on the Company,* a study sponsored by the Office of Special Studies, National Science Foundation, Contract NSF-C68, December 1959.
5. Cyert, Richard M., James G. March, and William A. Starbuck, "Two Experiments on Bias and Conflict in Organizational Estimation," *Management Science,* Vol. 7, No. 3, April 1961.
6. Dean, Joel, "Measuring the Productivity of Capital," *Harvard Business Review,* January-February 1954.
7. Edwards, Ward, "Behavioral Decision Theory," *Annual Review of Psychology,* Vol. 12, 1961.
8. Edwards, Ward, "The Theory of Decision-Making," *Psychological Bulletin,* Vol. 51, 1954.
9. Edwards, Ward, "The Prediction of Decisions Among Bets," *Journal of Experimental Psychology,* Vol. 51, 1955.
10. Flood, Merrill M., "Research Project Evaluation," In *Coordination, Control, and Financing of Industrial Research,* Albert H. Rubenstein (Ed.), King's Crown Press, Columbia University, New York, 1955.
11. Freeman, Raoul J., "An Operational Analysis of Industrial Research," Ph.D. Dissertation, Department of Economics, M.I.T., 1957.
12. Gloskey, Carl R., "Research on a Research Department: An Analysis of Economic Decisions on Projects," *IRE Transactions on Engineering Management,* Vol. EM-7, No. 4, December 1960.

13. Hertz, David B., and Albert H. Rubenstein, *Team Research*. Department of Industrial Engineering, Columbia University, June 1953.

14. Hess, Sidney W., *On Research and Development Budgeting and Project Selection*. Ph.D. Dissertation. Case Institute of Technology, 1960.

15. Mottley, C. M., and R. D. Newton, "The Selection of Projects for Industrial Research," *Operations Research*, Vol. 7, No. 6, December 1959.

16. National Science Foundation, "Funds for Research and Development in the United States 1953–59," *Reviews of Data on Research and Development*, No. 16, NSF 59-65, December 1959.

17. Olsen, Fred, "The Control of Research Funds," In *Coordination, Control, and Financing of Industrial Research*, Albert H. Rubenstein (Ed.), *op. cit.*

18. Rubenstein, Albert H., and Ira Horowitz, "Project Selection in New Technical Fields," Proceedings of the National Electronics Conference, 1959.

19. Rubenstein, Albert H., "Organization and Research and Development Decision-Making Within the Decentralized Firm," Proceedings of the Conference on the Economic and Social Factors Determining the Rate and Direction of Inventive Activity (in press).

20. Rubenstein, Albert H., and Dawson E. Brewer, "A Study of Research and Development in the Chicago Area Electronics Industry," presented to the National Electronics Conference, Chicago, November 1961.

21. Rubenstein, Albert H., and Robert W. Avery, "Idea Flow in Research and Development," Proceedings of the National Electronics Conference, October 1958.

22. Savage, L. J., *The Foundations of Statistics*, John Wiley and Sons, New York, 1954.

23. Sobelman, Sidney, "A Modern Dynamic Approach to Product Development," Picatinny Arsenal, Dover, New Jersey, December 1958.

24. Torrance, E. Paul, "Function of Expressed Disagreement in Small Group Processes," *Social Forces*, Vol. 35, No. 4, 1957.

25. U. S. Army, Department of Army Regulation No. 11-25, "Army Programs. Reduction of Lead Time," Washington, D. C., September 27, 1961.

26. Wallach, M. A., and N. Kogan, "Aspects of Judgement and Decision-Making: Interrelationships and Changes with Age," *Behavioral Science*, Vol. 6, 1961. pp. 23–36.

8

·

Adaptive Organization Structures for
Research and Development Activities,

Herbert A. Shepard

The purpose of this chapter is to explore the implications of thinking of a R & D organization as an adaptive system. This exploration will be preceded by a discussion of more general problems of human adaptation.

The word "adaptation" recalls the processes of biological evolution and the classical idea of the survival of the fittest. As applied to the human race, therefore, this chapter should be subtitled: "It'll be the death of you." That gloomy thought is better suited to the discipline of sociology than to the field of behavioral science. A generalization derived from studies of adaptive behavior, one of which is a theme of this paper, is that patterns of action which serve an adaptive purpose in one context acquire a sacred quality, and we continue to expect these bovine patterns to give milk in environments that provide no nourishment to the cow. Unlearning is such an important part of the adaptive process that the conditions adequate for its occurrence deserve much more study than they have received. "Old theories never die: their proponents pass away."

Adaptation is the keynote of living systems, and the central theme of evolution. Adaptation requires that the organism or organic system comprehend its internal state and the state of the external universe in a strategic way. "Strategic" means that the comprehension must be in terms that lead to the specification of action alternatives which will enhance the well-being of the comprehending system. The notion of strategic comprehension can be applied whether the comprehension is unsymbolized, as in the lower organisms, or partly symbolized, as in man.

Symbolization, or language, is a tremendous evolutionary invention to increase the adaptive capacity of a species without requiring further genetic change.   Before the emergence of man, new adaptive mechanisms of significance had always to be the product of genetic transformations.   With man, new comprehensions could be learned and transmitted verbally, rendering obsolete the slow, uncertain, and clumsy learning by genetic transformation.   To put it another way, the capacity for deutero-learning was now installed in each representative of the race; in most prior species the representatives were equipped for proto-learning, the possibility of deutero-learning residing only in the genetic mechanisms of evolution for the species as a whole.

The usual image for thinking about adaptation is the simple animal finding ways to meet its needs from the physical environment, and altering the environment in ways that make it a better source of need satisfaction.   This can be referred to as "primary adaptation."   When the animal is complex, and when it is in an environment containing many other comprehending, acting systems, a much more complex model for thinking about adaptation is required.   For example, concepts of symbiosis, of organization and specialization, of population control, of defense and offense are, so to speak, built into the systems of strategic comprehension of the lower organisms as methods for resolving problems of mutual adaptation.   In the language of this chapter, processes of mutual adaptation will be called "secondary."

In human affairs, problems of secondary adaptation are baffling. The point that patterns which serve us in one context are continued in inappropriate contexts holds more firmly for social systems than for individuals.   As we have increased our knowledge of adaptive processes in relation to the physical environment, i.e., primary adaptive processes, we have produced new problems of secondary adaptation and are continuing to use old solutions to social problems whose nature has changed.   Our systems for managing interdependence have become so unreliable that we have little energy available for using what we know at the level of primary adaptation.   We are in competition with one another instead of with nature.   We know how to produce enough of everything for everybody, and we know how to control our population, but we lack the secondary adaptive patterns for doing so—and it may be the death of us.

R & D, or more generally, scientific method, represents the greatest human refinement in applying our capacities for strategic comprehension.   The physical sciences are largely devoted to the problems of primary adaptation and the social sciences to problems of secondary adaptation. Persons concerned with management of research are inevitably concerned with secondary adaptation, too, since the focus of their attention is on developing organization for R & D of primary adaptive mechanisms.

Adaptive mechanisms at both the primary and secondary level can lose their adaptive character from a number of causes. Illustrations of several categories of adaptive malfunctioning at the secondary level can be found in any organization or society, but we are interested in those found in R & D organizations.

OBSOLESCENCE

A pattern may be used in a new context which served an adaptive function in a former context. It may be ineffective, or it may even make matters worse, when applied in the new context.

As an example in R & D organizations, consider status and pay. The announced purpose of a status system or salary system is to motivate the scientist to do his best work. There is a good deal of evidence that a scientist does his best work when he becomes almost totally preoccupied with a scientific puzzle of his own choosing. Instead, we find many scientists who are preoccupied with puzzles stemming from the status and salary systems. Some have either lost or never developed the capacity for choosing their own puzzles, let alone becoming preoccupied with them. They want to know what puzzles they are supposed to pretend to be preoccupied with in order to get higher status and pay. Whether we choose to regard our status and salary systems as obsolete or simply as inadequate adaptive mechanisms is not the main point. On the basis of a very small survey, it appears that if a really good scientist is asked as to what he wants to achieve in the next five years, his answer will deal with the research problem on which he is working. If this question is put to a mediocre scientist, he is more likely to express the wish to become a research associate. Whether the good scientist responds as he does because of, or in spite of, the status or salary system is a good question. But it is not obvious that the status salary or system helps the mediocre scientist to become preoccupied with a research problem.

CANCELING-OUT

Two or more adaptive patterns interfere with each other's functioning with resultant confusion, neutralization, or other undesired consequences.

In research organizations the measures taken to build R & D teams often cancel out or are canceled out by efforts to stimulate individual achievement. Consider the following mixture of secondary adaptive patterns sometimes encountered in research organizations.

1. Scientific organizational tradition in research. In this tradition, each person's colleagues are his competitors, collaborators, and judges. The effect is to put the scientist in a rather lonely situation: his contribution to knowledge is cleanly defined, and is taken as a measure of his personal competence and worth.
2. Bureaucratic organizational tradition in research. In this tradition persons of like specialization are grouped together under a supervisor. The supervisor is the judge of each scientist's technical performance, the reward system is based on rank ordering (or a similar principle), and the scientists are in competition with each other for raises and other forms of recognition.
3. Task-force, team, or project-group tradition in research. The structure in this tradition is not as clearly defined as in the other two, but in at least some organizations the emphasis is on team-products, creative social processes, and mixing of specialists from various disciplines. Individual contributions are less recognizable or comparable, and success or failure is a group rather than an individual experience.

The simultaneous existence of all three traditions in a laboratory sometimes leads to confusion. In many laboratories, pattern 2 is the dominant one, and it frequently cancels out efforts to adopt pattern 3.

INTENSIFICATION

Adaptive patterns may be put to intensified use when they fail to serve their purposes.

The recognition that a secondary adaptive pattern is not fulfilling its purpose often leads to the expenditure of even more resources in trying to make it work. The number of "vicious circles" in a society is a kind of measure of the extent to which the patterns of secondary adaptation are obsolescent, or are canceling each other out, or otherwise are not functioning adequately. Such a vicious circle is illustrated in international armament races. If the present supply of armaments does not provide us with security, we produce more armaments. If both sides to the controversy use intensification of this adaptive pattern as the route to security, the result is a vicious circle. What practices in a research laboratory are subject to intensification in this way? One thinks of the numerological theory that adding more people will get the job done faster; or of the theory of selection, placement, and replacement as the way to get a job done. In one laboratory, the person in charge of systems testing was replaced three times. At that point the director put "his very best man" in charge of testing. Two months later he was asked how the test division was performing. He responded, "Well, we're beginning to think no one is perfect." The problem could not be solved by replacement, but that adaptive pattern continued to be used.

Efforts to ensure continued support from clients or a parent organization are often subject to intensification. More and more effort goes into the phraseology of letters and reports, the rehearsing or presentations and the approval of programs, not because a little effort in these directions produced favorable results but because it did not. Getting messages across to research workers is similarly subject to intensification when they do not seem to hear the first time.

POISONING

Secondary adaptive patterns employed by one part of a complex organism may be poisoned by the secondary adaptive patterns employed by another.

Efforts of one part to control another are often met by poisoning. A headquarters staff man, who distrusted the quality control reports he received from the field laboratories, developed a separate method of acquiring data for checking on their accuracy. The field discovered his method and was able to poison the data he used so that they conformed to their reports. This is a special case of intensification or the vicious circle as well as a case of poisoning: the field was able to establish control over the control.

CONCLUSION

A final point about inadequate or inappropriate secondary adaptations: They represent fruitless expenditures of energy, time, and thought, and leave correspondingly less energy, time, and thought for the development of more strategic comprehensions. Worse yet, the managers are in a sense victims rather than masters of the malfunctioning secondary adaptive patterns. To illustrate the point: In research, creative insight is most likely to be gained when the scientist (or group of scientists) is preoccupied with a puzzle of his own choosing. In the field of management, the attractive puzzles are of the following type: What are the conditions (and how can they be provided) under which scientists can become preoccupied with relevant puzzles of their own choosing? By and large, the managers themselves are not operating under conditions which make it easy for them to become preoccupied with this puzzle. Like the scientists, their preoccupations are quite likely to be with issues of status, security of position, advancement in the hierarchy and so forth, and their time and energy are likely to be consumed in the maintenance of secondary adaptive patterns that are not functioning adequately.

Is there a way out of this vicious circle? It sounds as though a "bootstrap operation" is needed, a notion that is as improbable as perpetual motion. In fact, the way out is simple and, like many important discoveries, obvious. It involves the unlearning of some adaptive patterns whereby the individual treats his social environment (the other members of management) as though it were a part of his physical environment. He has adjusted himself to them, and developed some primary adaptive patterns toward them. He has developed extraction techniques for mining whatever rewards those above him control. His view downwards is often exploitative in the same way—he wonders how to use people effectively.

These primary adaptive patterns of members towards each other prevent the development of a more strategic comprehension which could lead to a more adequate secondary system. There is, of course, a tremendous adaptive potential if the managers' separate capacities for strategic comprehension could be jointly brought to bear on the issues. This requires the unlearning of such patterns as withholding expressions of certain attitudes, avoiding certain issues, and playing it close to the vest for the sake of harmony and friendliness, or with the hope of being the winner, or of at least surviving. It requires leveling, clearing the air, building trust and confidence, and developing objectives to which all can subscribe. It is not easy for a management group to undertake such a mission on its own; some help is usually needed because unlearning is difficult and people fear the consequences of risk-taking in previously forbidden areas. But openness, mutual support, and identification are necessary conditions in a management team before its members can become preoccupied with the most interesting puzzle in the world—how to develop a secondary adaptive system which will facilitate the invention of new primary adaptive mechanisms.

9
.

The Relation of Proposal Effort to Sales,

Herbert K. Weiss

"There is something fascinating about science. One gets such wholesale returns of conjecture out of such a trifling investment of fact" (Mark Twain, *Life on the Mississippi*). Mark Twain's comment is particularly relevant to the analysis of the process of making proposals against competition to obtain new business which, in turn, provides the funds for making additional proposals. The amount of relevant published quantitative data is scant; whatever analyses have been done in individual companies are proprietary and not generally available. It is still possible, however, to describe the process and to insert such data as are available. In this chapter a logical structure of the proposal process is developed, and available data are used to indicate the form of the basic relationships and to show how the analysis may be applied to assist decision making. This chapter is an extension of a portion of a paper, "Strategic Planning in an Industry with Rapidly Advancing Technology," presented by the author at the 7th Annual International Meeting of the Institute of Management Sciences on October 20, 1960, in New York.

THE PROPOSAL PROCESS

The awarding of contracts for the development and production of military and space systems in the United States is based upon competitive bidding. Although a company may occasionally receive a sole-source award as a result of a unique capability or a proprietary development achieved with its own funds, almost all weapon and space systems operational or under development today were initiated as the result of a series of competitions. The "eliminations" may begin with the selection of several contractors to perform concept studies, then a new selection is made (which may be open to new bidders as well as winners and losers of the concept investigations) for feasibility studies, and so on through development and production contracts.

It is the purpose of this chapter to analyze the bidding process from the bidder's viewpoint as a problem in allocation of proposal preparation effort. The elements of the process are simple. At periodic intervals (typically, annually with quarterly review and revision), a company allocates funds for proposal effort in selected "market" or "product" areas. As a result of prior presentation of company capability to the "customer" and currently expressed interest in specific "product areas," the company receives invitations to bid on projects ranging from study contracts to complete systems development and production contracts. From these opportunities the company selects some and declines others. It submits proposals in response to the selected requests for proposal (RFP's) in competition with from several to several dozen competitors, depending upon the magnitude and kind of effort required. Upon being selected to perform on a project, the winning contractor bills the customer for manpower and material as direct charges against the contract, for "overhead" charges (which include, among other costs, all or part of the costs of making new proposals) and, usually, a fee.

Note that the maintenance of the defense budget at a high level, the growth of the "defense business," and the adaptation by the "defense industry" of procedures developed in nonmilitary product manufacture and sales have led to the use of terminology that tends to obscure the fact that the purpose of all defense expenditures is to secure the military strength of the United States. The reader must remember that although each "bidder" suboptimizes his effort according to his company's profit or growth objectives, the whole process must be interpreted by the bid evaluators in terms of measures of national security. (See Chapter 1.)

This business of getting new business has many ramifications. It has associated with it a great deal of folklore well known to those who engage in it. This chapter is concerned, however, simply with an attempt to describe the structure of the proposal process in a form which leads to quantitative measures of its effectiveness, and to means for estimating the effect on future company success of current decisions. It must be remembered that no analysis can substitute for a manager who, through experience, judgment, intuition, and common sense, weighs the qualitative and quantitative factors in a problem and invariably comes up with the best decision. It may be hoped, however, that in the long run the results of analysis may assist a less perfect manager to be right more often.

The quantitative relationships involved will vary depending upon whether the company concerned is a prime or subcontractor, and whether its interest is in research only or in components or systems development and manufacture as well. This chapter is mainly concerned with a company emphasizing prime contracts, with an interest in the full spectrum of activities from research to manufacture.

The analysis has, as principal objectives:

1. Describing the structure of the process as a guide to analysis.
2. Developing a measure of how well proposal expenditures are being allocated.
3. Estimating the effect on future sales of current decisions and performance in winning proposals.

No matter how excellent managerial judgment may be, the bidding process is essentially probabilistic. Funds are assigned to a proposal in the expectation that company sales will result which generate (1) enough overhead to support future proposals and insure company survival, and (2) product sales and associated fees (or growth funds in the case of nonprofit organizations) to justify the employment of assets in this activity as opposed to, for example, investment in government bonds.

Since the maximum proposal effort as measured by the cost of proposal preparation which can be charged against sales tends to be proportional to sales, it is clear that the process tends to be one of *positive* feedbacks—as sales increase, they provide more funds for proposals and hence more opportunities for increased sales. Furthermore, a contract won tends to generate sales from several to 20 years, with corresponding opportunities to win additional contracts to maintain and expand the company's position. On the other hand, since the bid evaluator must consider the bidder's capacity for performing, an inhibiting factor on growth is the greater available capacity of a company nearing the completion of a contract as compared with one in an intensive growth phase, all other factors being equal. These and other aspects of the bidding process have been discussed by Friedman (Ref. 5).

OUTLINE OF METHOD

In attempting to quantify the structure of the proposal process, the method employed in this chapter is to examine:

1. The availability of opportunities.
2. The probability of winning as a function of proposal effort and bid value.

3. The distribution of sales generated by a winning proposal.
4. The expected return per dollar invested in proposal effort.
5. A simple dynamic model of sales/profit relationships.
6. The variance of predicted performance about the expected value.

As might be expected, the interpretation of the model developed in terms of real life has been hindered by the lack of appropriate data. Wherever possible, however, real data have been used to support the method. The complete process of model developments and application of available data suggest the form in which records on proposal effort should be kept to provide an operating tool for decision making.

Two levels of model building are employed: first, a simple model is generated that provides a useful initial measure of proposal effectiveness. Next, a more detailed model is developed that requires more detailed data and yields confidence limits of expected outcomes.

SIMPLE MODEL

A first approach to measuring the effectiveness of proposal effort is based on the following minimum set of data:

1. Annual sales.
2. Annual expenditures for proposals.
3. Fraction of annual sales generated by follow-on sales of current product lines.
4. Fraction of proposal effort devoted to new products.

It is desirable to have the data subdivided by product type.

A cursory examination of actual records indicates that in military system contracting the cost of obtaining follow-on contracts, compared with new product efforts, is a comparatively small fraction of total proposal effort; furthermore, the probability of success of such effort is comparatively high. We therefore direct most of our attention to the new contract area.

Again, by analyzing actual data,[1] it has been noted that, for the first 2 or 3 years of a contract's history, sales tend to grow in an exponential fashion; and if the examination is restricted to a particular system, a sales pattern can be drawn, assuming that the program continues successfully to completion. Figure 1 shows a typical pattern.

[1] The author is indebted to personnel at Aeronutronic and, in particular, to Mr. Steig Gavelin, for making available to him numerical records which served as a reference against which the analytic expressions of this chapter could be tested.

Some judgment is involved in selecting an appropriate pattern; for example, a second-generation weapon system will have a more condensed time pattern than a first-generation system (Titan vs. Atlas) and an earlier initial rise; a space vehicle contract will not ordinarily have a quantity "production" phase. Some study-type contracts may also, from the beginning, be recognized as having no follow-on prospects; it may be desired to undertake them, nevertheless, for the purpose of developing capability in advanced techniques.

It must be noted that Figure 1 represents "sales" associated with a typical program which continues to completion in a normal fashion. In using a curve such as Figure 1 for forecasting, it must be discounted for the ever existing possibility of program curtailment or cancellation. The appropriate corrections are discussed later under "Sales Forecasting."

As a system progresses through the various phases of Figure 1, the kinds of personnel and facilities employed to execute its requirements change. This requires the internal allocation and reallocation of analytical, research engineering, design, and manufacturing types of personnel—activities which will not be discussed here (see Chapter 5). The complex of effort generates charges which are here called "sales."

The growth of sales noted has been determined from a limited amount of actual sales data and for a particular system; and considering only continuing programs, the ratio of sales in year $n+1$ to sales in year n plots against n, as shown in Figure 2. The range of ratios for the small sample is shown, as is the same ratio derived

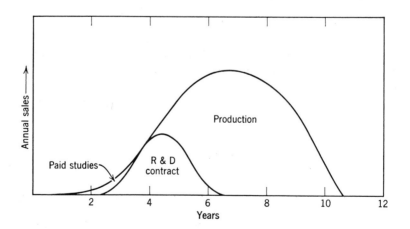

FIGURE 1.   Weapon system sales.

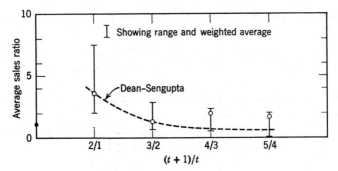

FIGURE 2.   Average sales ratios in successive years for continuing programs.

from the work of Dean and Sengupta (Ref. 1), who indicate that the
sales curve of a class of products may be represented by:

$$S(t) = kt^a e^{-bt}$$

$$a = 2.01 \quad b = 1.11$$

Note that there is good agreement between the actual data and the
Dean-Sengupta formula with the above parameters for the first three
years, but that in the class of effort represented by the data there is
a tendency for growth to continue for a longer time than given by the
particular a, b indicated.   Other values of a and b would bring the
formula into agreement with the present data.   Additional distribution of effort data has been generated by SCARDE (Study Committee for Research, Development, and Engineering).   (Refs. 6, 11, 12.)

Next, although the proposal effort is a discontinuous one, involving
preparation and submittal of a number of proposals of varying bid
value and cost, it will be approximated by a continuous process.
Symbolically:

$$S(t) = \int_0^T P(t - T)\, U(T)\, dT$$

where $S(t)$ = sales rate at time t

   $P(t)$ = proposal expenditure rate at time t

   $U(T)$ = a distribution function that describes how the expected
   sales generated by a single dollar of proposal effort are
   distributed in time

Defining:

$$A = \int_0^\infty U(T)\, dT$$

where A is the total expected dollar of sales generated per dollar of
proposal effort.

Stolze (Ref. 2) has discussed problems in measuring effectiveness of military marketing effort, and defines "bid effectiveness" as the ratio of dollars of business to the engineering cost of acquiring this business. The parameter A is thus analogous to Stolze's index of "bid effectiveness." Although Stolze states that the examples cited in his paper are fictitious, it may be noted that he gives a typical bid effectiveness ratio as 62.

If proposal and sales data are aggregated by full years, the integral equation for $S(t)$ may be approximated by:

$$S(t) = \Sigma P(t - j) \, U(j)$$

where t is in integral years, and $j = 0, 1, \cdots, t$.

It is possible to derive $U(T)$ by straightforward methods, given $S(t)$ and $P(t)$ for past sales and proposal effort. Johnson and Turner (Ref. 3) have described how to do this in a related application.

The author performed a similar computation on complete sales and proposal data for a large operation, involving a heterogeneous mixture of types of contracts, and assuming A to be a constant. It was, however, required that $U(T)$ be a smooth function. Figure 3 shows the resulting weighting function $U(T)$. More detailed examination of the data indicated, however, that the weighting function and, in particular, its initial slope $(T \leqq 2)$:

1. varied widely among the "product lines" comprising the aggregate;
2. had a marked trend with time in certain product lines, showing a consistent rate of change of proposal efficiency.

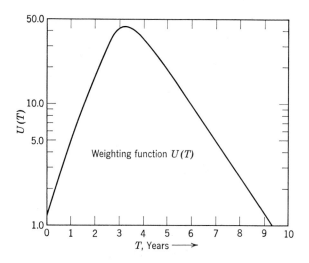

FIGURE 3.   Weighting function.

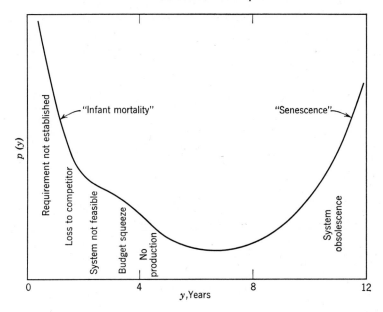

FIGURE 4.   Program mortality rate.

Interest in that portion of the analysis then shifted to a further de-composition of the factors comprising the weighting function $U(T)$. It is convenient to write:

$$U(T) = A \frac{\phi(T) \, w(T)}{\int_0^\infty \phi(T) \, w(T) \, dT}$$

where $w(T)$ is the distribution of R & D contract expenditures curve of Figure 1 normalized, so that

$$\int_0^\infty w(T) \, dT = 1.0$$

where $\phi(T)$ is the probability that a program will survive from initia-tion to time T; $A = A(t, S, C, \cdots)$ are the total expected dollars of return in sales per dollar expended of proposal effort. This may be a function of the time t at which a proposal is made, the size of the company S, the class of work being proposed on C, whether the market is growing or contracting, etc.

Once a program is under way, with an initial contract, it may be considered subject to attrition similar to the actuarial "force of mor-tality." Figure 4 shows a hypothetical shape for this function $p(y)$, where $p(y) \, dy$ is the conditional probability that, if a program sur-

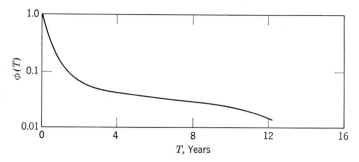

FIGURE 5.   Probability that a new concept will attain at least a specified age.

vives to an age of y years, it will be terminated in the next infinitesimal time period dy.

Then the probability that the program survives to a time T is

$$\phi(T) \simeq \prod_j [1 - p(y_j) \, \Delta y_j]$$

$$\phi(T) = \exp \left[- \int_0^t p(y) \, dy \right]$$

A typical curve showing the probability that a program survives to specified ages from "birth" is shown in Figure 5.

The fact that infant mortality of programs is much higher than middle-aged mortality means that

1. A program that has been under way for a few years is more likely to survive another year than a new program. This is shown in Figure 6.
2. The expected value of total future sales generated by a program increases as a program surmounts successive initial hazards and does not begin to decrease until obsolescence causes it to be supplanted by an entirely new

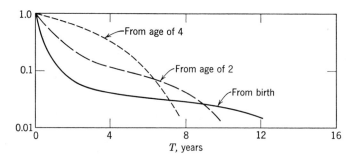

FIGURE 6.   Probability that program survives additional years as function of age.

system. This increase and decrease are shown in Figure 7. Clearly a program must not be proposed unless the expected profit for the $t = 0$ point is positive. On the other hand, the shape of the sales expectation curve of Figure 7 shows decisively why many companies engage in cost participation, waiving of fee, and other tactics in the first stages of a program to increase the probability of survival to the later, more remunerative, and less risky phases.

Some data has been obtained (Ref. 4) roughly in support of the function shown in Figure 6. Figure 8 has been plotted for a large number of missile programs, showing the funds expended and the duration of the program to the date of cancellation, termination, or redirection. It may be noted from this figure that expenditures (hence,

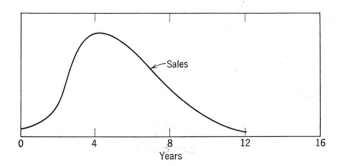

FIGURE 7.   Expected total future sales as function of program age.

sales) associated with these R & D programs at their end dates tend to increase exponentially with the duration of the program. (Of course, the scatter is very large because the programs ranged from small air-to-air missiles to the intercontinental Navaho.)

More programs were canceled in their first 6 years of life than after 6 years as the following table demonstrates.

Age of Program (years)	Number Canceled
0–2	7
2–4	9
4–6	8
6–8	5
8–10	1
10–12	4
12–14	4
Total	38

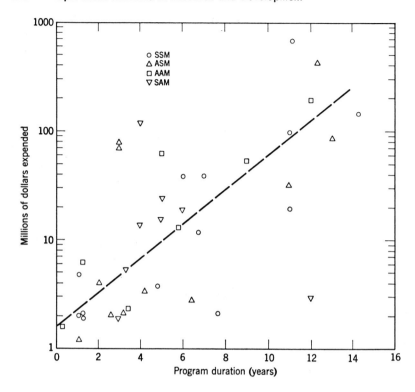

FIGURE 8.   Guided missile programs canceled, terminated, or reoriented.

Since this table does not include a very large number of study and feasibility programs which never survived to be dignified by project status, it is clear that the initial shape of the curve shown in Figure 4 is roughly correct.

As shown in the Appendix, if A can be assumed to be a constant, the proposal effort required in the steady state to secure a specified company growth rate is given approximately by

$$\frac{P(t)}{S(t)} = \frac{R^{T_m}}{A}$$

where T_m = that value of T for which $\phi(T)\, w(T)$ has a maximum (provided that $T_m > 0$)

R = ratio of each year's sales to preceding year's sales

Thus if $T_m = 4$, $A = 70$, and $R = 1.2$ (20 percent growth per year), $P/S = 3$ percent, i.e., 3 percent of sales must be devoted to proposal effort. Furthermore, if the company overhead structure will support some maximum ratio of proposal rate to sales rate λ_m, the company must achieve

$$A\lambda_m > 1.0$$

to hold its sales level constant.

Finally, if a choice must be made between increasing proposal effort above the maximum chargeable against overhead at the expense of profit, and an alternative investment of profit yielding an interest rate ρ is available, a simple profit model (as shown in the Appendix) requires that approximately

$$A(p_0 + \lambda_m) > e^{c_1 \rho T_m}$$

for the present profit to be diverted to present proposal effort. Here p_0 is profit as a fraction of sales when no profit is reinvested in proposal effort and c_1 is a constant, $2 > c_1 > 1$.

Since there appears to be a fair amount of stability in the program effort distribution function $w(T)$, whereas the survival probabilities $\phi(T)$ are largely beyond the control of the contractor once the program is under way, emphasis in evaluating proposal performance is focused on the coefficient A. A measure of A is the new sales generated in each year divided by the proposal effort in that year, with the ratio taken by program class. From this ratio, A itself can be computed on a continuing basis, by using typical $w(T)$ and $\phi(T)$ functions for the program class, and estimates kept up to date on whether the maintenance of the program line is expected to be successful.

Effect of R & D on Proposal Effectiveness

As is well known, one way of improving a company's competitive position is to engage in research supporting the product area of company interest. From research comes new information which can serve as the basis for new products or major improvements in current product lines. A company rich in proprietary resources generated by research may drastically reduce its proposal effort since its competitive advantage is great.

Research in defense product areas may be company-supported, in which case from a half to all of its costs represent potential profit reinvestment, with the remainder adding to overhead. It may be done under government contract, in which case the results are available after some time lag to competitors. Whichever way it is done, there is a substantial time lag between the decision to allocate funds to research and the realization of new sales.

The dynamic relationships between research investment and sales are not known at all quantitatively, although some data are beginning to be available (Ref. 16) which can serve as the basis for model construction. Hence, research investment will not be discussed in this chapter. A possible extension of the methods discussed here is, however, to consider that the effectiveness of a proposal effort is conditioned by past company research. Symbolically we have, as before,

$$S(t) = \int_0^t P(t - T) \, a(t - T) \, U(T) \, dT$$

where we now make

$$a(t) = \int_0^t R(t - u) \, h(u) \, du + a_0(t)$$

where $R(t)$ = rate of investment in research at time t

   $h(u)$ = a weighting function describing the rate at which research investment affects proposal investment effectiveness

   $a_0(t)$ = the value of $a(t)$ if no supporting research is performed

Unfortunately, no data are at hand to estimate $h(u)$, although a mean time lag of from 4 to 8 years between expenditure of a research dollar and effect on sales is reasonable in some industries (Ref. 1).

Sales Forecasting

The expressions generated thus far may be used to construct a sales forecast based upon the future potential of current contracts and the possibility of obtaining new contracts.

In forecasting future sales on current contracts in the τth year, a suggested function is (for the jth program, assuming it to be k years old in year t)

$$S_{jk}(t + \tau) = S_{jk}(t) \frac{w(k + \tau)}{w(k)} \exp \left[- \int_k^{k+\tau} p(y) \, dy \right]$$

By relating future sales to the present position of the program along its life curve $w(k)$, past errors of estimation are removed. The use of the exponential to include the chances that the program will come to an untimely end provides a more conservative and unbiased estimate than is usual in extrapolating current contracts by "judgment."

It is sometimes possible to combine sales under a number of contracts which originated in the same past year as "j-year-old money" and project their future potential as a block. One has for total expected future sales:

$$S(t + \tau) = \sum_j \sum_k S_{jk}(t + \tau)$$

This expression gives the future sales of current contracts; the earlier expression, computed with current estimates of A, provides an estimate of new sales as a function of the rate of proposal effort $P(t)$. The sum can be used to determine what level of proposal effort should be scheduled in the future.

MORE DETAILED MODEL

The simple model of the bidding process thus far presented provides a measure of bid effectiveness and a method for sales forecasting. We shall now sketch a more detailed model which recognizes that bids are made at discrete times, and that they vary in size, cost, and probability of winning.

Opportunities to Bid

A company's growth is limited by the size of the "market area" it has chosen to penetrate as well as by the actions of its competitors. The "defense market" has many of the characteristics of the commercial market. Growing demand for a particular product creates opportunities for new companies to enter the market; lessening demand squeezes out the less effective producers. A characteristic peculiar to the defense market is the very long period of time over which funds are committed to a single producer. In a commercial product line, individuals may shift from one make of automobile or washing machine to another and back in a few years' time; the B-52 bomber program continued for over a decade without major competition (although intensive competitions for its successor took place; the B-70, if procured, could have a similar program life).

This "budget momentum" associated with going programs is well known. Steiner (Ref. 14) has described how one may estimate the extent to which future space and security funds are already committed to known programs (and contractors). The subcontractor intrastructure is established later in a program's life; once established, it has a similar momentum.

Suppose, for example, that one considers federal expenditures for guided missiles. Total funds available in 1961 were of the order of 7 billion dollars. Almost all of these dollars were, however, expended

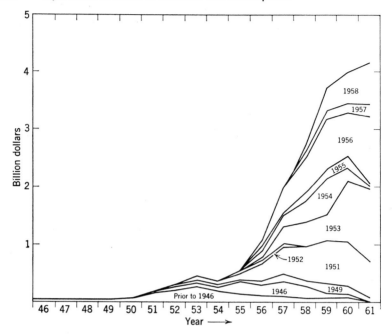

FIGURE 9. Annual expenditures for surface-to-surface missiles showing estimated year in which projects originated.

against programs initiated in earlier years. Figure 9 shows total expenditures for surface-to-surface guided missiles, with a rough guess as to the years in which the programs were initiated.

A more detailed examination was made of the composition of the Air Force RDT and E budget for 1962 as proposed in the hearings on the budget (Ref. 13). Of about 2 billion dollars in RDT and E, approximately 0.9 billion dollars were for systemlike developments, with 0.3 billion dollars for basic and applied research. Fifteen identifiable programs (Samos, Midas, STOL, etc.,) plus unidentified studies (5,000,000 dollars) totaled 890,000,000 dollars. The distribution of dollars by the estimated age of the program was as follows:

Program Age (years)	Percent of Dollars	No. of Programs
Over 6	8	5
5	12	2
4	33	2
3	44	5
2	3	2
1	Less than 1	?

From this table, one notes the uneven starting rate of major new programs (five in one year, compared with two each in three other years) and the growth in expenditures with program age. It may be noted that, if it were not for major external shocks applied to the weapons phasing problem, at a level budget rate, the annual distribution of funds among research, development, production, and operating costs would resemble the distribution of funds with program life (plus operating costs) as indicated in Figure 1, averaged over all types of weapon systems. An approach to this type of program analysis has been presented elsewhere by the author (Ref. 7).

Assuming, then, that a company has developed a competence in a selected area (we shall not discuss here how the area is to be selected), it receives opportunities to propose on studies, research and exploratory investigation, system feasibility examination, and component and systems development and production. The bid values on most of these opportunities will be small. In 1961, for example, out of 423,000,000 dollars placed in private industry by NASA, 250 contracts accounted for 292,000,000 dollars, 1,005 awards for an additional 88,000,000 dollars, with the remainder in awards of less than 25,000 dollars (Ref. 8). Thus, most of the opportunities received by a contractor will be small, but they must be carefully selected for growth into larger programs or for building the capability for the less frequent major proposals.

As is well known, and has been pointed out by Stolze (Ref. 2), there is a seasonal variation in the arrival of requests for proposal which is keyed to the budget cycle. Internal company planning allows the proposal effort to be phased to this variation.

To show the range of bid values, the distribution for one year of a company's operation was computed and is exhibited in Figure 10. The few large bids accounted for most of the total bid value, as evi-

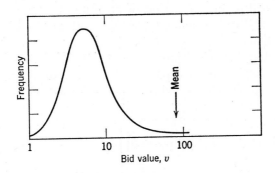

FIGURE 10.   Distribution of bid values.

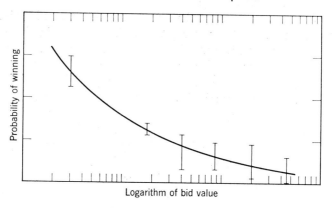

FIGURE 11. Probability of successful bid as function of bid value showing 50% confidence bands.

denced by the position of the mean. Most of the proposals were for much smaller contracts. The numerical values of the abscissa are omitted since the scale will vary widely across companies, depending upon company interests and estimates of its capability; the logarithmic-normal shape of the curve is, however, notable. The lognormal distribution has been discussed by Allais (Ref. 10), among others. The mean bid value v is given in terms of its median M and the variance of its logarithm σ^2 by:

$$v = Me^{\sigma^2/2}$$

and so the mean value will always be larger than the median, as noted in the figure.

In this particular case, distribution of opportunities selected for bid was similar to that of opportunities (i.e., many small opportunities and few large ones), and is probably typical of the industry. Since competition will be intense for major opportunities, one may also expect the probability of winning to decrease with bid value. Figure 11 shows probability of winning, with 50 percent confidence limits, based on a substantial number of proposals. Again, since the actual values will vary widely across companies, they are omitted. It appears, however, that probability of winning can be expressed as:

$$p_w = \exp\left(-a_1 v^{a_2}\right) \qquad a_2 < 1.0$$

Then the expected return per proposal is:

$$vp_w$$

which has a maximum, v_m, at

$$v_m{}^{a_2} = \frac{1}{a_1 a_2}$$

However, the cost of making a proposal increases with the bid value. A proposal for a small research study may cost 1,000 dollars or less. The preproposal and proposal effort for a program such as Apollo or Minuteman could be three orders of magnitude greater; and, in fact, the total expenditure by industry for proposal effort in a major competition has been itself a matter of concern and analysis by the contracting agencies.

Again, examination of data indicates that although there is wide variance (caused in part by variation in time to prepare proposals) in cost of a proposal, the effort can on the average be related to bid value simply as

$$c = b_1 v^{b_2}$$

where the coefficient b_1 depends on the type of system and

$$0 < b_2 < 1.0$$

The expected return per dollar of proposal effort, v_r, is then maximized for

$$v_r{}^{a_2} = \frac{1 - b_2}{a_1 a_2}$$

and

$$v_r < v_m$$

For one set of data analyzed

$$\frac{v_r}{v_m} = \frac{1}{8}$$

so that the maximum return per dollar expended occurs for a much smaller bid than that for which the maximum return per proposal occurs.

In expressing probability of winning as a function of bid value, computing best estimates from existing data, and then applying the parameters to forecasts of future sales, it is necessary to recognize the difference between the particular task being proposed on and possible future follow-on work on the same program.

In many cases major proposals represent proposals to execute development and production on a program which has already passed the preliminary study and feasibility obstacles of Figure 4. The probability that the program will continue and generate follow-on work is very high, and so expected future sales on the average may increase more rapidly beyond the magnitude of the work initially bid on. In systems work, therefore, maximum expected return per dollar invested over the possible program life may be attained at a higher v than given by the preceding expressions.

In this chapter, no discussion has been made of the variation in probability of winning as a function of the bid price for a given job. The price a company bids depends upon its assessment of the direct costs of doing the job plus its overhead and fee structure. Although the probability of winning is certainly influenced by the size of the bid compared with that of the competition, the author has not yet been able to develop a relationship for this parameter. Friedman (Ref. 5) has discussed this aspect of bidding comprehensively. Similarly, the amount of effort spent on a proposal must affect its probability of success; again, this influence has not yet been isolated.

Variance of Estimates

The more detailed model developed in the foregoing allows both the expected value of future sales and the variance about the mean to be computed. As developed in the Appendix, it is shown that, if a specific mean value of sales is set as a future objective, the variance about this mean is less if it is planned to be obtained as the result of a large number of small contracts rather than of a small number of large contracts. This, of course, agrees with common sense. Considering the rate of availability of opportunities, however, very high sales levels can be attained only by the acquisition of large contracts.

As more data accumulate, it should be possible to indicate the confidence with which various levels of future sales can be attained. A typical choice might be as shown in the following table.

	High-Risk Plan, Large Proposals (Million of dollars)	Low-Risk Plan, Medium-Sized Proposals (Million of dollars)
Expected sales rate in 5 years	200	50
Sales rate expected to be exceeded with 90 percent probability	30	45
Sales rate expected to be exceeded with 10 percent probability	300	55

CONCLUSION

A logical structure has been constructed for the process of getting new business by making proposals against competition. It has been possible to indicate the functional form of some of the relationships based on actual data. The model also shows the kinds of data which should be accumulated, analyzed, and estimated to obtain and improve estimates of business success.

A central and important index which can fairly readily be obtained is the new business received each year divided by the cost of obtaining that business, for each product area. This index contains the probability of winning against competition, perhaps the most sensitive determinant of over-all success. Combined with the growth rate of projects in house (a more stable function) and the probability of termination of going contracts (an external influence), estimates can be made of the total dollar return per dollar spent in getting new business. These results, inserted in a simple financial model, allow continuing forecasts of the probability of success in each product line.

APPENDIX

Assume that sales rate $S(t)$ can be represented as a linear function of proposal rate $P(t)$ by

$$S(t) = \frac{A \int_0^t P(t - T) \, \phi(T) \, w(T) \, dT}{\int_0^\infty \phi(T) \, w(T) \, dT} \tag{1}$$

where $S(0) = 0$, $t \leq 0$, A is total dollars of sales generated by a dollar spent on proposal effort, and $w(T)$ is a weighting function of the general form

$$w(T) = \frac{a^k T^{k-1} e^{-aT}}{\Gamma(k)} \tag{2}$$

such that

$$\int_0^\infty w(T) \, dT = 1.0 \tag{3}$$

Also assume that $\phi(T)$, the probability that a program will survive for a time T, can be written as

$$\phi(T) = e^{-bT} \tag{4}$$

More complicated functions for ϕ can be handled in a similar way or approximated as

$$\Sigma b_j e^{-b_k T} \tag{5}$$

The expression

$$w(T)\ \phi(T)$$

has a maximum at

$$T_m = \frac{k-1}{a+b} \tag{6}$$

First, consider a "growth company" with increasing sales. Let proposal effort increase at an exponential rate:

$$P(t) = P(0)e^{\beta t} \tag{7}$$

Taking Laplace transforms of Eq. 1:

$$S(s) = \frac{A\,P(0)(a+b)^k}{(s+a+b)^k(s-\beta)} \tag{8}$$

We are interested only in the "steady-state" solution after the terms in $e^{-(a+b)t}$ have become negligible. Then:

$$\frac{S(t)}{P(0)} \to \frac{Ae^{\beta t}(a+b)^k}{(a+b+\beta)^k} \tag{9}$$

$$\frac{P(t)}{S(t)} \to \frac{[1+(\beta/a+b)]^k}{a} = \frac{[1+(\beta T_m)/(k-1)]^k}{A} \tag{10}$$

For $k > 2$, we have that,

$$\frac{P(t)}{S(t)} \sim \frac{e^{\beta T_m}}{A} \tag{11}$$

If R is the sales ratio in successive years

$$\frac{P(t)}{S(t)} \sim \frac{R^{T_m}}{A} \tag{12}$$

For

$$T_m = 4 \text{ years} \qquad A = 140$$

The approximate values of P/S are as follows:

R	P/S (percent)
1.0	0.7
1.2	1.5
1.4	2.8
1.6	4.9
1.8	7.8
2.0	11.2

Next, consider the expected sales performance of a company when the proposal expenditure rate is held at a constant fraction of sales,

$$P(t) = \lambda S(t) + P(0) \tag{13}$$

where $P(0)$ is here assumed to be the proposal expenditure rate over a very short interval of time at $t = 0$.

Again employing Laplace transforms,

$$S(s) = \frac{P(0)\, w(s)}{[1 - \lambda w(s)]} \tag{14}$$

where $w(s) = \mathcal{L}[w(t)\, \phi(t)]$.

Then

$$\frac{S(s)}{P(0)} = \frac{Ac^k}{[(s + c)^k - \lambda Ac^k]}, \quad c = a + b \tag{15}$$

and by inspection, using the Laplace limit theorem,

$$\lim_{t \to \infty} S(t) = \infty, \quad \lambda A > 1.0$$

$$= 0, \quad \lambda A < 1.0$$

$$= P(0)\, \frac{Ac}{k}$$

$$= P(0)\, \frac{A}{T_m} (1 - k^{-1}), \quad \lambda A = 1.0 \tag{16}$$

The denominator of Eq. 15 is of the form $a^n - b^n$ which is known to have a factor $a - b$. Hence, for $\lambda A > 1.0$, the single exponential term in $S(t)$ which does not decay with time is

$$e^{c[(\lambda A)^{1/k} - 1]\, t} = e^{[(\lambda A)^{1/k} - 1]\, (k-1)t/T_m} \tag{17}$$

which describes the rate of sales growth. Now in practice there is another constraint on the availability of proposal opportunities; hence these simple expressions are an oversimplification for large $S(t)$. However, Eq. 17 may be considered indicative for fractional penetrations of a market.

Simple Profit Model

Suppose that it is possible to realize a profit p_0 as a fraction of sales. Then profit rate in dollars $F(t)$ is:

$$F(t) = p_0\, S(t) \tag{18}$$

There is some approximate maximum fraction of sales which can be assigned to proposals without reducing profit. Let this fraction be λ_m. It may be decided to increase proposal effort to $\lambda_m + \Delta$ at the expense of profit. Then

$$F(t) = (p_0 - \Delta)\, S(t) \tag{19}$$

Also, let us consider a simple model in which the proposal effort is got under way at time 0 by investment P_0 and that $S(0) = 0$.

Future profit is discounted by the average interest rate ρ available from alternate investments. Then the present value of the operation V is where

$$V = (p_0 - \Delta) \int_0^\infty S(t)e^{-\rho t}\, dt - P_0 \tag{20}$$

By recognizing Eq. 20 as a Laplace transform, we may write immediately:

$$\frac{V}{P_0} = \frac{(p_0 - \Delta)}{(H - A\lambda_m - A\Delta) - 1.0} \tag{21}$$

where

$$H = \left(1 + \frac{\rho}{c}\right)^k = \left[1 + \left(\frac{\rho T_m}{k-1}\right)\right]^k \tag{22}$$

By differentiating with respect to Δ, we find that it is desirable to reinvest profit in proposals as long as:

$$A(p_0 + \lambda_m) > \left(1 + \frac{\rho T_m}{k-1}\right)^k, \quad \Delta < p_0 \tag{23}$$

The logic of this inequality is evident by comparing the terms with Eq. 17 Even though $A\lambda_m$ may be less than 1.0 (and hence prevent growth without reinvestment of profit), there is enough reserve in profit to produce an exponential growth if it is diverted; as long as the growth rate is larger than ρ profit margin in dollars over the alternate investment will increase indefinitely (subject to limits not expressed by this simple model).

The corresponding criterion for no reinvestment of profit indicates that the operation is desirable if

$$A\lambda_m + p_0 > \left(1 + \frac{\rho T_m}{k-1}\right)^k \tag{24}$$

Variance of Estimates

At this point we summarize some of the useful relations involving characteristic functions. Let $p(x)\, dx$ be the probability density function of a continuous distribution. Then the characteristic function is

$$\chi(s) = \int_0^\infty e^{isx}\, p(x)\, dx \tag{25}$$

or if x takes on only discrete values x_j:

$$\chi(s) = \sum_j e^{isx_j}\, P(x_j) \tag{26}$$

The probability density function is obtained from the characteristic function by:

$$p(x) = (2\pi)^{-1} \int_{-\infty}^\infty e^{-isx}\, \chi(s)\, ds \tag{27}$$

The characteristic function of the sum of a number of independent variables is equal to the product of the individual characteristic functions.

Finally, given the characteristic function, the mean μ and the variance σ^2 about the mean are obtained simply from the relations:

$$\mu = i \frac{d}{ds} \ln \chi(0) \tag{28}$$

$$\sigma^2 = -\frac{d^2}{ds^2} \ln \chi(0) \tag{29}$$

To estimate the sales rate at time T in the future, make the following assumptions:

1. Proposal opportunities are selected at a mean rate $\nu(t)$ which may vary seasonally with time; the probability that a proposal is made in time dt is assumed independent of when any other proposal is made.
2. Each proposal bid value is assumed drawn at random from a population with probability density function $p(v)$; the associated probability of winning is $p_w(v)$.
3. If a contract is won at time t, it has a probability

$$\phi(T - t) = \exp\left[- \int_0^{T-t} p(y)\, dy \right] \tag{30}$$

of surviving to T.
4. If the contract survives to T, it generates a sales rate $vw(T - t)$.

Consider the characteristic function describing the sales generated by a contract originating in time-value increment $dv\, dt$. This is

$$\{p(v)\ \nu(t)\ dv\ dt\ p_w(v)\ \phi(T - t)[e^{isvw(T-t)} - 1]\} + 1 = J(v, t)\ dv\ dt + 1 \tag{31}$$

$$= e^{J(v, t)\, dvdt} \tag{32}$$

Now, thanks to the assumptions that sales rates generated by successive dv and dt increments are independent, the characteristic function of total sales is obtained by multiplying the individual characteristic functions. However, because of the exponential form of Eq. 32, this is equivalent to integrating the exponent over v and t, i.e.,

$$\chi_S(s) = \exp\left[\int_0^\infty \int_0^T J(v, t)\ dv\ dt \right] \tag{33}$$

Note that the expected number of contracts won in T and surviving to T is:

$$E(n) = \int_0^T \nu(t)\ \phi(T - t)\ dt \int_0^\infty p(v)\ p_w(v)\ dv \tag{34}$$

The expected bid value won is

$$E(v) = \int_0^\infty vp(v)\ p_w(v)\ dv \tag{35}$$

The expected value of the square of bid value is:

$$E(v^2) = \int_0^\infty v^2 \, p(v) \, p_w(v) \, dv \tag{36}$$

Also let,

$$U_1(T) = \int_0^T \nu(t) \, w(T - t) \, \phi(T - t) \, dt \tag{37}$$

$$U_2(T) = \int_0^T \nu(t) \, w^2(T - t) \, \phi(T - t) \, dt \tag{38}$$

We have, then, by applying Eqs. 28 and 29 to Eq. 33:

$$\mu = E(v) \, U_1(T) \tag{39}$$

$$\sigma^2 = E(v^2) \, U_2(T) \tag{40}$$

To obtain a rough idea of how large the variance is likely to be, assume that T is large enough so that the limit in the U integrals may be replaced by infinity, and that ν is constant. Then, for the weighting functions given by Eqs. 2 and 4:

$$U_1 = \nu \left(\frac{a}{c}\right)^k \tag{41}$$

$$U_2 = \nu \, \frac{a2k}{(a + c)^{2k-1}} \, C_m^{2m} \tag{42}$$

where $m = k - 1$ and C is the binominal coefficient.

Next, assume that all proposals are for the same bid value v and each costs C_p. Then, the rate of proposal expenditure is

$$P(t) = \nu C_p \tag{43}$$

and

$$A = \frac{v p_w(v)}{C_p} \int_0^\infty \phi(t) \, w(t) \, dt \tag{44}$$

$$A = \frac{v p_w(v)}{C_p} \left(\frac{a}{c}\right)^k \tag{45}$$

whence

$$\mu = PA \tag{46}$$

$$\sigma^2 = \frac{PAvC_m^{2m}(ac)^k}{(a + c)^{2k-1}} \tag{47}$$

For a given mean set as an objective, therefore, the variance is smaller if it is planned to achieve the objective by a large number of small contracts rather than a small number of large contracts.

Variance of Sales Forecast for Current Contracts

It is assumed that to begin with one has for each current contract a weighting function $w(T)$ and a mortality function $p(y)$, as described in the main text of this chapter. As a minimum, one can assume a $w(T)$ based on the cost/time schedule on which the contract is operating, with a conservative total production run based on a minimum estimate of customer needs. $p(y)$ can, in the absence of better information, be taken as a constant, but should never be taken to exceed 80 percent survival probability per year. Then, as described earlier, for the jth contract of age k,

$$S_{jk}(t + \tau) = G(j, k, t, \tau) \, \phi(k, \tau) \tag{48}$$

where

$$G(j, k, t, \tau) = \frac{S_{jk}(t) \, w(k + \tau)}{w(k)} \tag{49}$$

$$\phi(k, \tau) = \exp\left[- \int_{k}^{k+\tau} p(y) \, dy \right] \tag{50}$$

The characteristic function for the jth contract is

$$\chi_{j,k}(s) = \phi e^{isG} + (1 - \phi) \tag{51}$$

Sales in year $t + \tau$ equal the sum of sales on all contracts; hence, the characteristic function of total sales is the product of the individual characteristic functions:

$$\chi_t(s) = \prod_{j,k} \chi_{j,k}(s) \tag{52}$$

Whence, by applying Eqs. 28 and 29, the expected sales are

$$S(t + \tau) = \sum_{j,k} G\phi$$

and the variance about the mean is

$$\sigma^2(t + \tau) = \sum_{j,k} G^2\phi(1 - \phi)$$

REFERENCES

1. Dean, Burton V., and S. Sengupta, "On a Method for Determining Corporate Research and Development Budgets," in *Management Sciences, Models and Techniques,* Vol. 2, Pergamon Press, New York, 1960, pp. 219–225.
2. Stolze, William J., "Measuring the Effectiveness of Technical Proposals and Marketing Effort in Military Electronics," *IRE Transactions on Engineering Management,* Vol. EM-7, No. 2, June 1960.
3. Johnson, Gordon K., and Inez M. Turner, "Use of Transfer Functions for Company Planning," *Operations Research,* Vol. 4, No. 6, December 1956, pp. 705–710.
4. Department of Defense Appropriations for 1961, Hearings before the Subcommittee on Appropriations, U. S. Senate, Part 2, Washington, 1960, p. 1388.
5. Friedman, Lawrence, "A Competitive-Bidding Strategy," *Operations Research,* Vol. 4, No. 1, February 1956, pp. 104–112, *see also:* C. W. Churchman, R. L.

Ackoff, and E. L. Arnoff, *Introduction to Operations Research,* John Wiley and Sons, New York, 1957, Chapter 19, pp. 559–577.

6. Norden, P. V., "The Study Committee for Research, Development and Engineering (SCARDE): A Progress Report and an Invitation to Participate," *IRE Transaction on Engineering Management,* Vol. EM-8, No. 1, March 1961, pp. 3–10.

7. Weiss, Herbert K., "Weapon System Phasing for Ready Forces," *IRE Transactions, on Engineering Management,* Vol. FM-8, No. 1, March 1961, pp. 30–34.

8. Wilson, George C., "U. S. Plans to Control Space Dollar Impact," *Aviation Week and Space Technology,* November 13, 1961, pp. 30–32.

9. Weiss, Herbert K., "Long-Range Planning for Space and Defense," *Aerospace Management,* Vol. 4, No. 10, October 1961, pp. 28–33.

10. Allais, M., "Method of Appraising Economic Prospects of Mining Exploration over Large Territories: Algerian Sahara Case Study," *Management Science,* Vol. 3, No. 4, July 1957, pp. 285–347.

11. Norden, P. V., "On the Anatomy of Development Projects," *IRE Transactions, on Engineering Management,* March 1960, pp. 34–42.

12. Norden, P. V., and A. V. Bakshi, "Internal Dynamics of Research and Development Projects," in *Management Sciences, Models and Techniques,* Vol. 2, Pergamon Press, New York, 1960, pp. 187–205.

13. Department of Defense Appropriations for 1962, Hearings before the Subcommittee on Appropriations, U. S. Senate, Washington, 1961.

14. Steiner, George A., "How to Forecast Defense Expenditures," *California Management Review,* Vol. II, No. 4, 1960, pp. 84–99.

15. "Aerospace Facts and Figures," *American Aviation Publications,* Washington, 1961. The estimates for specific programs have been assembled from Hearings on the Department of Defense Appropriations, supplemented by judicious guesswork.

16. Horowitz, I., "Regression Models for Company Expenditures on and Returns from Research and Development," *IRE Transactions of Engineering Management,* Vol. EM-7, No. 1, March 1960, pp. 8–13.

10
.

Development Evaluation and Specification
Modification, *Raoul J. Freeman*

The advent of PERT has filled a great need in the area of development management and control (see Chapter 4). However, the full impact and usefulness of such network techniques will not fully be felt until cost, reliability, and specification (specs) changes are incorporated into the sphere of analysis. This chapter is concerned with the subject of specs changes, and an analytic system designed to handle this concept is outlined in the following.

DESM (Development Evaluation and Specs Modification System) is a planning and control tool which relates a generalized network development scheduling scheme to a statistically designed hardware testing program. The results of the latter are fed back to determine possible specs changes in the hardware, development "time savings," and the critical path of the network. These, in turn, influence the further design and nature of the testing program.

This system will tend to reduce "overdesign" and development-production time, assuming that desired performance is attained. It will give management and engineers a display device for observing proposed specs changes and their effects. Furthermore, the system will serve as an integrator to bring design, fabrication, and testing into an over-all optimization scheme.

STATEMENT OF THE PROBLEM

Consider the manufacturing stage in the development of a hardware system. Specifications have been set, plans have been drawn, and

239

fundamental technological feasibility has been established. Various component parts of the system must be manufactured, assembled, and tested. Some of the manufacturing processes are intricate, so that instead of specified design characteristics a component will have actual values which may be at some disparity with the desired values. There is only limited information available about the statistical nature of this disparity. The system, being composed of numerous component parts, comes to the testing or firing line with actual characteristics on many components being different from the design specs. The problem is to determine whether the differences of actual measurements and specifications for various components are significant in affecting the test performance of the system.

A network diagram has been drawn up showing the fabrication and assembly process of the entire system. However, unlike the usual PERT diagram, this is a generalized network representation showing a relationship between time and specifications on every activity. For example, if a component has certain specifications, our knowledge of the characteristics of the fabricating process permits us to determine that on the average not more than, say, one out of three produced parts will meet these specifications. Rework or discard is then necessary on two out of three. However, if the specifications were loosened somewhat, then perhaps two out of three might be acceptable at the first inspection. There are limitations on the amount of money and facilities that are available for production of these components. In the short run, improvement of the manufacturing process is too time-consuming a proposition to consider. Thus, the question is whether or not the specifications can be relaxed without impairing the performance of the entire system. This question may occur in many system components.

The relating of test performance data to specific causes is difficult. However, attributing a certain test performance to one of a known selected group of causes is a feasible proposition. Then by utilizing statistical techniques in the testing (given a series of items to be tested each with a certain set of measurements and deviations from specifications), some stochastic information can be obtained from the technological results. The information thus derived is fed back into the design system so as to relax the specs on some components. This is done so as to arrive at a production plan which will yield specified technical performance and still be accomplished in an acceptable period of time.

THE DESMS MODEL

Generalized Network System

To view an activity as "given" and then obtain time estimates for its completion is a somewhat oversimplified viewpoint for the technological problem described in the foregoing. It seems more realistic to view an activity as consisting of some work which can be done according to various specifications. Let us consider three categories of specifications—acceptable rigid, acceptable nonrigid, and unacceptable. Field data indicate that a sufficient number of the produced parts is usually in the two "acceptable" categories. If such a sufficient acceptability fraction is not achieved, then the manufacturing process must be investigated. Of the ones which fall into the acceptable ranges, the largest number are usually acceptable nonrigid. The latter category, in essence, means that it is worth while to use the component in question, but that it does not come up to design specifications. The dividing line between acceptable rigid and acceptable nonrigid at the beginning of a project is provided by the design engineers, and is later modified as a result of the testing program described in the following. Of course, any items which can be altered in a short period of time so as to be classified in the acceptable rigid class are so altered.

From the actual measurements made on finished components, one can estimate the percentage of completed items which *a priori* fall into the acceptable rigid category, and therefrom calculate the production time per acceptable rigid unit. Furthermore, it is possible to estimate how much this production time would be reduced by reducing the aceptable rigid level. Thus, a large gain in time in such an instance would make it advisable to determine, via the testing lines, the technical effects upon the entire system of such changes. This can be done by suitable statistical design and decision techniques on the testing line.

The network is "given" in the sense that the diagram of events is specified. However, each activity has a "specification-time" trade-off function attached to it. The production time estimates are based on the early models that have already been fabricated and on the opinions of the supervisors of the activities. Unlike PERT, only one estimate is made per performance level, and thus the PERT probability ideas are not used. The network that is finally derived is really a generalized "technological" version of critical path planning.

Cost considerations are not explicitly considered, but the model could be expanded to include them.

At the beginning of a project, the network scheme described here can be used like any other network device to identify the critical path, to set starting dates for certain activities, etc. However, the real effectiveness of the model comes into play after the system tests have begun.

Statistical Testing Program

A series of finished models of the system, whose components have certain measurements which may be at some variance with design specifications, are tested and their performance characteristics noted. This information yields statistically valid conclusions about component and system interaction. However, the network model described in the foregoing now gives a *value* function to the information that is derivable. For, if there are any large gains in time available through small specs changes via the "time-performance" functions of individual parts, then a statistical testing program designed to find the sensitivity of the system performance to changes in the technical specifications for these individual components is of quite some importance. However, it is truly of high value in time-savings potential *only* if the component lies on the *critical* path of the network. A production time reduction on a high-slack event is of negligible value from the total system point of view. Thus, experiments or testing schedules are so designed as to shed light on the areas most important from a potential *reduction of production time* point of view. It should be noted that resultant changes could alter the critical path, and thus a feedback loop is established.

The schedule of tests should be so arranged as to produce information on the effects of changes in specific parts on system performance, as well as to satisfy objectives of other organizations. Some delays in testing should be tolerated so as to obtain sequential information. To a valuable degree, what will be known and what will not be known from any test can be precalculated, and the order of items to be tested can be so arranged that an "optimal" testing sequence is constructed. Where appropriate, tests should make use of the theory of statistical design of experiments.

DESM Procedures

We have described the component parts of our model and turn briefly to a description of the DESM procedures. A generalized net-

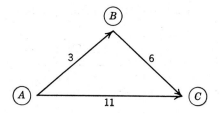

FIGURE 1.   Time network diagram of a hardware system.

work diagram is drawn up that contains "performance-time" trade-off functions of the various activities.   The critical path is determined, based upon the original design specifications of the components. Several items are produced, assembled, and then tested.   The component characteristics of these do not necessarily meet the design specifications.   Various testing orders are precalculated in terms of the information that they will yield with regard to valuable production time-savings (in terms of loosening component specifications). The network data are constantly revised as additional items are produced.   This, in turn, influences the testing schedules currently underway.   When something definitive in a stochastic sense has been ascertained, the specs on a component are relaxed and a new critical path is calculated.   This, in turn, influences the values of the information derivable from the continuing testing program.

Input data to the model of DESM are the original network, system design specifications, initial estimates on time and time-performance relations, actual measurements on the components and systems that have been fabricated, and actual test performances of the completed systems.

The computer program calculates performance-time trade-off functions, critical paths, information content of various testing sequences, and develops an optimal test program.   It maintains current information and constantly revises it by means of the feedback mechanism which has been described previously.   The iterative processes of this analytic model thus help to determine suitable component specs which minimizes production time consistent with providing specified system performance levels.

NUMERICAL EXAMPLE

Consider the time network diagram (Figure 1) of a hardware system with critical path AC:

Performance-time trade-off functions are given as follows:

Task

	AB	BC	AC
$(a - r)*$	3	6	11
$(a - n - r)\dagger$	1.5	3	6

* $(a - r)$ = acceptable rigid.

$\dagger$ $(a - n - r)$ = acceptable nonrigid.

Note: The table elements are in "time" units. The development of this matrix takes place during the course of the project, and there are bound to be inaccuracies in its formulation.

There are several pieces of completed hardware having component characteristics as listed below. We can assume that there may be several items of types I, II, and III.

Task

System	AB	BC	AC
I	$(a - n - r)$	$(a - r)$	$(a - n - r)$
II	$(a - r)$	$(a - n - r)$	$(a - n - r)$
III	$(a - r)$	$(a - r)$	$(a - n - r)$

From the "value" viewpoint, it is most important to investigate possible loosening of the specs of activities on the critical path. Thus, we wish to see if specs on AC can be loosened. This might dictate testing a few of type III first. In the general case, much information could be gathered from an experimental design of various configurations. We would wish that design or sequence that will give the maximum value in terms of information content. The value function is supplied by the updated network.

Suppose we establish that it seems feasible (at given required systems performance level) to reduce the specs on AC. A reduction of specs on AC immediately alters the critical path, as shown in Figure 2. The critical path is now AB–BC. Testing might now concentrate on critical-path activity BC as reflected in configuration II. Thus, the procedure utilizes test information to modify subsequent testing.

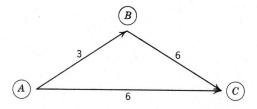

FIGURE 2.   Effect of reducing specs on critical path.

This example was highly oversimplified to show the effect of the feedback mechanism that is set up. It should not be interpreted as an illustration of the functioning of DESMS.

ADVANTAGES AND LIMITATIONS OF THE MODEL

This model, as any other network model, demands as inputs a realistic network diagram and detailed technical estimates. However, this model applies to "late-development, prototype-production" phases of projects, and thus the foregoing input requirements are more likely to be available. By isolating performance factors, we believe that we tend to lose much available information.

An advantage of this model is the interconnection that is established between design, testing, and scheduling. Inherent in this structure is a value analysis approach in a "time" sense. A large amount of data is processed by this analytic system, and the information contained therein is used to the full benefit of the system under development.

The implications of sudden changes in the technological specs can be calculated utilizing this model. Conversely, the technological changes necessary to speed up production can be established. Extensions of this model are possible so as to include costs and major design changes in the analytic structure. Research in these directions is definitely indicated.

CONCLUSION

The system as described herein does not represent all the work that has been done along the general lines of this problem area. DESMS has been more fully developed, but we are still somewhat short of the point of writing a general computer program for it. What remains to be done is the adaption of the model to fit different technologies and development situations. However, general understanding and principles have been obtained. In work completed to-date, we have managed to connect the testing and planning stages of a development project, by a feedback loop from a statistical testing program, to a generalized network scheduling planning system.

Simple network systems, although subject to much theoretical criticism, have served the purpose of awakening the R & D industry to the potentialities of R & D planning. The generalized successors to these first systems definitely have a role in R & D operations. Further research into such methods is very much worth while. As well as being of value *per se*, all "research on research" sheds light upon the basic decision processes in research and creativity. This contributes towards man being ultimately able to influence the rate of technological progress, and thus perhaps appreciably affect the course of human civilization.

REFERENCES

1. R. J. Freeman, "An Appraisal of Scientific Methods in R & D Management." *Proceedings of IRE Winter Convention on Military Electronics,* February 1962.
2. R. J. Freeman, "A Generalized Network Approach to Project Activity Sequencing," *IRE Transactions on Engineering Management,* September 1960.
3. R. J. Freeman, "A Stochastic Model for Determining the Size and Allocation of Research Budgets," *IRE Transactions on Engineering Management,* March 1960.
4. R. J. Freeman, "A Generalized PERT," *Operations Research,* March 1960.
5. R. J. Freeman, "Quantitative Methods in R & D Management," *California Management Review,* Summer 1960.
6. T. L. Healy, "Activity Subdivision and PERT Probability Statements," *Operations Research,* May 1961.
7. J. J. Schwab, "What Do Scientists Do?," *Behavioral Science,* January 1960.

11

.

Models, Rules of Thumb, and
Development Decisions, *Thomas A. Marschak*

This chapter presents the argument that highly simplified and abstract models, unrealistic as they may be, have an important role in the study and improvement of R & D management. The central point is that, although no human activity is harder to describe and predict than the R & D activity, the managers of R & D are nevertheless continually forced to make several kinds of choices. In making these choices, they quite properly use certain general rules of thumb which seem intuitively reasonable or which seem, over repeated trials, to work fairly well. It is, therefore, legitimate and instructive to "test" these rules of thumb—to construct simple models which, although they abstract from the real situation, nevertheless capture some of its more important elements—and then to see whether the rules of thumb can be proved, in the context of these models, to be optimal, or, putting it another way, to find those assumptions under which the rules of thumb *are optimal*. If the result is that certain assumptions have to be met in order that a given rule be optimal, and if the R & D manager is very reluctant to accept these assumptions, then he ought to re-examine very carefully his acceptance of the rule of thumb. It is possible that he is being seriously inconsistent.

THE FRAMEWORK

We will be concerned, first of all, with development and not with basic research. We define a task as being a development task when its logically possible outcomes are well defined *before* it is under way and for which the developer is able to express as a probability his degree of belief that a given outcome will occur. More specifically, we can think of development as the attainment of some item which can be characterized by a number of performance magnitudes. The developer, namely, the manager of development, might divide the space of these performance magnitudes into two parts—a satisfactory part and an unsatisfactory part. The development task consists then of achieving some point in the satisfactory region of the space. One kind of possible outcome, about whose likelihood we can question the developer, is then the attainment of some point in a given region of the space (e.g., the satisfactory region) *if X dollars and T units of time* are made available to him for this purpose.

The developer can be asked to attach a (personal) probability to the outcome (event) of "attainment of a point in region R of the performance space with not more than X dollars and T time units being devoted to the effort." He is asked to do this for some set of non-overlapping regions which, together, exhaust the performance space. The set of probabilities which he announces for this set of regions add up to unity. That such probabilities can be elicited from anyone, even when the events are unique (as they certainly are in the case of development), has been persuasively argued by Savage and his followers.[1] We shall repeat no aspect of the argument. The probabilities can be elicited, if necessary, by asking the developer some *hypothetical* questions: "Suppose you were given the choice of (1) receiving D dollars if region R is attained (for the given maximum expenditure of time and money) and nothing if it is not attained, or (2) receiving D dollars if you draw a red ball and nothing if you draw a black ball from an urn containing a proportion p of red balls and $1 - p$ of black balls. What would p have to be in order that you would be indifferent in regard to the two options?"

To assert that the developer is simply unable to answer such a question is to accuse him of a degree of ignorance that his observed day-to-day behavior continually denies. He does, in fact, repeatedly choose between alternative options, each of which can have a number of possible outcomes, and yet he is uncertain about which outcome of a given option will, in fact, be observed.

If he is at all consistent[2] and does not make his decisions by purest whim, then he is, in fact, repeatedly posing to himself and answering

[1] L. J. Savage, *The Foundations of Statistics,* John Wiley and Sons, 1954. A good, short account is in R. D. Luce and H. Raiffa. *Games and Decisions: Introduction and Critical Survey,* John Wiley and Sons, 1957, Chapter 13.

[2] In a sense made precise by Savage in the form of some behavior axioms.

hypothetical questions of the same form as the one just illustrated, except that both of the options compared have to do with development. The answers, and the personal probabilities, are based on his experience with similar development tasks, his knowledge of others' experience, or the opinions of experts in his employ.

So even though a development activity is perhaps the most clearly unique (nonrepeated) of productive activities, probabilities, in the sense of personal degrees of belief, can be attached to development outcomes.

Besides the class of outcomes just considered, another important class consists of the amount of time and money which will turn out to be *necessary* to achieve a given region of the performance space if the development is undertaken in a certain way. (We leave the meaning of "way" vague for the moment.) In important cases the developer must attach probabilities to alternative amounts of time and money for given regions and given "ways."

Having now a clearer idea about what a development task is and about the nature of the developer's knowledge of an uncompleted task, we can proceed to classify the development problems or models that can be studied. It is useful, for example, to classify them with respect to the following four dichotomies:

1. Is there, in the development tasks that the model describes, just *one* "decision stage," or *review point*, to introduce a term we shall use? Or is there *a sequence of review points* at each of which the developer makes decisions, using the knowledge then available?
2. The item being developed is characterized by a number of performance magnitudes. Over the space of all possible combinations of these magnitudes, the developer has certain preferences. Is a function defining these preferences (i.e., a function assigning a higher value to that one of two points that is preferred) *two-valued* or *many-valued*. Does the developer, in other words, merely denote one region of the space as satisfactory and the rest of it as unsatisfactory (the possibility discussed above), or does he divide the space into more than two regions which he is willing to rank?
3. For the purpose of analyzing the development decisions, do we regard the item being developed as having *one component* or *many components?*
4. Does the world outside the developer's control *stay the same* during the course of development or does it *change* (i.e., does the "state of the art" change or the external data which affect the developer's preferences over the performance space)?

In a realistic model, of course, the second alternative in each dichotomy would have to be true. But to make any progress at all, we must simplify. We shall assume here, that preferences are two-valued, that a one-component item is being developed,[3] and that no changes in the outside world occur in the course of development.

A SIMPLE MODEL: CHOICE AMONG PARALLEL APPROACHES—THE CASE OF A SINGLE REVIEW POINT[4]

Consider now a developer starting the development of a one-component item under the assumed conditions. The choice he has to make immediately is among, what we may call, *approaches* to the development task—to the task of attaining a version of the item whose performance magnitudes lie in the satisfactory part of the performance space. The definition of approach is very broad. An *approach* may be the pursuit of a particular *design* for the item, initially specified to some degree; or it may be the attempt of a particular *group of people* (a particular firm, laboratory, or laboratory group) to develop a satisfactory version of the item.

For each approach there exists, we shall assume, a *unique* amount of time and of money which would, in fact, be required if that approach were followed all the way, until it yielded a satisfactory item. Thus an approach, as we shall think of it here, does not allow substitution between money and time.

If, for example, the same initial design is pursued by using two different amounts of money, the larger amount of money "buying" a reduced development time, then the two efforts are regarded as different approaches. In a later section we shall sketch very briefly how this definition of approach can be relaxed somewhat so as to take specifically into account the fact that the same design may be pursued with different degrees of intensity and that these alternative efforts bear a special relation to each other.

The unique amount of time and money that each approach requires is not initially known to the developer. If it were, the developer would have virtuallly no task at all. He would pick that approach, among all those proposed to him, that had the "best" time-money combination and would discard all others. He could then retire from the scene.

We must leave this unrealistic extreme of complete certainty, but not before clarifying the meaning of "best" time-money combination,

---

[3] The decisions that a developer has to make having specifically to do with the "matching" of components are, for the time being, disregarded.

[4] The single-review-point parallel-approach problem discussed in this section was formulated first by R. R. Nelson in "The Economics of Parallel R & D Efforts," RAND Corporation Research Memorandum, 1959.

i.e., clarifying the developer's goals. The developer has preferences over all the possible time-money combinations that could be spent in attaining a satisfactory version of a given item. These preferences are determined by the alternative uses to which time and money could be put by the developer or by the enterprise to which he belongs —alternative development projects or productive activities other than development. In the short run, those preferences may have very sharp "corners," especially with respect to money (i.e., any time-money combination involving more than a certain amount of money is extremely undesirable).[5] In a longer run, more money can always be obtained *somewhere* at some cost in terms of opportunities fore-gone (and, with respect to time, no deadline is completely immutable). The developer's preferences can be summarized, in any case, by any function $U(M, T)$—where M is the total money and T the total time required to develop satisfactorily the given item—such that if one time-money combination yields a lower value of U than another, then the first combination is preferred. Combinations yielding the same value of U are indifferent; within such a set of combinations, time and money can be traded against each other.

Under complete certainty the developer's goal is then, of course, to achieve as low a value of U as possible. Among all the approaches proposed to him, he chooses, in the case of complete certainty, a single one, for which time and money required yield the lowest value of U. To put the developer's problem in this way (for the certainty case) seems much more realistic, natural, and general than to assume that he has a fixed inviolable budget constraint, a fixed immutable deadline, or both. We shall refer to $U(M, T)$ as the "total time-and-money-cost of development" when a total of M dollars and T time units are spent.

Now what about the true development case—the case of uncer-tainty? We shall assume in general (and not just in the parallel-approach model investigated in this section) that the developer al-

[5] In the time-money space, in other words, indifference curves might look like this:

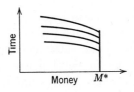

The lower the curve the more desirable it is, and M^* designates an amount of money beyond which it is extremely undesirable to go.

ways wants to make such a decision or set of decisions as to minimize the expected value of $U(M, T)$ where, in computing the expected value of $U(M, T)$ for a proposed decision or set of decisions, he attaches personal probabilities to the alternative possible values of U that could result. That this properly describes the developer's goals under uncertainty can be deduced from several axioms about his preferences—reasonable axioms which he would probably accept.[6] Note that we have not ruled out by any means the developer who feels quite differently about a 50 percent chance of (M_1, T) and a 50 percent chance of (M_2, T) than he does about $[\frac{1}{2}(M_1 + M_2), T]$ occurring with certainty. If he dislikes risk with respect to money, time, or both, this is expressed in the "shape" of the function U.

We return now to our parallel-approach model in the case of uncertainty about the time and money that will turn out to be required (and hence about the value of $U(M, T)$ that will turn out to be experienced) for each proposed approach, if that approach alone is pursued and is carried out until development is complete. We could simply say that the developer's task before development starts is now, for each proposed approach, to attach probabilities to the alternative values of $U(M, T)$, to select that approach for which the expected value of U is smallest, and immediately to discard all other approaches. At that point he can, again, retire from the scene.

But if that were our model, it would leave out an essential part of the developer's role. For development is the acquisition of knowledge, and the developer's responsibility is to respond to such knowledge as it becomes available. This means that he must not be totally committed to a single approach at the very start—if he were he could never take advantage of the knowledge obtained in the course of pursuing that approach as to how "good" an approach it is. He must, in general, pursue *more* than one approach for some time at least.

It is true that, for a different definition of approach than ours, there could still be work for the developer to do after he makes an initial once-and-for-all choice of approach. We might, for example, think of a single approach (say, the pursuit of a given initial design) as involving a sequence of decision points at each of which some *one* of a number of possible choices has to be made by the developer—choices with respect to alternative characteristics of the item under development (performance magnitudes, internal design characteristics, etc.). Indeed this clearly occurs in development all the time. An "approach," then, would no longer have a unique true time-and-money-cost to completion, the actual cost of pursuing it would depend on the

[6] See Luce and Raiffa, *op. cit.*, Chapter 2.

sequence of choices actually made. But if these are the only kinds of choices the developer has to face, then there is not much that a formal analysis, at the present level of generality, can tell him about what the best choices are. We can merely say that, for each of a given set of choices, the developer wants (ideally) to find the expected value of $U(M, T)$, assuming that *all subsequent choices* will be optimal; he then wants to make that current choice for which this expected value is least. However, this statement does not express anything very useful, interesting, or unexpected.

The models worth exploring, however, are those in which, under fairly general assumptions, analysis reveals properties of the developer's best responses that are interesting and not obvious. The simplest of such a model does seem to involve approaches as we have defined them in the foregoing, and hence it involves, in general, *the simultaneous pursuit of more than one approach*. This simplest model is as follows.

Assume that the developer's "time-and-money-cost" function is of the form

$$U(M, T) = aT + bM + c, \quad a > 0, \quad b > 0 \quad \text{(Assumption 1)}$$

An amount of time T has a money "equivalent" aT, and U is an increasing linear function of the total "money equivalent" spent. In particular, since U is purely ordinal (i.e., any nondecreasing function of U represents the developer's preferences, or "costs," just as well), we may take U to equal the money spent:

$$U = aT + M + c \quad \text{(Assumption 1a)}$$

For convenience we also assume $c \geqq 0$, so that U is never negative.

Now consider, for each of the approaches among which the developer initially chooses, the time-and-money cost of development that would be observed if that approach were pursued to completion, excluding any pursuit of another approach. Denote this by $u(m, t)$, where m and t are the total amounts of money and time required to complete the approach. Consider Eu, the expected value of u. Note that for each of the approaches among which the developer initially chooses Eu is exactly the same. This is so because, under our general assumption about the developer's goals under uncertainty, for any two proposed approaches the only initial information that he needs in order to determine which he prefers is the expected value of u for each of them. He will, therefore, immediately select from all the approaches first proposed to him those with the lowest value of Eu. The selected approaches, from which choice is then to be made, therefore have the same initial value of Eu. (For each proposed approach, the developer's task of deciding on an Eu—on the *mean* of his personal probability distribution over the possible values of u—may be a far easier task than that of eliciting from him the entire personal probability distribution; and Eu is all that is required.)

Assume next that the additional knowledge acquired during the course of development presents itself at one and only one point of time—called the *review point*. For any approach that is pursued, there becomes available at the review point (which occurs at the same point of calendar time for all simultaneously started approaches) an *estimate* $\hat{u}$ of the true time-and-money-cost u for that approach. This estimate constitutes *more accurate knowledge* of the true u than does the developer's initial knowledge of the true u (namely, the mean Eu). To be more precise, the estimate $\hat{u}$ is, we assume, an "unbiased" estimate of the true u in the sense that

$$E(u|\hat{u}) = \hat{u} \qquad \text{(Assumption 2)}$$

The conditional expected value of u, given that the particular estimate $\hat{u}$ has been observed, is equal to that estimate. Assumption 2 immediately implies that $E\hat{u} = Eu$.[7]

We could now express the condition that $\hat{u}$ imparts more knowledge about the true u than does Eu (that $\hat{u}$ is a "better" estimate of u than is Eu) in a number of ways. A reasonable and convenient one is simply

$$E(\hat{u} - u)^2 > 0 \qquad \text{(Assumption 3)}$$

To interpret this assumption, observe that under Assumption 1 we can write (letting $\bar{u}$ henceforth stand for Eu),

$$E(\hat{u} - \bar{u})^2 = E(u - \bar{u})^2 - E(\hat{u} - u)^2 \qquad (1)$$

The first term on the right of the equality[8] measures the dispersion of the true time-and-money-cost of completing an approach about the mean $\bar{u}$; and $\bar{u}$ is the only information the developer has at the

---

[7] Since, if $\hat{u}$ has the density function $f(\hat{u})$,

$$Eu = \int_0^\infty E(u|\hat{u}) f(\hat{u}) \, d\hat{u} = \int_0^\infty \hat{u} f(\hat{u}) \, d\hat{u} = E\hat{u}$$

[8] The equality is proved as follows. Let $f(\hat{u})$ be the density of $\hat{u}$. Observe first that $E(u\hat{u}) = \int_0^\infty E(u\hat{u}|\hat{u}) f(\hat{u}) \, d\hat{u} = \int_0^\infty \hat{u}(Eu|\hat{u}) f(\hat{u}) \, du$, which, by footnote 7, equals $\int_0^\infty \hat{u}^2 f(\hat{u}) \, d\hat{u} = E\hat{u}^2$. Then $E(u - \bar{u})^2 - E(\hat{u} - u)^2 = Eu^2 - \bar{u}^2 - E\hat{u}^2 + 2Eu\hat{u} - Eu^2 = Eu^2 - \bar{u}^2 - E\hat{u}^2 + 2E\hat{u}^2 - Eu^2 = E\hat{u}^2 - \bar{u}^2 = E(\hat{u} - \bar{u})^2$.

start of an approach.   If this term is large, therefore, the developer's initial information about the true time-and-money-cost of an approach is ("on the average") small.   The second term on the right of the equality measures the dispersion of $\hat{u}$—the second piece of information acquired by the developer—about the true u.   If this term is large, then the developer's information at the review point about the true cost of an approach is small.   The equality shows, however, that under Assumption 3 *the second term on the right is smaller than the first term*.

The developer's information about the true u for a given approach *increases* between the start of development (when only Eu is known) and the review point.   And a reasonable measure of the increase (of the amount learned) is $E(\hat{u}-\bar{u})^2$.   (It may seem paradoxical at first sight that the larger the dispersion of $\hat{u}$ about its mean, the greater the information that $\hat{u}$ provides about u.   The paradox is resolved, to put it very roughly, if one realizes that a large dispersion of $\hat{u}$ about $\bar{u}$ means that given $\bar{u}$—the initial information—it is hard to predict what $\hat{u}$ will be and, hence, what u will be.   Therefore, *knowing* what $\hat{u}$ is constitutes a large gain in information about the approach in question and about its true u.)

Now the developer has to make two decisions: (1) He has to decide how many of the initially "equally good" approaches available to him—let there be M of them—to pursue up to the review point. Let $n \leqq M$ denote the number chosen.   (2) At the review point he has to decide, after looking at the estimates $\hat{u}$ for all the approaches which he has pursued up to the review point, which one to pursue up to the end (which is to be the *surviving approach*).   All the rest will be discarded, for we are assuming that no further opportunity arises to take advantage of the additional knowledge gained in carrying them further.

But the second decision is obvious: the chosen surviving approach will be the one with the lowest estimate $\hat{u}$ (or, if there are several with lowest $\hat{u}$, any of these).

Under our assumptions moreover, the optimal value of n is easy to characterize in a compact way.   For each approach is completely characterized by two numbers, the estimate $\hat{u}$ and the true time-and-money-cost u.   The M initially available approaches and the n approaches chosen from among them to be pursued to the review point may be regarded as random samples, of size M and n, respectively, from a two-dimensional population $(\hat{u}, u)$ such that $E(u|\hat{u}) = \hat{u}$ and $Eu = E\hat{u} = \bar{u}$.   In deciding to pursue an approach, the developer can think of himself as drawing a ticket from an urn full of tickets. On each ticket are two non-negative numbers—a value of $\hat{u}$ and a value of u—and the above conditions on the two numbers are satisfied. The developer does not get to look at the first number, however, until the approach has reached the review point; and he only gets to look at the second number if he pursues the approach until a satisfactory version of the required item is obtained.

If then n approaches are pursued, the expected value of the estimate $\hat{u}$ for the surviving approach equals $E\hat{u}_n$, where $\hat{u}_n$ *is the smallest first number in a sample of n tickets drawn from the urn described.* And since $E(u|\hat{u}) = \hat{u}$, we also have that $E\hat{u}_n$ equals the expected value of u for the surviving approach, if n approaches are pursued to the review point.

If n approaches are pursued, therefore, and if, as we shall assume, it costs one money unit to perform an approach up to the review point, then, under Assumption 1, the expected value of the *total* time-and-money-cost of pursuing n approaches up to the review point and the surviving approach thereafter is[9]

$$\bar{u}_n \equiv E\hat{u}_n + n - 1 \tag{2}$$

Now it is easily established that the expected value of the minimum of a sample of n from a given population[10] declines as n increases, *but declines at a decreasing rate.* Hence for any $n \geqq 2$, $E\hat{u}_{n-1} - E\hat{u}_n > E\hat{u}_n - E\hat{u}_{n+1} > 0$.

There are "diminishing returns" to the addition of more and more approaches—a property that is not intuitively evident and is true without any restrictions whatever being placed on the probability distribution of the $\hat{u}$. This means that the developer has to calculate, for successive values of n up to $n = M$, the quantity $E\hat{u}_{n+1} - E\hat{u}_n$. *As soon as he reaches an n for which*

$$|E\hat{u}_n - E\hat{u}_{n-1}| > 1 \quad \text{and} \quad |E\hat{u}_{n+1} - E\hat{u}_n| < 1 \tag{3}$$

he has found an optimal n. And the diminishing-returns property assures him that there does exist an n (though it may be an $n > M$)

---

[9] If the surviving approach requires a time t^* and an amount of money m^* to completion, then, by Assumption 1a, the time-and-money-cost for that approach alone is given by $u^* = at^* + m^* + c$. But the total money required for development is $m^* + n - 1$ (and the total time is t^*). Hence the total time-and-money-cost of development is $at^* + m^* + n - 1 + c = u + n - 1$. If the surviving path is always the one with the lowest $\hat{u}$, then the expected value of $u^* + n - 1$ is $E\hat{u}_n + n - 1 = \bar{U}_n$.

[10] A population with a lower bound.

for which this is the case. The n satisfying Eq. 3 is optimal (if it is $\leq M$) because at that point running one more approach drops the expected value of the surviving approach's time-and-money-cost by less than the extra cost of pursuing that approach to the review point. On the other hand, reducing the number of approaches by one increases this expected value by more than the reduction saves. If there exists no $n \leq M$ satisfying Eq. 3, then the developer's optimal course is to pursue all of the M available approaches to the review point. To make this optimal choice of n, the developer needs to know only his (personal) probability distribution of the numbers $\hat{u}$. He can then, for example, use the easily established formula

$$E\hat{u}_n = \int_0^\infty [1 - F(x)]^n \, dx \tag{4}$$

where F is the (continuous) cumulative density function according to which $\hat{u}$ is distributed.

Recall now that $E(\hat{u} - \bar{u})^2$, the variance of the $\hat{u}$, is a reasonable measure of the *amount learned* in pursuing the "average" approach up to the review point. Let $\hat{n}$ denote the optimal number of paths pursued to the review point. An important question is this: How does $\hat{n}$ change as the "average" amount learned [as measured by $E(\hat{u} - \bar{u})^2$] increases?

Ordinary economic intuition would suggest that $\hat{n}$ increases, as long, at least, as $\bar{u}$ does not change much: the more learned from an approach the more approaches it pays to carry. In fact, if $\bar{u}$ does not change at all, it seems intuitively reasonable that $\hat{n}$ increases *only if* $E(\hat{u} - \bar{u})^2$, the expected amount learned from an approach, increases. We might recommend to the developer a *rule of thumb*, taking either the *strong* form or the *weak* form:

1. *Rule of thumb, strong form.* Suppose, when turning from one development task to another, the expected value of the time-and-money-cost to completion for the (initially equally good) approaches available at the start of development remains roughly the same (as does the cost of pursuing any approach to the review point). Then the number of approaches initially pursued should be increased, as compared to the previous task, *if and only if* the expected amount learned from pursuing an approach to the review point is greater now than it was before.
2. *Rule of thumb, weak form.* Same as above with "if" replacing "if and only if."

Like all rules of thumb, these would have the entirely legitimate purpose of simplifying the job of decision making. They require only the knowledge that the probability distribution (of $\hat{u}$) characterizing the approaches for the new development task has a higher variance than the same distribution for the old task (and a similar mean). These rules of thumb would make it possible to avoid the somewhat cumbersome analysis just described.

Would we be right in recommending either of these apparently reasonable rules to the developer? The answer is, *in general*, "no." For it is simply not true, in general, that, if two populations have the same mean but one has a higher variance than the other, the one with higher variance has a lower expected value for the minimum of a sample of n. Yet that would have to be true always if the weak rule of thumb were valid—if increasing the variance $E(\hat{u} - \bar{u})^2$ meant that pursuing n approaches now yields a better (lower) value of $\tilde{U}_n$ than it did before (so that the previously optimal number $\hat{n}$ is now too small).

The strong rule of thumb, moreover, would clearly only be valid if the mean and variance of the distribution of $\hat{u}$ uniquely determines $E\hat{u}_n$. For the rule requires that, if $f(\hat{u})$, $g(\hat{u})$ are two distributions (density functions) with the same mean, then the second has a smaller value of $E\hat{u}_n$ if it has the larger variance, a larger value of $E\hat{u}_n$ if it has the smaller variance, and the same value of Eu_n if it has the same variance.

The case of two-point distributions provides counterexamples to the validity of both rules of thumb. Let $\hat{u}$ equal a with probability $1 - p$ and b with probability p, where $0 < a < b$. Then $Eu = \bar{u} = (1 - p)a + pb = a + (b - a)p$ and $E\hat{u}^2 = (1 - p)a^2 + pb^2 = a^2 + (b + a)(b - a)p$. Now consider the case $n = 2$. Here $\hat{u}_2$, the minimum of a sample of two, equals a with probability $1 - p^2$, b with probability p^2. Hence $E\hat{u}_2 = (1 - p^2)a + p^2b = a + p^2(b - a)$. Now let us *fix* $\bar{u}$ and fix $E\hat{u}^2$ at some level, say, K. (We have then also fixed the variance of $\hat{u}$.) We have

$$E\hat{u}^2 = a^2 + (b + a)(\bar{u} - a) = K$$

$$E\hat{u}_2 = a + p(\bar{u} - a)$$

Fixing $\bar{u}$ and K still leaves freedom in selecting a, b, and p: We can find at least two sets of values of (a, b, p) such that $0 < a < b$, $E\hat{u} = \bar{u}$, and $E\hat{u}^2 = K$, whereas for one set, $E\hat{u}_2$ has a different value than for the other set. Thus the strong rule of thumb cannot be valid.

Consider next the two two-point distributions, shown in Table 1, both having mean 1.

TABLE 1

Two-Point Distributions*

	Distribution 1	Distribution 2
a	$\frac{1}{2}$	$1 - \sqrt{\dfrac{\sqrt{2} - 1}{2 - \sqrt{2}}}$
b	$\frac{3}{2}$	$1 + \sqrt{\dfrac{2 - \sqrt{2}}{\sqrt{2} - 1}}$
p	$\frac{1}{2}$	$\sqrt{2} - 1$
$E\hat{u}$	1	1
$E\hat{u}^2$	$\frac{5}{4}$	2
$E\hat{u}_2$	$\frac{3}{4}$	$1 + (3 - 2\sqrt{2}) \sqrt{\dfrac{2 - \sqrt{2}}{\sqrt{2} - 1}}$
		$+ (2 - 2\sqrt{2}) \sqrt{\dfrac{\sqrt{2} - 1}{2 - \sqrt{2}}} \sim 1 + 0.216 - 0.217 > \frac{3}{4}$

*$\hat{u} = a$ with probability $1 - p$, b with probability p.

The second distribution has a higher variance than the first, and it also has a *higher* expected value for the minimum of a sample of two. Suppose a developer first faces a task whose approaches are characterized by distribution 1, pursues one approach only there, and is pretty sure this is the optimal thing to do. Suppose he then faces a second task in which the available approaches are, in fact, characterized by distribution 2, although all that he wants to convince himself of is that the new distribution has higher variance and a similar mean. He decides, in accordance with the weak rule of thumb, to pursue two approaches in the new situation. He has then been misled. If it did not pay to pursue two approaches in the first situation, it pays *even less* to do so in the new situation. The weak rule of thumb is invalid.

It becomes valid (as does the strong rule) if certain conditions on the probability distribution of $\hat{u}$ are fulfilled—conditions which are slightly peculiar and may be quite unpalatable to the developer. One such condition is that $\hat{u}$ be always some linear transform $rZ + s$ of a random variable Z whose mean is zero and whose variance is one. More precisely, there exists a distribution (a cumulative density function) $G(Z)$ with mean 0 and variance 1 such that for every distribution (cumulative density function) $F(x)$ belonging to a class of distributions containing all possible distributions of $\hat{u}$, there exist numbers $r \geqq 0$, $s \geqq 0$ for which, for any x, $F(x) = G[(Z - s)/r]$. The requirement that $F(x) = 0$ for $x \leqq 0$ imposes the further condition that $G(Z) = 0$ for $Z \leqq s/r$.

We then have $E\hat{u} = s$ and $E(\hat{u} - E\hat{u})^2 = E(r^2 Z^2 + 2rsZ + s^2 - s^2) = r^2$. But also it is easily shown that $E\hat{u}_n = rEZ_n + s$ (where Z_n is the minimum of a sample of n from the Z-population). Hence the expected value of the total time-and-money-cost of development when n approaches are pursued is $\tilde{U}(n) = rEZ_n + s + n - 1$. Since $EZ = 0$, clearly $EZ_n < 0$ for fixed n and fixed $E\hat{u} = s$, therefore, $\tilde{U}(n)$ decreases if and only if $E(\hat{u} - E\hat{u})^2 = r^2$ increases. The strong and, hence, the weak rules of thumb are valid.

The developer, to summarize, is inconsistent if he does not accept a specific (and possibly peculiar) condition like the one just stated and, at the same time, insists on accepting the "reasonable" rules of thumb.

PARALLEL-APPROACH MODELS WITH MORE THAN ONE REVIEW POINT

The foregoing model may be expanded to allow for a sequence of two or more review points, say, R of them. At review point r, $r = 1$, $\cdots$, R, an estimate u_r is available for each approach pursued up to that point. We assume $E(u|u_r) = u_r$. The greater r is, the more information the estimate u_r provides about u, the true time-and-money-cost for the path in question; i.e., $E(u_r - Eu_r)^2$ increases as r increases.

At each review point the developer has to decide how many of the approaches carried up to that point should be pursued up to the next point—should it be the approach with the lowest estimate u_r, the two approaches with the two lowest estimates, the three approaches with the three lowest estimates, etc.? The case $R = 2$ has been "solved," in the same sense that the case $R = 1$ was solved in the discussion of the previous section. The optimal sequence of decisions usually cannot be compactly characterized without further restrictions on the joint probability distribution of the estimates $u_1, \cdots, u_r$. There is, though, a general method of *finding* a compact characterization (or, more accurately, proving that a conjectured characterization is correct), once a probability distribution has been specified.

We cannot go into these results here. We remark only that *at least two further rules of thumb* which seem intuitively reasonable turn out to be *not* generally valid for the R-review-point case. One rule says:

The more "varied" are the estimates u_r that are obtained at review point r for the appraoches carried to that point (as measured, e.g., by their mean squared deviation), the more approaches should be pursued to the subsequent review point.

If all the u_r are the same, for example, it would seem likely that the true u are very nearly the same for the approaches that have been pursued—hence to pursue many of them still further seems to be "wasteful duplication."

A second rule has to do with the diminishing-returns property. It says:

Suppose no use has been made of a given review point r^*, i.e., all the approaches pursued up to r^* are going to be pursued to $r^* + 1$, no matter what the estimates u^* turn out to be. Suppose further that there are diminishing returns to increasing the number of approaches *initially pursued* (pursued to the first review point) when optimal decisions are made at all points other than r^*. If it is then decided to *make use* of review point r^* after all (to choose at r^* the optimal number of approaches rather than all that are available), the diminishing-returns property still holds.

This rule, which would be useful in deciding whether or not to "use" a given review point, is generally invalid.

MODELS IN WHICH DIFFERENT APPROACHES MAY BE PURSUED WITH DIFFERENT INTENSITIES

We can give here only the barest sketch of another class of models, more general than those just considered, in which we admit the possibility of *shortening* the time required for development, in a given approach, by pursuing it more intensively, i.e. by spending more money on it. The term "approach" must then be redefined. In the completely nonsequential case (in which the developer has to make all his decisions once and for all at the start of development), we define an approach as a family of (personal) probability distribution of *time to completion*,[11] each distribution in the family corresponding to a different total amount of money to be spent on the approach. (In the sequential case, money is not allocated to an approach once and for all, but rather in a sequence of parts, one at each of a sequence of review points; in this case the definition of approach, which we omit

[11] That is, time required to attain a satisfactory version of the item being developed.

here, is somewhat complex but is still an extension of the definition just given.)

Spending more money on an approach (in the nonsequential case) lowers the expected time to completion. Various assumptions can be made about the shape of the curve relating expected time to money spent. For each assumption, the optimal choice of number of approaches (if all are initially indistinguishable) and of the amount to be spent on each can be investigated. The developer (in the nonsequential case) pursues all the chosen approaches at the chosen intensities until one of them yields a satisfactory version of the required item; at that instant, all approaches are dropped. (A simplifying assumption is that the money chosen to be spent on the dropped approaches is already committed and is lost, even though they are not completed.)

One intuitively reasonable rule of thumb for the simple nonsequential case is this:

Suppose there are "diminishing returns," in the expected time for spending of additional amounts of money on the given approach. Then the function relating the *total* money spent on all approaches (the developer's total budget) to the expected development time also exhibits diminishing returns *if the budget is optimally allocated among approaches.*

This would be a useful rule of thumb for it would mean (under Assumption 1) that, if the money–expected-time curve has the required shape,[12] there exists a unique optimal budget beyond which the spending of another dollar decreases expected development time by less than a "dollar's worth."

Unfortunately the rule of thumb is again not generally valid. Under a variety of conditions, a curve of the shape shown is consistent with a *constant-returns* or even an *increasing returns* shape for the curve relating total budget to expected development time.

CONCLUSION

The models reported in the foregoing (and all the models so far worked on) have been approximations to reality. Many more elements of the development process could be incorporated into them,

---

[12] As for example, if the way in which a given approach (design) is pursued more intensively would mean having more groups of people of identical size working on it separately or running more and more "approaches" in the sense discussed in the section entitled "A Simple Model." Then the diminishing-returns result described in that section implies that the money—expected—time curve has the required shape.

and for each of them a host of alternative assumptions could be explored (especially alternative probability distributions over the quantities which are unknown until development ends). But the simple models described have already sufficed to make the point that "reasonable" rules of thumb invite further scrutiny.

There is, moreover, no *a priori* reason whatever to believe that, when a simple model (such as the simplest parallel-approach model) has called into question a rule of thumb (such as the weak and strong rules), then complicating the model to make it more realistic will "salvage" the rule of thumb (or its analogue in the more complex model). On the contrary, it seems likely that the conditions under which such a rule of thumb *is* valid are even more "special" in the complex model than in the simple one. This is a crude conjecture, however, and much more research would be needed to defend it.

12
.

Case Studies in Network Planning, Scheduling, and Control of Research and Development Projects,

William F. Ashley and Milton T. Austin

INTRODUCTION

In a few years, a new and powerful technique to plan, schedule, and control projects has grown from theory to widespread acceptance by business, industry, and government. Generally called a network technique, it was developed concurrently and independently by industry and by the military. Industry developed the technique under the names Critical-Path Method (CPM) and Critical-Path Scheduling (CPS). On the military side, the Navy initiated the Program Evaluation and Review Technique (PERT). At one time, the Air Force used a different name, Program Evaluation Procedure (PEP), for what was essentially PERT, but this name was later dropped in favor of the standard PERT designation.

History

A brief history of the major industrial and military systems, and of the persons and groups most closely associated with their development, follows. Late in 1956, the Integrated Engineering Control Group (IEC) of E. I. duPont de Nemours and Company began to explore possible alternatives to traditional project planning and scheduling procedures. At the time, Du Pont recognized the deficiencies of the conventional methods and felt that a high degree of coordination could be obtained if the planning and scheduling information of all

264

project functions were combined into a single master plan. IEC therefore initiated a survey of the prospects for applying electronic computers to the complexities of managing engineering projects. The firm sought help from the Univac Applications Research Center, then under the direction of John W. Mauchly, who assigned James E. Kelley, Jr., to work with Morgan R. Walker, of Du Pont. The results of the Kelley-Walker effort were CPM and Minimum-Cost Expediting (MCX).

Critical-Path Method (CPM)

In basic CPM, a pictorial representation of a project is developed with a closed network of arrows, joined head to tail. The completed network shows the relationship of activities; the juncture of arrow head and tail is an event—a point in time—whereas the arrow itself represents a discrete activity. This representation, then, is activity-oriented, each activity having an assigned duration used to calculate all activity times and the duration of the entire project. The longest path in terms of time through the project is known as the critical path. Its length represents the project duration, and the activities on it all are critical; that is, each must begin as soon as its predecessor is completed and each must be completed within the time allotted to it, if the project is to be completed on time. The project can be expedited only by compressing activities on the critical path. Activities not on the critical path are said to have slack, because there is more time available to complete each activity than the activity itself requires. Therefore, the activity can begin or end at a number of different times. What is now known as MCX (Minimum-Cost Expediting) was also a part of the original CPM system devised by Kelley and Walker.

By May 1957, the theoretical effort had advanced far enough for a practical test. Remington Rand provided computer programs and Du Pont supplied a small pilot project. The results in the test demonstration of September 1957 were most promising, and three months later, a team of six engineers was trained in the new method, their goal being to apply CPM and MCX to the construction of a 10,000,-000-dollar chemical plant. Thus, the first project and case study came into being. Since this was the first of its kind, Du Pont decided to plan and schedule this project by traditional methods as well as by the new CPM approach. The former would be used for the actual administration of the project. Traditional analysis indicated 156 critical items in the project. CPM indicated seven critical items, three of which were not included in the 156 designated by traditional means of planning and scheduling. By April 1958, sufficient evidence had been gathered for Remington Rand and Du Pont to consider the joint effort successful.

Program Evaluation and Review Technique (PERT)

In January, 1958 the United States Navy established a team representing its own Special Projects Office, the Lockheed Missile System Division, and the management consulting firm of Booz, Allen, and Hamilton. The team's task was to develop a technique that would yield continuous evaluation of the Polaris Fleet Ballistic Missile Program. By July, 1958, the team had worked out the essentials of PERT. The feasibility of this tool was examined and authorization was obtained to enter the second phase of the task—application. By the end of 1958, the application of PERT to the Polaris program appear to be successful (see Chapter 4).

Like CPM, the PERT system is based on a network. But in this network the focus is the event, that is, a clearly defined point in time is the essential element in this approach. The difference is clear, if one compares a generalized CPM network for a sample missile-guidance system R & D program (Figure 1) the same project in a PERT configuration (Figure 2). The first application of PERT—a large R & D program including more than 3,000 contractors and subcontractors—required the consideration of several unknowns. Therefore, statistical methods were associated with PERT. Where CPM uses one time estimate for each activity, PERT uses three—an optimistic, a pessimistic, and a most probable. The expected time between events is obtained from the three estimates by the formula:

$$t_e = \frac{a + 4m + b}{6}$$

where t_e equals the expected time between two events, a is the optimistic time, m the most likely time, and b the pessimistic time. The variance or standard deviation for each activity is evaluated by using the optimistic and pessimistic estimates to indicate the range of probable completion for each activity.

The probability of meeting scheduled dates is then calculated. If the calculated and scheduled dates are equal, the probability for reaching the milestone on time is 0.5. If the calculated (or expected) completion time is greater than the scheduled completion time, the probability of meeting the scheduled date is less than 0.5. If the calculated time is less than the scheduled time, the probability is greater than

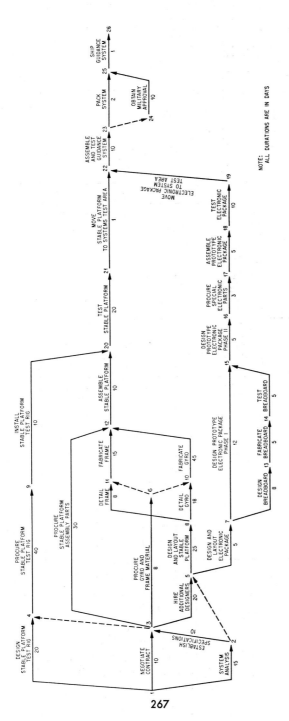

FIGURE 1. Sample missile guidance system research and development program (CPM).

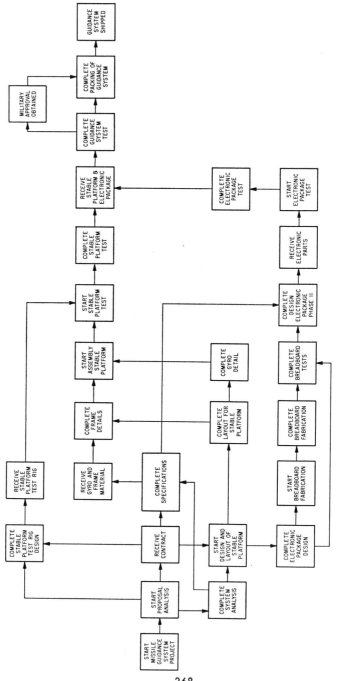

FIGURE 2. Sample missile guidance system research and development program (PERT).

268

0.5.   For the method of making the calculation, refer to PERT Summary Report Phase I, Special Projects Office, Bureau of Naval Weapons, Department of the Navy, Washington, D. C. and Chapter 4.

Comparison of CPM and PERT

In addition to the consideration of time, there are other basic differences between CPM and PERT. For example, PERT was until recently based solely on time, while CPM and its extensions take into consideration the resources of dollars, manpower, space, and equipment. CPM techniques alone allow job weights to be built into the calculations.

Recently, PERT techniques have undergone a number of modifications, all tending to make PERT and CPM more closely resemble one another. Some users of PERT have gone to a single time estimate; some, while using the three time estimates, have eliminated the calculation of probability; others have begun to emphasize the activity rather than the event. Some focus attention on both the activity and the event. Obviously, the project analyst who can use whatever system is required by the project and by the contract will perform the greatest service for management. PERT, modified and extended suitably to the project and the purpose, is flexible and workable to the degree that the planner can shape this tool to his needs.

Basically, however, event-oriented PERT is most satisfactory for the evaluation of project status at a high management level. This is so because events are not adjustable. They are points in time and represent only the completion or noncompletion of a job. Work cannot be controlled if the graphic depiction of activities between events is so general that neither the job nor the person or group responsible for it can be identified. If the number of events is developed to the level of detail necessary for control, the network then becomes prohibitively complex for convenient management of the network. PERT is most useful, then, when a project is to be evaluated and reviewed at a high level.

In our experience, CPM is useful for controlling projects by virtue of its activity orientation. While it serves the same purposes for high-management evaluation that PERT does, CPM functions also on the first level of a project, the level where the detailed activities are physically carried out. That is, activity orientation answers the two basic questions—(1) what jobs must be done, and (2) by when.

An integral part of CPM is the MCX technique. In this technique, dollars are associated with each activity, especially the dollars-per-day required to expedite the activity. A computer can then select those jobs that are least costly to expedite and give management cost figures on compressed schedules of various lengths, as well as new durations for the activities comprising the project. Thus, the project analyst can quickly offer management an array of schedules so that management can decide which time compression of the project, or of any portion of the project, is the most economical and/or the most feasible. A recent development has extended the usefulness of CPM very markedly. This is the Resources Planning and Scheduling Method (RPSM), which permits consideration of resource limitations. The equipment and manpower required for a schedule may exceed those available or may fluctuate violently over the course of the project. Similarly, a project schedule may require that money be spent faster than it can be raised, or it may tie up funds that could be used profitably elsewhere. The RPSM technique permits the project analyst to specify such things as the availability of equipment, money, and labor by crafts and crew compositions, as well as the limitations of materials and working space. This information is input to a computer, which schedules the project by working out a solution compatible with the model and determining the usage curve for each resource over the project duration. If the output is not desirable, the input can, of course, be modified until acceptable results are obtained.

CASE STUDIES

The experience of the authors and their associates on a number of R & D projects has included the application of CPM, with its extensions, and of PERT—the latter being sometimes rather drastically modified. Each of the case histories that follows has, what one might call, a moral of its own; what they all have in common is the further establishment of the significance and strength of the application of network techniques to a wide range of activities and projects.

Case 1.   Implementation of Network Techniques

A multimillion-dollar, two-year project called for the design, prototype fabrication, test, and production manufacturing of a major subsystem for a missile. The over-all contract requirement was to control the project in-house and to report to the customer with a PERT network. The company was having a variety of problems, including the following:

1. Management did not have a complete view of the total organization, to the extent that one man had the job of coordinating the activities of three

different sections of the over-all project—and all three were at different plants.

2. A number of conflicts of responsibility occured in the firm; for example, between engineering and manufacturing.

3. No integrated project plan existed with which to evaluate the total impact of deviations on the project.

After careful consideration of the problem, the contractor concluded that he required an activity-oriented system in order to maintain the required project control. A modified PERT system was devised, which was activity-oriented at the line level but which produced a conventional event-oriented PERT network which satisfied the contractual requirement.

For this project, as for any other of long duration with many contributing departments, a complete monitoring and reporting system was necessary for effective project management. The system used in this case required the following preparations as a foundation for operations:

1. All personnel who were to establish networks, determine the duration of the activities, and submit biweekly reports on the project to a central agency were carefully trained. The training was successful in that, among other things, the personnel satisfied the contractual requirement for early start and early completion dates, slack specification, and clear definition of department responsibility on each job.

2. A program planning group was established to serve as the central agency between the persons who were to submit bi-weekly reports and project management. This group had responsibility for maintaining the networks and updating and distributing schedules. New in the organization of this company, the group eliminated from the reports of individual departments the information that need not concern management, thus creating an environment in which the management-by-exception principle could in fact operate. Through this planning group passed networks that were consolidated into summary networks for management. For the project over-all, some 10,000 activities were recorded on the detailed, activity-oriented PERT networks. The program planning group prepared four summary networks of 150 events each for management review (Figure 3). Finally, one summary network of only 100 events resulted, for presentation to top management.

3. Computer programs were obtained and subsequently modified. The project analysts made use of an IBM 7090 program, prepared originally by Douglas Aircraft, for updating the schedule and otherwise keeping the PERT activity-oriented network current.

Fundamental to the operation of the system used here is that the computer should do as many tasks as possible, thus making the re-

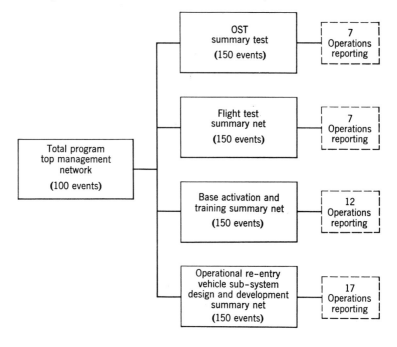

Notes:
1. Summary nets are keyed to the working nets and used to conduct PERT review meetings.
2. Department reports are based on computer runs of the working nets.
3. Working nets under each summary net are combined as required to facilitate computer operation.

FIGURE 3.   Reporting system, PERT activity-oriented networks.

porting and updating of schedules as quick and easy as possible for all concerned.   The departmental representative was assigned by the department manager and represented the department in all matters pertaining to planning and scheduling.   In the periodic reporting by the program planning group, there were four possible cases for consideration—completed jobs, canceled jobs, revised jobs, and new jobs.

The department representative noted all jobs for which the early finish date preceded the reporting date.   If jobs were completed, he recorded the completion dates on the report form, and if they had been canceled, the date of cancellation.   If jobs were neither completed nor canceled, a revised completion date was reported.   Finally, he recorded all new jobs established during the previous reporting period and their scheduled completion dates.   This completed the information necessary for the computation of a new schedule.

The report forms went to the planning group, where they were scanned for obvious errors. Since dates were submitted directly to the computer, updating the input deck was relatively simple. For example, for a completed job, all that was required was that the completion date be added to the input card. The computer then converted the completion to the appropriate duration. Incidentally, all completed and canceled jobs dropped out of the schedule so that only jobs remaining to be done appeared for consideration.

When the input deck was updated, a new computer run was made and a review meeting was held with all department representatives, a member of the program planning group, and project management. At this meeting, first consideration was given to all jobs which affected key dates by exceeding their allowable time for completion. Since these slippages created additional critical paths, a careful review was necessary. Then, all jobs supposedly in progress were reviewed— were they actually in progress, and if so, would they be complete by their predicted finish dates? This particular review covered the situation in which a job might be of long duration and was not required to be reported on the report form. The progress of all such jobs was discussed biweekly; thus, control was maintained over these jobs. If the review meeting generated enough new information, a new schedule was computed and disseminated for the next review period, thereby continuing the reporting cycle, which ran for the life of the project. In this case, only time was considered. Of course, a complete reporting cycle must take into consideration all resources—time, manpower, money, equipment, materials—not time alone. A dynamic CPM reporting cycle is shown in Figure 4.

The discussion of this case has been extensive and detailed because the project itself was the largest and the most complex of those reviewed in this chapter. At this time, the project is still under way. It is on schedule. Making a PERT network operate on an activity basis worked many benefits, both large- and small-scale. Not only is the project running on schedule but the analysts called in initially to set up and operate the network system trained employees of the contractor, who now are continuing to implement the system themselves, most satisfactorily.

Case 2. Updating and Rescheduling by CPM

A large corporation had bid successfully on a contract for the development of equipment for a defense warning system. The project, actually of multiproject scope, involved the development of electronic equipment, the assembling of many subassemblies, appropriate check-

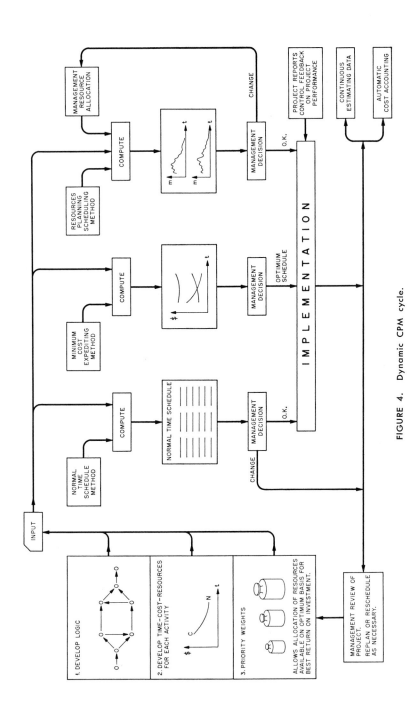

FIGURE 4. Dynamic CPM cycle.

274

out and testing of the initial system, and a series of follow-on systems, to be produced during the final stages. Internally, the orientation of the company was both functional, by department, such as engineering or manufacturing, and by project. Consequently, project managers worked across functional department lines. This arrangement eventually proved beneficial to management insofar as completeness of information was concerned.

Before consultants were engaged, the company was in the ironic, although by no means unusual position of not being able to handle a rush of contracts that had been awarded almost simultaneously. One of the most serious problems was a shortage of manpower, not only in professional and scientific areas but in many labor craft areas. Further, management had no over-all, complete picture of its work situation, although on the projects under way the company was operating at a commendable level of efficiency and the dollar volume of business was not only good, but improving.

In general, this firm's difficulties clearly reflected the inadequacy of the planning and scheduling techniques then in use. The company relied on a system of bar charts for information, and it faced several concurrent problems: the failure of the bar charts to show interrelationships among the jobs; failure to define the criticality of the jobs, and the inadequacy of the system to show the total project plan. The bar charts fell into two extreme categories—either they showed only a fraction of the total number of jobs, because they were drawn by one man and his knowledge was limited, or the volume of the charts inundated management, because too many engineers and administrative personnel had been preparing them (see Chapter 4).

Among the most significant tasks the consultants carried out were these:

1. All specific jobs were reviewed. This review required the interviewing of key personnel on the multiproject activity in considerable detail, until the consulting analysts could establish the total number, duration, and interrelationships of all activities through the CPM arrow diagram. The mere creation of the arrow diagram, was effective in that, for the first time, it gave management a clear picture of all the activities and their significance, critical or noncritical, in the total scheme. At this point, the application of CPM techniques showed that the project was running about three months behind the contract duration.

2. Management decided upon a major reorientation of the program, on the basis of the analysts' data, designed primarily to bring the individual projects into line and bring the end date back to the contract commitment. As an example of reorientation—previously, all 80 subassemblies

were to be worked on without regard to their place in the project time-scale. The new plan called for the main work effort to be applied toward the 15 subassemblies destined for the first system to be delivered. The remaining 65 were to be packed and stored for later shipment; sufficient float, or slack time, was available to permit these subassemblies to wait for subsequent work.

3. The analysts strongly advised the firm to take a stand on its objectives with respect to satisfying those contracts already in the house and planning new ones according to the most effective use of available resources.

4. Resources planning and scheduling computer runs were made for manpower, which at the time posed the most serious resource problem. In one professional category, the company had only three persons of the 25 needed. The analysts carried out a parametric manpower-leveling computer run to determine what number of men in this category management needed to complete the project within the contract time.

Parametric leveling is a stepwise method of determining the manpower to be hired. Requirements based on unlimited availability are found first. Limits of 90, 80, 70, and 60 percent of the level found under that first assumption are then imposed. The extension of the project duration is observed as a function of the various limits of availability. Time extensions which are too great can then be excluded. An acceptable combination of time-extension and availability level to be met by hiring personnel can then be selected.

The entire program has now been updated. One part of the project is ten days ahead of schedule. To accomplish this, in addition to the work already described, subnetworks were created and revised, two of them being completely updated three times. A reporting and monitoring system was installed, much like that described in case 1, the differences being ascribable largely to the differences in company organization. Review meetings are now held regularly and the ideal of management-by-exception is being realized.

Case 3.   A Project Characterized by Vagueness

After a project involving an application of atomic energy had been underway for more than a year, the following conditions characterized it:

1. Many of the problems, technologies, and skills demanded were so new that research and processing were in effect going on in parallel, or nearly so. The project suffered from unexpected damage to equipment from combinations of materials, from the breakdown of equipment, and from other technical problems.

2. Because of emergencies that constantly arose, no one could predict any end-date for the project.

3. Because the project plan was undefined manpower needs were undetermined, and the various requirements for scientific, professional, and labor craft personnel were also not clearly defined.

4. Since manpower was in short supply in most categories and since the real significance or criticality of many activities was unknown, management tended to work all jobs that appeared to be critical on an expedited basis, thus creating unnecessary tensions throughout the project. Later, when CPM analysis was applied to these jobs, some of them were found actually to have 60 to 90 weeks of slack time.

The analysts' first major job was to interview all project engineers and project supervisors at considerable length, in order to gain an understanding of all the activities, a reasonable estimate of their durations, and an over-all view of their interrelationships and then to rid the project as soon as possible of duplication of effort. It was not surprising to find that no one had a clear picture of the entire project. Such was precisely the situation in many other large and complex projects on which even the most responsible, capable, and efficient managerial persons did not have the tools or techniques available by which they could be sufficiently informed.

The first result of presenting the arrow diagram to management was that an over-all picture was at last available. An initial revision of this network resulted in reducing the original project duration by 32 weeks. Critical jobs were defined and the talents of the company were directed towards those activities. Meanwhile, a monitoring and reporting system was organized along the lines detailed in Case 1 of this chapter. Relatively soon, management received regular and up-to-date information in summary form of the progress of the entire undertaking. RPSM techniques were used to achieve the most efficient distribution of the limited manpower. Data generated by the RPSM computer runs enabled management to direct work efforts to the activities of greatest priority.

The remaining cases in this chapter will be discussed in somewhat less detail, not because the problems and attempted solutions were any less significant but because the basic concepts in the applications of network analysis, the leveling of manpower and other resources, and the considerations of time-cost relationships were constants throughout these research and development activities.

Case 4. Activity Orientation Was Necessary

A 70-event network had been established for the design and fabrication of a computer to be used for training purposes to simulate the countdown procedures during a missile firing. The company found that this event-oriented PERT network was too general for a project on which great detail was essential for tight control. Just for bimonthly evaluation of the schedule on this basis, one man had the full-time job of gathering information.

As a remedy, the analysts developed an activity-oriented network of 600 jobs, still working within the framework of the logic as originally developed by management. The task of developing this network was of course preceded by much effort in interviewing supervisors and managers on the job, working up accurate activity definitions, descriptions and durations, and fitting together this mass of information into the arrow diagram. However, once the project was broken down in detail and responsibility was defined for each activity, evaluation became simpler. Furthermore, the necessary information for the over-all event network was generated as the project went along and the full-time effort at information gathering was no longer necessary. Management was convinced, as a result of this experience, that at the working level the network should be activity-oriented, with event-oriented networks used only at the highest levels.

The first use of an activity-based network generally enlightens management in this way. The gains include a greater quantity and quality of intelligence about the project, better information on which to base decisions, increased understanding of network techniques within the company staff, and an appreciation for the entire program as an integrated endeavor. The next case will illustrate how the acquisition of information contributes to the making of more intelligent decisions.

Case 5.   A Metallurgical Problem Proved Critical

This company was developing a new turbine engine. When the arrow network diagram was created, one of the critical activities proved to be the casting of blades that would have to withstand speeds of 100,000 rpm. Having been informed of the true significance of this metallurgical problem, management shelved the development of the new engine and approved the effort necessary to concentrate on the metallurgical problem. Much effort and money were saved on this project because, instead of depending on intuition and plunging into all aspects of the project with equal applications of resources, management concentrated on a problem which it had not previously recognized as critical.

Case 6.   A Critical Activity Was Thought Trivial

On this project for the design, fabrication, and test of a variable-thrust vernier rocket engine, one critical item was the procurement of a flowmeter. But a second critical activity was one that, at first glance, seemed to be so trivial that no one was inclined to take it seriously. The portion of the project on which both of these activities were critical involved the conversion of a previously used test cell to one for the new engine.

The CPM analyst informed the project manager that the vendor could not expedite the delivery of the flowmeter, but that a crude meter of only 50-percent accuracy could be used at the beginning of the project. The manager ordered the design and fabrication of this meter, which was used satisfactorily up to the point where the new meter was genuinely needed. At that point, delivery of the flowmeter was possible and the entire project continued on schedule.

The second critical activity was one to which no one had given any attention—the removal of old equipment from the test cell. The CPM network showed nearly four months available for completion of this activity, actual working time for which was perhaps one day. The analyst called to the attention of management, however, the need to secure Air Force clearance for removal of old and obsolete military equipment. Further investigation established that at least six weeks, and possibly two months, would be the lead time for the completion of all the paperwork. Therefore, management immediately began securing Air Force approval. The test cell was in fact cleaned and ready on time for the installation of new equipment.

Case 7. CPM Techniques Permitted Flexibility

On a one-year project for the design, fabrication, and test of a liquid-cooled rocket nozzle, a number of unexpected and difficult situations arose, some of them before network analysts were engaged, some of them after. Among other things, the logic of the project had to be drastically changed midway, the expediency of overtime had to be applied to the design and drawings of a critical part when the project was well underway, and the entire test facility blew up when the program was nearly completed.

Analysis of the arrow diagram showed that the original project duration was six weeks longer than necessary because the unavoidable lead time on the manufacture of tungsten parts had not been recognized as slack time and had mistakenly been added to the length of the project. Associated with this problem was the fact that the test and manufacturing facilities for the tungsten parts were physically distant. Because of these and other conditions, available slack time for the manufacture of a tungsten nut began to disappear as the project continued. When the analysts informed management that the manufacture of this small part would become critical, the project manager approved the application of overtime to the completion of design and drawings for the tungsten nut, so that the manufacturing process would not force an extension of the entire program.

Another revision of logic was necessary when the entire test facility exploded. Because the CPM network technique was being used, the schedule could be reevaluated relatively easily. All necessary repairs were made, with the necessary expediting of critical activities, and the project was completed on time.

This case brings out not only the flexibility with which changes can be made within the framework of a fixed project duration, but the importance of getting full and accurate information back to management quickly for use in the making of decisions. Furthermore, the reporting system used in this case and in others—although in most applications it is a minimum system that does not take into account updated cost figures, a comparison of dollars spent against the total allocation, or some other significant information—provides management with accurate information about time elapsed and time available, and is therefore a useful management tool.

Case 8.   A Need For Daily Rescheduling

By way of contrast to the preceding cases, the following is a six-week project. It was not a research and development project but it is included here, to illustrate the usefulness of the ability to update a schedule regularly with a computer run of a CPM program.

The project called for a public demonstration in Florida of a machine commonly called an "air car." Management was not only contractually obliged to have the machine on site and operating six weeks from the start of the project, but it had publically committed itself to the demonstration through a series of press releases. The air car had to be completely checked out, disassembled, overhauled, reassembled, and painted. Because of the short time available, the project analysts reevaluated the schedule daily. Every afternoon at 5 o'clock the day's accomplishments (or lack of accomplishments) were fed into a computer for any necessary rescheduling. By 8 o'clock the next morning, management could examine the new schedule and indicate what activities had to be expedited. In the end, the vehicle was shipped to Florida on time, minus certain parts which then were flown in, in time for final assembly. The demonstration took place on schedule. The panicky application of expensive expediencies, which within the environment of conventional planning and scheduling methods probably would have resulted, was never even considered in the case of the air car.

IMPLEMENTATION

The application of network techniques in numerous situations has provided considerable experience in management training and the development of implementation requirements.

Management can be conveniently divided into four categories—the general manager and his staff; line management; task and subtask leaders, and key persons who report into the system. The general manager and his people must know how network techniques compare with conventional methods; their commercial and military applications, and what the practical results can be in terms of decreased operating costs, on-time completion of a project, and effective project control.

Personnel at the line level must know what demands the system will make on their time; the type of control it will effect, and how it can simultaneously satisfy the objectives of both the functional manager and the project manager. They also will have questions about its contribution to cutting schedule time and costs and increasing the possibility of controlling and adjusting schedules.

Task and subtask leaders are the lowest managerial level that must be informed about the network system. Therefore, they need the most detailed information, along these lines—the techniques, the mechanics of monitoring, reporting methods and tools, how to update schedules and the significance of flagged jobs. Of course, they also must understand the benefits of a plan that is easily adjustable, definite, and that renders erratic and incomplete rescheduling unnecessary.

The fourth category of management to be informed are those key persons, at several levels, who report into the system. These men must be trained to develop the logic of the system, provide reports for updating, and communicate between the functional and project managers, and the work force. Experience has indicated that a five-day training course is necessary for this group of personnel, but that one- or two-day seminars are sufficient for management at the top, intermediate, and lower levels.

Implementation includes arrangements to have the networks developed by trained persons, to set up computer runs, to establish monitoring and reporting systems, and to ensure that management-by-exception will be the standard procedure. When the system has been set up, the key person responsible for the program control office should be a senior executive with initiative and a good knowledge of the company. He must be able to communicate at all levels of management. His own staff needs no special skills other than the ability to take part in the area of planning and scheduling. All the new information and techniques he will need can be developed in a five-day training course and during the subsequent implementation period.

The limitations we have found in practice may be summarized most significantly under these categories: size of networks, costs of system development control, and errors in estimating costs and times. The largest practical network is between 900 and 1,200 jobs. For networks that contain up to 150 or 200 jobs, the calculations can be done by hand; thereafter, it is more economical to use a computer. Networks in excess of 1,500 jobs are cumbersome and lose their usefulness, because no one can assimilate this amount of data and control this number of jobs. In large projects, large networks should be broken into subnetworks.

The cost of having a working system based on CPM or PERT can be compared with present system costs by entering the appropriate values in the following equation:

[(hours/week for scheduling) (engineers' hourly rates)
    + (hours/week for meetings) (engineers' hourly rates)] 52
$$= \text{annual cost}$$

Implementation costs range between 0.5 and 1.0 percent of the total contract value of the project to which the network method is applied.

Initial errors occurring in time and cost estimates in our experience have been no greater than those in conventional systems. In addition, refinements obtained by reducing tasks to basic jobs in terms of weeks or days tend to reduce estimating errors. Furthermore, the updating system allows improvement of estimates, thereby reducing or nullifying initial errors.

COMPUTER RESEARCH AND DEVELOPMENT

Program Development

The techniques described in this chapter are without exception computer oriented, even though some of them may be performed by hand. Du Pont's original purpose in approaching Remington Rand in 1956 was to seek assistance in determining whether computers could be used to enable more scientific scheduling and control of large projects.

James E. Kelley, Jr., of Mauchly Associates has been responsible for the basic algorithms on which MCX and RPSM are based, as well as for much of the initial implementation of these techniques in the field. He continues to do original work in this area, his latest contribution being a technique for interproject scheduling.

As a result of Kelley's work, programs for basic CPM (including MCX) and RPSM now exist for a number of computers. Mauchly Associates themselves have written programs for the IBM 650. They assisted General Electric in writing programs for the GE 225 and are now assisting another client in writing programs for the IBM 1620. R & D in this area will, of course, continue.

Hardware Development

John W. Mauchly has taken still another approach to the problem of getting from algorithm to useful result. Early in 1962, he announced SkeduFlo[1] MCX-30 a portable analog computer capable of showing the critical path in a project by means of indicator lights and of generating the time-cost curve used in MCX in a matter of seconds. The number of jobs that SkeduFlo can handle at the present time is limited and the first model is intended for use either at the top-management level, where it is desirable to consider summary networks only, or at the job-management level where the number of activities is small but where the day-to-day situation may be very fluid. If MCX is not desired, but only critical-path determination, other models of SkeduFlo can handle a very respectable number of jobs. Parameters are changed simply by adjusting knobs and the new results are obtained immediately without waiting for a digital computer run, evaluation of the run, and a rerun with new parameters. SkeduFlo is accurate to within 3 to 5 percent of full scale, which is acceptable for use in estimating.

Network computers have in the past been designed and used primarily for linear flow problems, such as occur in power distribution systems. SkeduFlo uses nonlinear network elements, and is the first electronic model for problems which include upper and lower bounds on flow capacity, a *sine qua non* for generating the time-cost curve.

SUMMARY AND CONCLUSIONS

Of the new management tools for intelligent decision-making, based on the application of network techniques, only the CPM and PERT have been used widely. Associated with CPM are the MCX technique and RPSM, both of which have been applied to research and development projects. MCX is a tool that gives management information on the basis of which it can decide which of several time-

[1] Trademark of Mauchly Associates, Inc.

compressions of a project, or of any portion of a project, is the most feasible and the most economical. A new analog computer, SkeduFlo, is available which enables management to see instantaneously the effects of changing various parameters of the network without waiting for the results of a series of digital computer runs. RPSM is a technique that permits the consideration of limited resources. With RPSM, a project analyst can correlate the availabilities of all resources—men, money, time, crafts, equipment, material, space—and utilize a computer program to work out a solution compatible with the project requirements, determining the usage curve for each resource over the duration of the project.

These techniques have been applied to a number of R & D projects, on most of which a competent and efficient management was struggling with older planning, scheduling, and control techniques that neither gave them sufficient information nor enabled them to see the entire range of activities and the interrelationships of those activities. Using the tools of network analysis, R & D management is beginning to note such major benefits as these:

1. Critical activities are identified.
2. The entire project is seen as an entity.
3. Interrelationships and responsibilities are defined.
4. Duplication of effort is minimized.
5. Activities are tightly controlled at the working level.
6. An effective monitoring system gives management current information at any desired interval.
7. Activity and project times and costs are correlated. The costs of activity compressions or stretchouts are known and a decision on time can be made with full knowledge of the effect on costs.
8. Manpower can be leveled efficiently, according to availabilities and the project duration.

The newer technique, RPSM, is beginning to be applied in more companies. Although the MCX technique has been available for several years, the simpler network method had to be implemented first. It is expected that the use of MCX will grow as management learns to use economic decision methods. With MCX, the minimum-cost plan for any expedited project can be determined. When known, the application of resources ensures management of the best and most realistic mode of operation.

Finally, it is reasonable to expect further refinements and extensions of the techniques now gaining in use among R & D managers. One new technique, for which the mathematical model has been developed, is interproject scheduling. This system will enable project analysts to consider the resources across a number of projects entailed in a major undertaking, along with activity and project priorities with respect to time, costs, manpower, equipment, materials, and working space.

REFERENCES

Anonymous, "New Tool for Job Management—Perini Corporation, Pioneers CPM," *Engineering News Record,* January 26, 1961.

Anonymous, "Faster Phased Plan Speeds Plant Building," *Chemical Week,* August 26, 1961, pp. 50–51.

Astrachan, A., "Better Plans Come From Study of Anatomy of an Engineering Job," *Business Week,* March 21, 1959, pp. 60–66.

Berman, Herbert, "The Critical-Path Method for Project Planning and Control," *The Constructor,* September, 1961.

Christensen, B. M., "The Critical-Path Method," General Electric Computer Department, Phoenix, Arizona, 1961.

Fazar, Willard, "Progress Reporting in the Special Projects Office," *Navy Management Review,* April, 1959, pp. 9–15.

Ford, L. R., Jr., and Fulkerson, D. R., "A Simple Algorithm for Finding Maximal Network Flows and an Application to the Hitchcock Problem," *Canadian Journal of Math.,* Vol. 9, 1957, pp. 210–218.

Fulkerson, D. R., "A Network Flow Computation for Project Cost Curves," Rand Paper P-1957, March 18, 1960.

Gass, S., and Saaty, T., "The Computational Algorithm for the Parametric Objective Function," *Naval Research Logistic Quarterly,* Vol. 2, 1955, pp. 39–46.

Kelley, James E., Jr., "Computers and Operations Research in Roadbuilding," *Operations Research, Computers and Management Decisions,* Symposium Proceedings, Case Institute of Technology, January 31, February 1, 2, 1957.

———, "The Construction Scheduling Problem (A Progress Report)," UNIVAC Applications Research Center, Remington Rand UNIVAC, Philadelphia, April 25, 1957.

———, "Parametric Programming and the Primal-Dual Algorithm," *Operations Research,* Vol. 7, No. 3, 1959, pp. 327–334.

———, and Walker, Morgan R., "Critical-Path Planning and Scheduling," *Proceedings of the Eastern Joint Computer Conference,* Boston, December 1–3, 1959, pp. 160–173.

———, "Critical-Path Planning and Scheduling: Mathematical Basis," *Operations Research,* May–June, 1961, pp. 296–320.

———, and Walker, M. R., "Critical-Path Planning and Scheduling: An Introduction," Mauchly Associates, Incorporated, Fort Washington, Pennsylvania, 1959.

Malcolm, D. G., Roseboom, J. H., Clark, C. E., and Fazar, W., "Application of a Technique for Research and Development Program Evaluation," *Operations Research,* Vol. 7, 1959, pp. 646–669.

Reeves, Eric, "Critical-Path Speeds Refinery Revamp," *Canadian Chemical Processing,* October, 1960.

Steben, Major E. S., "The Critical-Path Method as Used in the Canadian Army," Mauchly Associates, Incorporated, Fort Washington, Pennsylvania, May 12, 1961.

Index

287